Third Edition

Automotive collision work

ERNEST VENK
M.A. Voc.Ed.

Assistant Dean, Emeritus, Technical
Division, Henry Ford Community College,
Dearborn, Michigan. Formerly, Instructor
Auto and Aviation Mechanics, Fordson
High School.

EDWARD D. SPICER

Supervisor of Service Training and
Publications, Lincoln-Mercury Division of
Ford Motor Company. Formerly Body Design
Engineer; Aircraft Stress Engineer.

editorial consultant
EWART J. DAVIES
B.Sc.

Journeyman Machinist, Mechanical Engineer,
Teacher, Principal, Inspector of Technical
and Academic Subjects and Retired Assistant
Superintendent of Secondary Education,
Ontario, Department of Education.

AMERICAN TECHNICAL SOCIETY
CHICAGO, ILLINOIS

Library of Congress Catalog Card Number: 64-18557

PRINTED IN THE UNITED STATES OF AMERICA

FOREWORD

Eleven and one half million automobile accidents!

The National Safety Council estimates that there will be eleven and one half million accidents this year. Almost eighty-three million automobiles are on the roads and highways of the United States this year. The number of motor vehicles on the road is increasing at the rate of three million per year. Inevitably, the number of accidents will increase too. Whatever else accidents may mean, they mean crumpled fenders, misalignment of frames, damaged finish and the need for many forms of auto body repair. Collision work has ballooned to proportions that give repairmen a gross income of more than $500,-000,000 per year. For the properly trained technician, lucrative pay and steady employment are almost assured.

This revised edition of *Automotive Collision Work* covers the collision man's work in all its aspects. Building from the basic concepts of body and frame construction in Chapter One, the book works step by step through tools, welding repairs, repair of doors, hoods, deck lids, and frame alignment.

New material has been added to keep pace with the fast moving automotive industry. The unitized body has been given added emphasis. New tools which speed the job, new materials which the repairman must know, as well as low cost, short duration repairs are now explained and discussed in detail.

Ernest Venk and Edward D. Spicer were chosen to revise this book because of the breadth and depth of their experience. They make an ideal combination. Mr. Venk has a Master of Arts degree in Vocational Education. He worked as an automobile mechanic and is an experienced instructor of aviation and automotive mechanics. He has trained thousands of mechanics in his thirty-six years of teaching experience. He held the position of Assistant Dean of the Technical Division of the Henry Ford Community College in Dearborn, Michigan. In addition, he has served as an advisor to schools throughout the country in establishing successful programs for automotive mechanics. Mr. Venk also has proven ability as an author, having had a vital part in the authorship of *Automotive Engines—Maintenance and Repair; Automotive Fundamentals; Automotive Maintenance and Trouble Shooting;* and *Automotive Suspensions, Steering, Alignment and Brakes.*

iii

FOREWORD

Edward D. Spicer complements Mr. Venk's teaching and writing experience. Mr. Spicer is highly regarded in several fields, as a technical writer, a body design engineer and as an aircraft stress engineer. His experience and skill have provided him with the knowledge required for the task of producing this practical manual for collision repairs.

Ewart J. Davies served as the editorial consultant throughout the preparation of *Automotive Collision Work;* his special knowledge and experience—both as educator and as engineer—have helped to maintain this book as a leader in its field.

This revision has retained all the features which have long made *Automotive Collision Work* a standard in its field, and the material which will keep the worker up-to-date has been added.

THE PUBLISHERS

ACKNOWLEDGMENTS

The publishers, editors, and authors wish to acknowledge and express their appreciation to the following companies who supplied artwork and information used in this volume:

Allen Electric and Equipment Company
American Motors Corporation
Anzick Manufacturing Company
Bear Manufacturing Company
Blackhawk Manufacturing Company
Buick Division, General Motors Corporation
Chicago Pneumatic Tool Company
De Vilbiss Company
Ditzler Color Division, Pittsburgh Plate Glass Company
Dodge Division, Chrysler Corporation
Ford Motor Company
Thomas M. Galey
General Electric Company
Guy-Chart Tools Limited
Hobart Brothers Company
Lincoln Electric Company
Linde Air Products Company
Minnesota Mining and Manufacturing Company
H. K. Porter
Purity Cylinder Gases Incorporated
Rinshed-Mason Company
Smith Welding and Cutting Equipment Company
Tripo Engineering Company
Tri-Saw Corporation
United Shoe Machinery Corporation

CONTENTS

CONTENTS

BODY AND FRAME CONSTRUCTION

Automotive engineers strive constantly to make the automobile more durable, safe and functional, and also more attractive and comfortable for the passengers.

Strength is of prime importance in a car body and frame. How metal is formed to provide strength is discussed in Section I.

Two types of construction are used in automotive vehicles. One is the separate frame and body arrangement used since auto building began; the other is "unit body construction" in which the body provides the strength and rigidity necessary for safety, and eliminates the need for a separate frame.

The two types of construction including major body and frame parts are covered in Sections II, III, IV, V, VI, VII, and IX. Study them thoroughly. Detailed knowledge of auto construction is needed to become an expert body repairman.

Section VIII deals with the methods employed to seal bodies and cabs against dust and water.

Section X will acquaint you with the principles of measurement necessary to determine whether or not a frame or body is misaligned.

Aside from the fact that damage to an automobile body is generally unsightly, anything which happens to loosen or distort the body or frame may constitute a hazard to any individual operating the vehicle.

I. HOW METAL IS FORMED TO PROVIDE STRENGTH

In early automobiles, strength was obtained where metal was used by making the members of extremely heavy gauge sheet metal. An example of this practice was the heavy gauge stock from which fenders were constructed.

As research continued, several ways to give strength to body panels were found. The automobile bodies and fenders of today are made from light gauge metal. However, when this light gauge steel is shaped and assembled, strength and rigidity are added by the contours into which it is formed.

This section gives you an accurate word picture of how metal is formed to obtain strength. Each type of forming is discussed under a heading descriptive of the method at that particular point. Illustrations of each method of forming metal are included for each.

a. Crowns. Probably the most commonly encountered formation of metal in a body or fender is a curved surface. Curved surfaces are commonly called crowns. A crowned surface is shown in Fig. 1.

CROWN

Fig. 1. Crowned Surface

A crowned surface may be crowned in one direction only, or in all directions from any given point on the surface.

A sheet of metal that is crowned is much stronger than the same sheet would be if it were flat. The crowned sheet will resist any influence to change its shape. It will also have a permanent tendency to return to its original crowned shape, provided it is not distorted beyond its point of elasticity. This is true only when the sheet has been formed into its original shape by a press, pressing gives the sheet a permanent shape. One surface of the sheet is made shorter than the other. Each surface of the sheet is more dense than the metal at the center of the sheet. When a sheet is formed, the last operation of the press squeezes the surfaces together. This causes the molecules in the metal to be crowded closer together at the surface than they were originally. For this reason, the sheet will be stronger than it was before. Both surfaces will resist any influence to move in any direction.

The more a surface is crowned, the greater is its tendency to resist movement and to return to its original shape if it is distorted.

When a surface has a small crown or is not curved very much, it is called a *low crown* surface. An example of a low crown surface with which you will be working is the almost flat portion of an all-steel top or hood.

When a·surface has a lot of crown, or is, in effect, a corner rounded in all directions, it is called a *high crown* surface. Contrary to a popular belief, a curved surface in an automobile body need not have a true radius; the designer can create a curved surface by laying out points which, when connected, form a smooth, curved line.

b. Angles and Flanges. Another method of shaping metal to gain strength is to form angles or flanges along the edges of large sheets or panels.

An angular or, as it is sometimes called, "corrugated" type of construction cannot be used when a smooth surface is required, but it is widely employed in the inner construction of automobile bodies. Every time a panel or bracket is given a right-angle bend, it becomes stronger. Fig. 2 shows an inner door panel which has a right-angle bend all

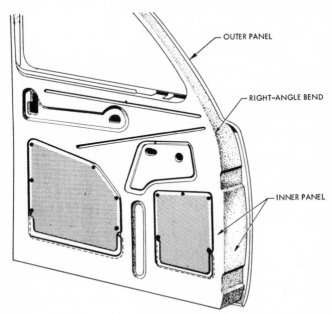

Fig. 2. Inner Door Panel Showing Right-Angle Bend

around the door. It is this bend which provides the depth for the inner workings of the door. However, an even more important function is that it supplies as much strength as would a frame of special construction.

You can acquaint yourself with the strength imparted by a right-angle bend in a piece of metal by the following experiment:

Form a flange approximately one inch wide across one end of a piece of thin, flat, sheet steel, then try to bend the sheet crosswise to the angle. You will find that you will encounter difficulty in bending it after the flange is made.

Flanges are, in effect, right-angle bends. Some panels on cars require a flange, because it gives stiffness to any unsupported edge. You will find flanges around the edges of most fenders and hoods. These flanges provide the rigidity necessary for these panels to be functional even though great portions of them are unsupported. These flanges are commonly called *beads*.

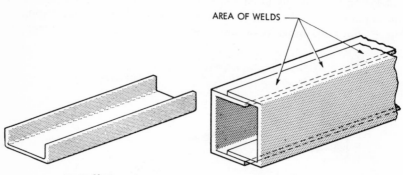

AREA OF WELDS

Fig. 3. **U** Channel

Fig. 4. Box Construction

c. U Channels and Box Sections. A **U** channel is just what you would expect from the name. It is a flat piece of metal with two edges turned at right angles in the same direction (Fig. 3). **U** channels are widely used in the inner construction of automobile bodies. Much more strength can be gained by making a **U** channel instead of a single-angle bend in any reinforcement bracket. The **U** channel is also the most common type of section used in the construction of automobile frames.

Another type of construction composed of two **U** channel sections nested together is called box section construction (Fig. 4).

Box section construction is obtained by overlapping the free edges of two **U** channel sections and either welding, riveting, or bolting them together. Box section construction is used in conjunction with **U** channel construction in the manufacture of automobile frames when great strength is necessary.

You will find by closely inspecting the construction of an automobile that the panels, brackets, braces, etc., all have one or more of the types of construction mentioned in this section. You will also see many odd seeming types of construction. However, they will be only a variation of one of these basic shapes.

II. FRAME CONSTRUCTION

An understanding of the construction of the frame is extremely important, because it is the foundation on which the car is built. Frames of all types to fit all conditions are described and illustrated in this section.

Frames can be constructed from **U** channel, I beam, box sections, angle, **T** stock, **Z** stock, tubing, flat plates, or combinations of any two or more of these stocks. Frames are usually made wider at the rear than at the front. This permits a shorter turning radius by allowing more room for the front wheels. It also allows more space for supported load-carrying at the rear. The heaviest cross member is usually mounted somewhere under the front portion of the engine.

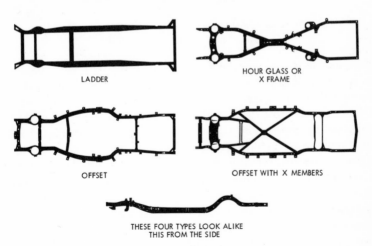

LADDER

HOUR GLASS OR
X FRAME

OFFSET

OFFSET WITH X MEMBERS

THESE FOUR TYPES LOOK ALIKE
THIS FROM THE SIDE

Fig. 5. Four Types of Passenger Car Frames.

(Blackhawk Manufacturing Company)

a. Passenger Car Frames. Several types of passenger car frames are shown in Fig. 5. One frame has an **X**-shaped member for added strength. You can also see from this illustration what is meant by the term "drop center" used in connection with a frame. The main part or center of the frame is dropped down between the front and rear wheels to lower the vehicle.

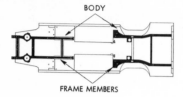

Fig. 6. Bottom View of Frame Constructed Integrally with Underbody

(*Blackhawk Manufacturing Company*)

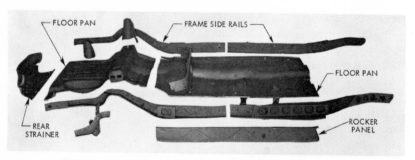

Fig. 7. Exploded View of Frame Constructed Integrally with Underbody
(*Courtesy American Motors Corporation*)

In some automobiles, the frame is incorporated with the body. This is a form of unit body construction which is thoroughly discussed in Section V of this chapter. Some feel that frames built in this manner are stronger and more durable than conventional type frames. Frames constructed integrally with the underbody are shown in Figs. 6 and 7.

b. Commercial Vehicle Frames. With the exception of the lighter vehicles, commercial vehicle frames are usually built flat. Light commercial vehicles are usually built on passenger car frames or on a reinforced passenger car frame.

Large truck and bus frames are made flat without any drop, since a flat floor for the cargo or passenger carrying space is highly desirable. A low center of gravity is not as important a consideration with regard to commercial vehicles of this type as it is with passenger cars. A typical, large truck frame is shown in Fig. 8. In this illustration, you can

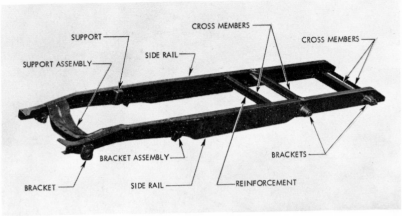

Fig. 8. Typical Large Truck Frame
(Courtesy Dodge Division, Chrysler Corp.)

see that even though this frame has no drop, the side members are made wider where the load strain is greatest.

III. CONVENTIONAL BODIES AND CABS

The passenger carrying compartment of a car is called the body proper. It is to the body that all of the doors and fenders attach to form a complete body assembly. In trucks, the passenger compartment is called the cab. The cab is the nucleus around which the complete body assembly is constructed.

Bodies and cabs differ a great deal in construction because of the different purposes for which they are intended. However, one factor is common to both. Each has outer and inner construction. These terms are used frequently in any discussion of automotive body construction.

Outer construction can be likened to the skin. In fact, some body experts use the term "skin" when referring to the outer surfaces of an automobile. Outer construction is usually considered as that portion of a panel, or panels, which is visible from the outside of the car.

Inner construction is considered as all of the braces, brackets, panels, etc., that are used to give the car strength. Inner construction usually cannot be seen from the outside of the car. In some cases, entire panels are inner construction on one make of car, and a combination of inner and outer construction on another. The discussions in this section of the major panels which make up a body or cab, will enable

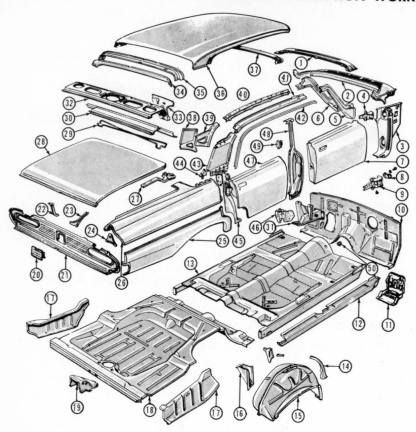

Fig. 9. Four-Door Pillar Sedan Body Panels
(*Courtesy Lincoln-Mercury Division, Ford Motor Company*)

NO.	DESCRIPTION
1	WINDSHIELD HEADER
2	COWL TOP PANEL
3	PILLAR AND COWL SIDE
4	UPPER DOOR HINGE
5	OUTER FRONT BODY PILLAR
6	INNER FRONT BODY PILLAR
7	FRONT DOOR
8	DOOR CHECK
9	LOWER DOOR HINGE
10	DASH PANEL
11	DASH TO FRAME BRACE
12	ROCKER PANEL
13	FRONT FLOOR PAN
14	REINFORCEMENT
15	QUARTER WHEELHOUSE
16	DOOR HINGE TO WHEELHOUSE BRACKET

NO.	DESCRIPTION
17	REAR FLOOR PAN TO QUARTER PANEL EXTENSION
18	REAR FLOOR PAN
19	FUEL TANK FILLER PIPE HOUSING
20	FUEL FILLER LID
21	LOWER BACK PANEL
22	LOWER BACK PANEL TO FLOOR BRACE
23	LOWER TROUGH
24	QUARTER PANEL REAR FILLER
25	LOWER QUARTER PANEL
26	UPPER QUARTER PANEL
27	LUGGAGE COMP'T. DOOR HINGE
28	LUGGAGE COMP'T. DOOR
29	TORSION RODS
30	UPPER BACK PANEL
31	BRAKE PEDAL SUPPORT
32	PACKAGE TRAY PANEL
33	PACKAGE TRAY STRAINER

NO.	DESCRIPTION
34	ROOF PANEL REAR EXTENSION
35	BACK WINDOW UPPER FRAME
36	ROOF PANEL
37	ROOF PANEL CENTER REINFORCEMENT
38	REAR SIDE RAIL
39	ROOF REAR UPPER SIDE RAIL
40	ROOF INNER SIDE RAIL
41	ROOF OUTER SIDE RAIL
42	SIDE FINISH MOULDING
43	ROOF SIDE REAR EXTENSION
44	ROOF REAR LOWER SIDE RAIL EXTENSION
45	QUARTER LOCK PILLAR
46	LOWER REAR DOOR HINGE
47	REAR DOOR
48	CENTER PILLAR
49	UPPER REAR DOOR HINGE
50	TRANSMISSION INSPECTION COVER

you to quickly determine which is outer and which is inner construction.

a. Body Construction. The body construction discussed here is the conventional type utilizing a full frame. Several types of bodies are available in most car lines. The most popular are the regular four-door sedan, of which the major panels are shown in Fig. 9, and the hardtop four-door shown in Fig. 10. The difference between these two styles is in the center pillar construction. The center pillar is the vertical member between the rear and front doors. On the pillar sedan, the center pillar attaches to both the floor pan and the roof side rails. This gives great strength to the body sides. In the hardtop sedan, the center pillar attaches to the floor pan only, and is only as high as the lower door panel "reveal line," leaving an uninterrupted opening from front to rear when the windows are open. A typical station wagon construction is shown in Fig. 11. The differences are easily seen.

In the following paragraphs, the major panels are discussed under descriptive headings. The panel names should be carefully noted, as they are typical of the terminology used by most car companies in their service and parts publications. Figs. 9, 10, and 11 will be referred to freely throughout the balance of this discussion.

(1) *COWL AND/OR DASH ASSEMBLY.* The cowl and/or dash panel forms the front end of the body. This panel usually is formed by assembling together several smaller panels. These are the cowl upper panel and the cowl side panels, which are joined by welds into one integral unit.

In some cars, the windshield frame is integral with the cowl panel. The cowl extends upward around the entire windshield opening so that the upper edge of the cowl panel forms the front edge of the roof panel. In this case, the windshield pillars are merely part of the cowl panel. The windshield pillars are the narrow sloping construction at either side of the windshield opening.

In some cars, only a portion of the windshield pillar is formed as part of the cowl.

The cowl is sometimes called the *fire wall* because it is the partition between the passenger compartment and the engine compartment. Some of the controls for operating the vehicle extend through the cowl from the passenger compartment into the engine compartment. The cowl is provided with openings to accommodate whatever controls, wiring, tubing, etc., that extend from one compartment to the other.

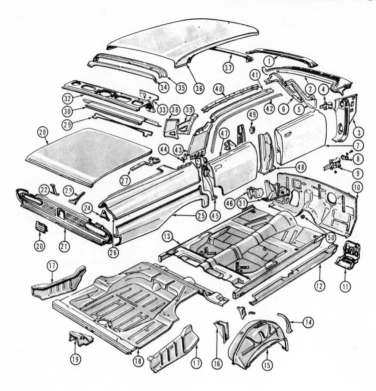

NO.	DESCRIPTION	NO.	DESCRIPTION	NO.	DESCRIPTION
1	WINDSHIELD HEADER	17	REAR FLOOR PAN TO QUARTER PANEL EXTENSION	34	ROOF PANEL REAR EXTENSION
2	COWL TOP PANEL	18	REAR FLOOR PAN	35	BACK WINDOW UPPER FRAME
3	PILLAR AND COWL SIDE	19	FUEL TANK FILLER PIPE HOUSING	36	ROOF PANEL
4	UPPER DOOR HINGE	20	FUEL FILLER LID	37	REAR PANEL CENTER REINFORCEMENT
5	OUTER FRONT BODY PILLAR	21	LOWER BACK PANEL	38	REAR SIDE RAIL
6	INNER FRONT BODY PILLAR	22	LOWER BACK PANEL TO FLOOR BRACE	39	ROOF REAR UPPER SIDE RAIL
7	FRONT DOOR	23	LOWER TROUGH	40	ROOF INNER SIDE RAIL
8	DOOR CHECK	24	QUARTER PANEL REAR FILLER	41	ROOF OUTER SIDE RAIL
9	LOWER DOOR HINGE	25	LOWER QUARTER PANEL	42	SIDE FINISH MOULDING
10	DASH PANEL	26	UPPER QUARTER PANEL	43	ROOF SIDE REAR EXTENSION
11	DASH TO FRAME BRACE	27	LUGGAGE COMP'T. DOOR HINGE	44	ROOF REAR LOWER SIDE RAIL EXTENSION
12	ROCKER PANEL	28	LUGGAGE COMP'T. DOOR	45	QUARTER LOCK PILLAR
13	FRONT FLOOR PAN	29	TORSION RODS	46	LOWER REAR DOOR HINGE
14	REINFORCEMENT	30	UPPER BACK PANEL	47	REAR DOOR
15	QUARTER WHEELHOUSE	31	BRAKE PEDAL SUPPORT	48	CENTER PILLAR
16	DOOR HINGE TO WHEELHOUSE BRACKET	32	PACKAGE TRAY PANEL	49	UPPER REAR DOOR HINGE
		33	PACKAGE TRAY STRAINER	50	TRANSMISSION INSPECTION COVER

Fig. 10. Hardtop Four-Door Sedan Body Panels

(*Courtesy Lincoln-Mercury Division, Ford Motor Company*)

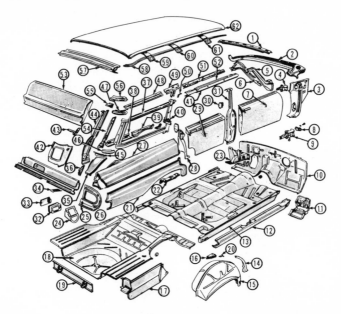

Fig. 11. Four-Door Station Wagon Body Panels

(Courtesy Lincoln-Mercury Division, Ford Motor Company)

NO.	DESCRIPTION
1	WINDSHIELD HEADER
2	COWL TOP PANEL
3	PILLAR AND COWL SIDE
4	UPPER DOOR HINGE
5	OUTER FRONT BODY PILLAR
6	INNER FRONT BODY PILLAR
7	FRONT DOOR
8	FRONT DOOR CHECK
9	LOWER DOOR HINGE
10	DASH PANEL
11	DASH TO FRAME BRACKET
12	ROCKER PANEL
13	FRONT FLOOR PAN
14	QUARTER PANEL (LOCKSIDE) LOWER REINFORCEMENT
15	QUARTER WHEELHOUSE
16	REAR SEAT BACK STOP SUPPORT
17	REAR FLOOR PAN TO QUARTER PANEL EXTENSION
18	REAR FLOOR PAN
19	REAR FLOOR REAR SILL
20	REAR SEAT BACK STOP WHEELHOUSE BRACKET
21	LOWER REAR QUARTER PANEL

NO.	DESCRIPTION
22	SEAT CUSHION SUPPORT RISER
23	BRAKE PEDAL SUPPORT
24	FUEL TANK FILLER PIPE HOUSING
25	LOWER REAR QUARTER PANEL EXTENSION
26	QUARTER PANEL REAR FILLER
27	UPPER REAR QUARTER PANEL
28	QUARTER LOCK PILLAR
29	REAR DOOR
30	REAR DOOR UPPER HINGE
31	CENTER PILLAR
32	FUEL FILLER OPENING COLLAR
33	FUEL FILLER LID
34	LOWER BACK PANEL BRACE
35	UPPER REAR QUARTER PANEL EXTENSION
36	FILLER (QUARTER PANEL) UPPER REAR TO LOWER REAR EXTENSION
37	QUARTER WINDOW FRAME
38	REAR QUARTER BELT RAIL
39	FRONT QUARTER BELT RAIL
40	CENTER LOWER INNER ROOF SIDE RAIL
41	FRONT ROOF RAIL OUTER EXTENSION
42	REAR QUARTER PANEL LOWER REINFORCEMENT

NO.	DESCRIPTION
43	TAILGATE HINGE
44	OUTER REAR CORNER PILLAR
45	QUARTER PILLAR EXTENSION REINFORCEMENT
46	QUARTER PANEL REINFORCEMENT BRACKET
47	REAR ROOF RAIL OUTER EXTENSION
48	INNER REAR ROOF SIDE RAIL
49	CENTER, UPPER INNER ROOF SIDE RAIL
50	QUARTER WINDOW OPENING REAR CORNER UPPER FRONT FILLER
51	INNER FRONT ROOF SIDE RAIL
52	OUTER FRONT ROOF SIDE RAIL
53	TAILGATE ASSEMBLY
54	UPPER INNER REAR CORNER PILLAR
56	BACK WINDOW HEADER EXTENSION
56	INNER REAR ROOF SIDE RAIL EXTENSION
57	BACK WINDOW HEADER RAIL
58	ROOF DRIP SIDE MOULDING
59	ROOF PANEL REAR REINFORCEMENT
60	ROOF PANEL CENTER REINFORCEMENT
61	ROOF PANEL FRONT REINFORCEMENT
62	ROOF PANEL

The instrument panel is usually considered as part of the cowl panel, although it is a complex panel in itself. The instrument panel portion of the cowl provides a mounting for the instruments necessary to check the performance of the vehicle during operation. The instrument panel usually is fastened to the major portion of the cowl with bolts and sheet metal screws. It is bolted at each end and secured along the lower edge of the windshield opening with sheet metal screws.

Cowl panels usually have both inner and outer construction. However, on some cars only the upper portion of the cowl around the windshield is visible as an outer panel. On most cars, the front door hinge pillar is an integral part of the cowl. A typical arrangement is shown in Fig. 12.

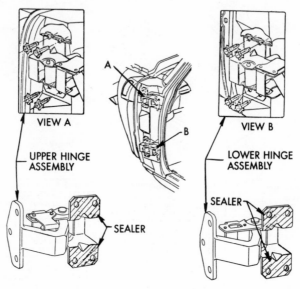

Fig. 12. Front Door Hinge Assembly
(*Courtesy Lincoln-Mercury Division, Ford Motor Company*)

(2) *ROOF PANEL OR ASSEMBLY.* The roof panel is one of the largest of all major body panels, but it is also one of the simplest in construction (Figs. 9, 10, and 11).

Usually, the roof is of all-steel, one-piece construction. The area the roof encompasses, however, varies between different makes and models of cars. On some cars, the roof panel ends at the front at the windshield. On others, it extends downward around the windshield, so that the windshield opening is actually in the roof.

On some cars, the roof ends above the rear window at the rear. On others, it extends downward at the rear so that the rear window opening is in the lower rear roof. When this is the case, the roof forms the top panel around the rear deck opening.

Some special body designs incorporate different methods of rear window construction which affect the roof panel. This is particularly true of "hard top" convertibles. On these cars, the top is joined to the rear quarter panels by another smaller panel which is part of the roof assembly. In other special designs, the roof panel is completely covered with a waterproof vinyl plastic. This arrangement is merely for the sake of eye appeal.

Most roof panels have stiffeners, which are small metal strips, placed crosswise to the roof at intervals along the inside surface. These stiffeners are welded in place and provide the necessary tacking strips for securing the headlining and inside trim in place.

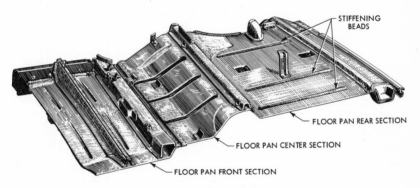

Fig. 13. Top View of Typical Floor Pan

(3) *UNDERBODY.* The underbody (Fig. 13) is commonly called the *floor pan*. The floor pan is usually composed of several smaller panels which are either welded together or secured to one another by bolts to form one single unit. All floor pans are reinforced on the underside by floor pan cross bars (Fig. 14).

Most floor pans are irregularly shaped for several reasons. They are formed with indentations or "beads," (Fig. 13) to strengthen the pan. A floor pan must be shaped to fit around the chassis units and the frame. The passengers' feet are often accommodated by recessed areas in the floor. The most noticeable irregularities in floor pans are usually the transmission "hump" and the driveshaft "tunnel" (Fig. 14).

(4) *REAR QUARTER PANEL.* The rear quarter panel is often integral with the rear fender on late model cars. An example of this type of arrangement is shown in Fig. 15. However, the common con-

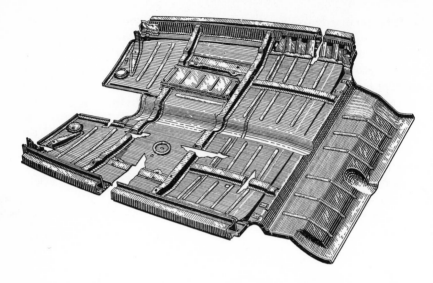

Fig. 14. Bottom View of Floor Pan Showing Floor Pan Cross Bars

ception of what is meant by rear quarter panels is illustrated in Figs. 9, 10, and 11.

The quarter panel has both inner and outer construction. The outer construction or outer panel is, of course, smooth, except for the breaks caused by the design of the car. The outer panel wraps around the inner construction at the edges which are exposed at fender openings or door openings. Both welding, and bolts and screws are used to secure the outer panel to the inner construction.

Fig. 15. The rear quarter panel is integral with the rear fender on this car.
(*Courtesy Lincoln-Mercury Division, Ford Motor Company*)

The inner construction of a quarter panel is made up of many strong reinforcement brackets welded or bolted together to form a single unit. The quarter panel inner construction usually extends across the vehicle at the rear of the passenger compartment. This provides a support for the rear seat back if the car is so equipped, or it provides a partition between the luggage compartment and the passenger compartment. The most important function of these reinforcements is to provide additional strength across the rear quarter panel area of the car. A typical quarter panel, lower section arrangement, forward of the rear wheel, is shown in Fig. 16.

(a) QUARTER PANEL WHEELHOUSE. On some cars, the rear wheelhouse is constructed as an integral part of the inner construction of the rear quarter panel.

A sectional view of a typical quarter panel wheelhouse arrangement

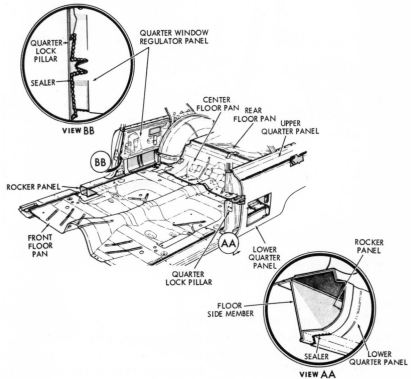

Fig. 16. Lower Section of Quarter Panel Forward of Rear Wheel

(*Courtesy Ford Motor Company*)

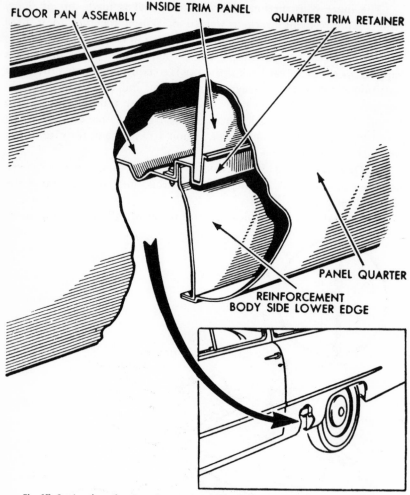

FLOOR PAN ASSEMBLY   INSIDE TRIM PANEL   QUARTER TRIM RETAINER

PANEL QUARTER

REINFORCEMENT
BODY SIDE LOWER EDGE

Fig. 17. Section through a Rear Quarter Panel Wheelhouse at Center Line of Rear Wheel
(Courtesy Ford Motor Company)

is shown in Fig. 17. As you can see from this illustration, the wheelhouse is usually of two-piece construction. The pieces comprising the wheelhouse are either welded or bolted together. The wheelhouse is then attached as an integral part of the quarter panel.

(5) *CENTER BODY PILLAR.* The center pillar in Fig. 9 is a typical arrangement for a four-door sedan body. In this type of construction, the center pillar acts as the central roof and side support between

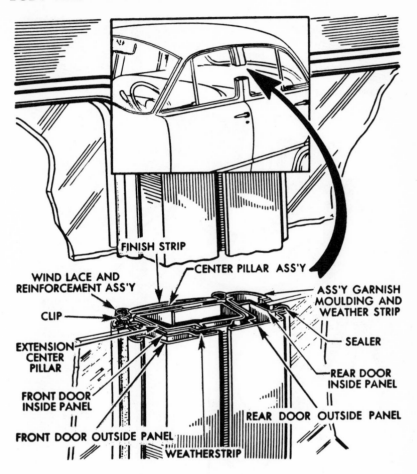

FINISH STRIP

WIND LACE AND REINFORCEMENT ASS'Y

CENTER PILLAR ASS'Y

CLIP

ASS'Y GARNISH MOULDING AND WEATHER STRIP

EXTENSION CENTER PILLAR

SEALER

REAR DOOR INSIDE PANEL

FRONT DOOR INSIDE PANEL

REAR DOOR OUTSIDE PANEL

FRONT DOOR OUTSIDE PANEL

WEATHERSTRIP

Fig. 18. Center Pillar Section above Window Opening
(*Courtesy Ford Motor Company*)

the rear and front of the car. For this reason, it is made from heavy stock and is constructed sturdily. In this type of arrangement, the center pillar acts as the hinge pillar for the rear doors and as the lock pillar for the front doors.

In some other makes of cars, the pillar is constructed similarly, but is visible from the outside when the doors are closed. In these cases, the pillar is wide with an outer panel surface. The sectional views in Figs. 18 and 19 show a typical arrangement where the pillar is not

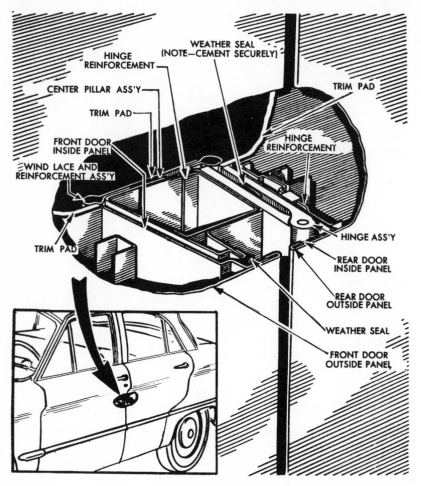

Fig. 19. Center Pillar Section below Door Handle
(*Courtesy Ford Motor Company*)

visible with the doors closed. The component parts of the pillar, including the trim parts and weather seals used around the center pillar, are also visible in these illustrations. On two-door sedan type bodies, the center pillar is incorporated into the rear quarter side panel. It does, however, perform the same structural function on a two-door as on a four-door.

The most common arrangement with two-door type cars is to have the center pillar act as the lock pillar for the door.

You can see from Figs. 18 and 19 that the center pillar is made from several pieces. These pieces are either welded or bolted together to form a single, strong unit.

The center pillar is usually irregular in shape. In fact, the center pillar design changes with each body style. The pillar must conform to the outside contour of the body as well as the contour of the door opening. Depressions are formed into the pillar at the time it is manufactured to accommodate the door lock striker plates and hinges, depending upon the body style.

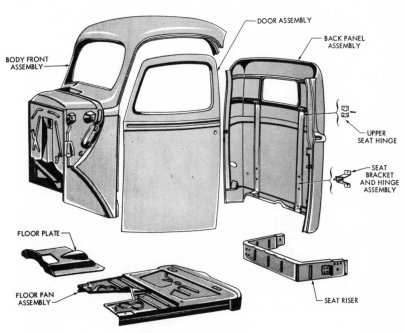

Fig. 20. Typical Closed Cab
(*Courtesy Ford Motor Company*)

b. Cabs. As explained before, a cab is the passenger compartment of a truck. All cabs are not alike, however, but vary in size and arrangement according to the purpose for which the truck is intended.

A typical closed cab is shown in Fig. 20. All of the component parts of a closed cab are clearly labeled in this illustration.

A typical cab over engine type cab is shown in Fig. 21, with all the major panels labeled clearly.

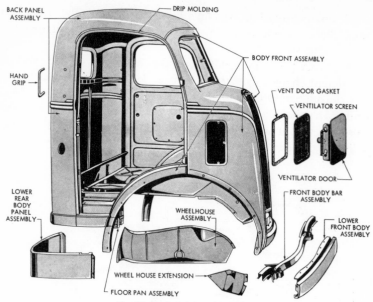

Fig. 21. Typical Cab over Engine

(*Courtesy Ford Motor Company*)

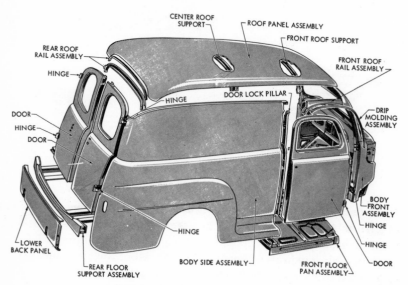

Fig. 22. Typical Panel Delivery Truck Body

(*Courtesy Ford Motor Company*)

Still another type of truck cab is integral with the body. This type of arrangement is called a body instead of a cab. This arrangement is popular for use in light delivery work. This type of truck usually is built on a passenger car chassis. A typical panel delivery truck body is shown in Fig. 22.

In Figs. 23, 24, and 25, several sections through different locations on truck cabs and bodies are shown which illustrate typical construction.

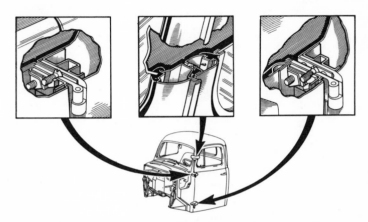

Fig. 23. Sectional View of Front Pillar and Upper and Lower Door Hinges
(Courtesy Ford Motor Company)

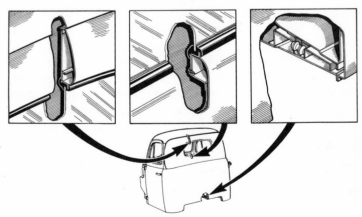

Fig. 24. Sectional View of Top of Rear Window, Bottom of Rear Window, and Bottom of Cab
(Conventional Cab)
(Courtesy Ford Motor Company)

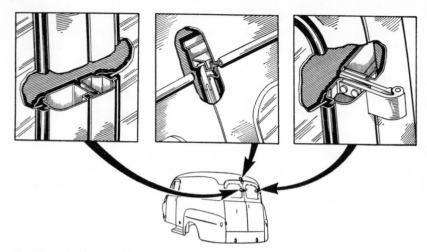

Fig. 25. Sectional View of Rear Door at Drip Rail and Door Latch, Rear Door at Center, and
Door Glass and Upper Hinge (Panel Delivery)

(*Courtesy Ford Motor Company*)

You can easily see from these illustrations that the major panels of
a truck cab, or body, and those of a passenger car body differ considerably. The same principles of construction are used on truck cabs and
bodies as on passenger car bodies, however, even though the panels differ in size and appearance.

You will undoubtedly encounter truck cabs and bodies which differ
in appearance from those that have been shown. However, the construction in these instances will be similar to the cabs and bodies previously illustrated.

In some designs, the entire cab is hinged to the lower front body
and can be unlatched at the lower rear edge and tilted forward. This
arrangement is desirable in some instances because of the necessity of
gaining access to otherwise inaccessible chassis components.

c. Body and Cab Assembly. At the time of original manufacture, the
major panels of bodies and cabs are joined to one another in huge jigs
or fixtures. The subassemblies are first assembled in smaller jigs and
fixtures into the major panels. The major panels are then clamped into
a large body fixture and are joined by welding, riveting, or with bolts
and nuts. The most common method of securing the panels to one another is spot welding. The spot welders usually are an integral part of
the body fixture. The spot welds are made about an inch and a half to
two inches apart. On certain panels, the welds are spaced much closer—

no more than half an inch apart. These are areas along the bottom of the body where the side panels are joined to the floor. The welds, being closer together, add strength to the structure and lessen the probability of dust and water leaks.

Huge jigs and fixtures for reassembly are too expensive for anyone in the collision business; less expensive methods of body and cab reassembly will be discussed later in this book.

(1) *COWL AND ROOF ASSEMBLY*. The cowl panel and roof panel are joined to one another by welding. The break between these two panels differs among manufacturers, so some are joined by continuous welds and some by spot welding. When the roof panel comes down below the windshield, it is joined to the cowl along the front edge by spot welding. When the cowl and roof panel break at the center of the windshield pillar, a continuous weld is made all around the pillar. When the cowl extends above the windshield, as is the case on many truck cabs, a continuous weld is made all along the edge where the two panels join.

(2) *UNDERBODY*. The underbody is secured to the cowl panel at the front, to the quarter side panels and pillars on the sides, and to the lower back panel at the rear. It is usually joined to the other panels by spot welding. It is not only welded directly to the panels, but also to numerous brackets and braces which have previously been secured to the cowl or quarter panels. The welds are spaced approximately one-half inch apart along the seam where the floor pan joins with the cowl or quarter panels.

(3) *CENTER BODY PILLAR*. The center body pillar joins to the roof panel at the top and to the floor pan at the bottom. It is usually secured by a continuous weld all around the edge at both the top and bottom.

(4) *REAR QUARTER SIDE PANELS*. These panels are spot welded all along the edge where they join with the roof. They are joined together at the rear by the lower back panel, which is not usually considered as a major body panel. All of the joining around the lower back panel is done by spot welding.

When the rear fender is not integral with the rear quarter side panel, it is fastened to the quarter panel. The quarter panel in this case has holes punched around the fender opening for the screws which secure the fender.

IV. UNIT BODY CONSTRUCTION

Unit, or *unitized* body construction is not a new engineering concept. Unitized body construction employs the same principles of design that have been used for years in the aircraft industry. The main goal has been strength and rigidity without unnecessary weight. Unit construction does not employ a conventional frame to which suspension, engine, and other chassis and power train components are attached.

(a) **Underbody.** The major difference between a conventional body and a unitized body is in the design and construction of the floor pan. In a unitized body, the floor pan area is generally called, the *underbody.* The underbody is made up of formed floor pans, channels, box sections, formed rails, and numerous reinforcements (Fig. 27).

In most unitized underbodies, a suspension member is incorporated at both the front and rear (Fig. 26). The suspension members have very much the same appearance as a conventional frame from the underside. However, the front suspension members terminate at the cowl and the rear suspension members terminate just forward of the rear "kick-up." With the floor pans, side rails and reinforcements welded to them, the suspension members become an integral part of

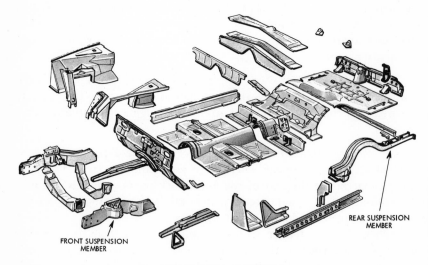

FRONT SUSPENSION MEMBER

REAR SUSPENSION MEMBER

Fig. 26. Typical Unitized Underbody

(*Courtesy Lincoln-Mercury Division, Ford Motor Company*)

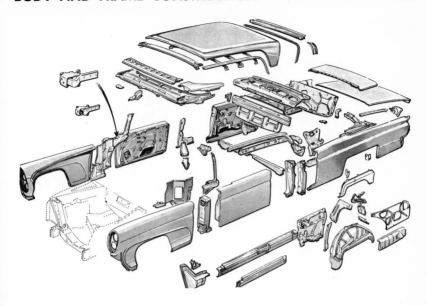

Fig. 27. Typical Unitized Upper Body

(Courtesy Lincoln-Mercury Division, Ford Motor Company)

the underbody. The suspension members become the supports for engine, front and rear suspension and other chassis components.

There is a marked difference between the floor pan of a unitized body and the single thickness floor pan of a conventional body. In the unitized body the floor pan is usually of double thickness and has one or more box sections and several channel sections which may either run across the floor pan from side to side, or from front to rear. The major differences between various underbody constructions are due largely to the differences in wheelbase, length, and weight of the car involved.

(b) Upper Body. A typical upper body for a unitized construction car is shown in Fig. 27. As you can see, the construction is very near the same as a conventional body. However, the major difference lies in the package tray area in the rear and in the construction which joins the front fenders at the front. A typical front fender and related supporting parts are shown in Fig. 28.

The construction in the area to the rear of the back seat is much heavier in a unit construction body than in a conventional body. The same is true of the attaching members for the front fenders. Rigidity

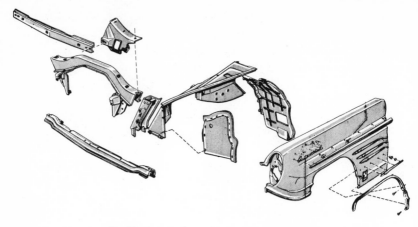

Fig. 28. Front Fender and Supporting Construction
(*Courtesy Lincoln-Mercury Division, Ford Motor Company*)

in the structure is necessary in these two areas to complement the cowl and floor pan construction and give strength and stability to the overall body structure.

(c) Unitized Body Variations. As with any automotive components, there are variations in construction methods among the various car

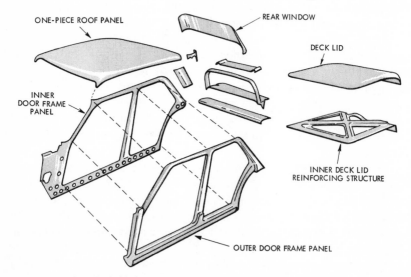

Fig. 29. Welded One-Piece Body Side and Door Frame Construction
(*Courtesy Lincoln-Mercury Division, Ford Motor Company*)

makers. In some forms of unit construction, the entire front end area forward of the cowl is joined to the cowl with bolts. With this construction, the bolts at the cowl can be removed and the entire front end replaced as an assembly in the event of extensive damage.

In yet another and more recent development, the entire body side or door frame construction is of one piece (Fig. 29). Notice that there is both an inner panel and an outer panel which make up the total structure. These are welded together and are therefore very strong.

V. DOORS AND DECK LIDS

The openings through which the passengers gain access to the body interiors are merely referred to as doors. The door through which access to the rear luggage compartment is obtained is called a deck lid.

In station wagon bodies, the opening into the passenger compartment through the rear of the body is generally termed a *tail gate*. Tail gates are two-piece. The lower half is hinged at the bottom and swings outward and down to form a platform when open. The upper half is hinged at the top to swing outward and upward when open to give easy access to the rear of the passenger compartment.

a. Doors. Several doors are used on each type of vehicle built, whether it is a car or truck. The construction of doors is similar, regardless of the location of the door on the vehicle.

A door is composed of two main panels: an outer panel and an inner panel (Fig. 30). Both panels are of all-steel construction. The door derives most of its strength from the inner panel, since the inner panel

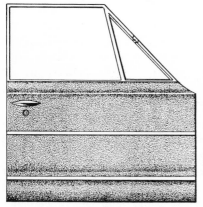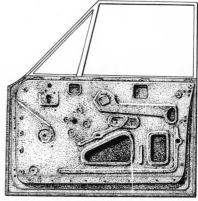

Fig. 30. Door Outer Panel (left) and Inner Panel (right)

is constructed primarily to act as a frame for the door. The outer panel flanges over the inner panel around all edges to form a single unit.

The inner panel is made with offsets and holes for the attachment of door inner hardware. This hardware consists of the window regulator assembly and the door locking mechanism. A typical installation of door locking mechanism is shown in Fig. 31. These assemblies are installed through the large openings in the middle of the inner panel.

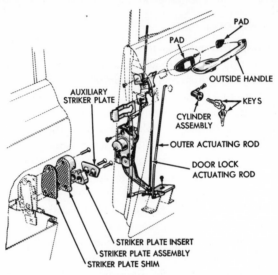

Fig. 31. Typical Door Locking Mechanism
(*Courtesy Ford Motor Company*)

Much of the thickness of the door is due to the depth of the inner panel, which is necessary to accommodate the door latch and window mechanisms. The inner panel forms the lock pillar and also the hinge pillar sections of the door (Fig. 32). Small reinforcement angles are usually used between the outer and inner panels, both where the lock is inserted through the door and where the hinges attach to the door.

The outer panel is provided with an opening through which the outside door handle protrudes. In some instances, a separate opening is provided for the lock (Fig. 31).

The upper portion of the door is a large opening which is closed by glass. The glass is held rigidly by the window regulator assembly. A channel is secured in the opening between the outer and inner panels in the upper portion of the door. When the window is raised, it slides

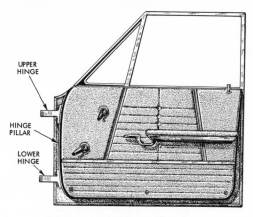

UPPER
HINGE

HINGE
PILLAR

LOWER
HINGE

Fig. 32. Hinge Pillar Section of Door
Panel

in this channel. When it is fully closed, the window seats tightly in
this channel, effectively sealing out the weather.

Most vehicles incorporate a ventilator window in front doors. Such
an arrangement is shown in Fig. 33. A bar is placed upright in the door
window opening, dividing it into a relatively large rectangular opening
and a smaller triangular opening. This smaller window is the vent
window. The vent window is sealed by weather stripping so that it is
weathertight. Different methods of control are used; some cars have a
crank and gear arrangement for opening and closing the vent; others
have a thumb latch next to the division bar.

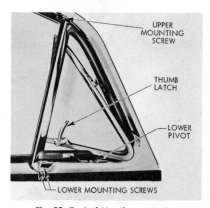

UPPER
MOUNTING
SCREW

THUMB
LATCH

LOWER
PIVOT

LOWER MOUNTING SCREWS

Fig. 33. Typical Ventilator Window

When rear doors have a vent window, the construction is similar to that used for front doors. In some cases, two-door rear quarter windows lower part way only. In others, it cannot be lowered at all because of interference with the wheelhouse and rear quarter panel. Some two-door models are equipped with only a ventilator type quarter window.

b. Deck Lids. The deck lid is really another door which allows access to the luggage compartment in the rear of cars. A typical deck lid is shown in Fig. 35.

A deck lid is composed of an outer panel and an inner panel. These

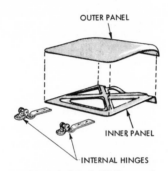

Fig. 34. Typical Deck Lid Construction

(Courtesy Lincoln-Mercury Division, Ford Motor Company)

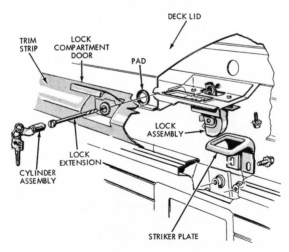

Fig. 35. Rear Deck Lid and Latch Mechanism without Handle

(Courtesy Lincoln-Mercury Division, Ford Motor Company)

panels are spot welded together along their flanged edges to form a single unit in the same manner as is a regular door. The inner panel construction is shown in Fig. 34. This also shows one type of hinge arrangement (internal). Some cars use external hinges, while other cars have concealed hinges attached to the inner panel only.

A latch is sometimes provided at the bottom rear of the deck lid and is controlled by an external handle. This external handle is sometimes concealed from the eye under a molding or some other type of trim.

In some models, there is no handle on the rear deck lid (Fig. 35). Instead, the hinges are spring-loaded so that when the deck lid is unlocked, it automatically raises part way and is held in the open position by the springs in the hinge mechanism.

VI GLASS

Various methods are used to hold glass in place, depending on where the glass is used. Some windows remain stationary while others are movable. The different methods of glass installation are shown in this section.

Certain general precautions should be taken whenever any kind of glass is installed. Exercise care against straining or chipping the glass during the installation procedure, as breakage may result. Be sure that the glass used is the proper size for the body or cab on which you are working. Always use a drop cloth to protect interior and exterior surfaces from being marred or soiled and to prevent glass breakage.

Glass often cracks for no apparent reason. Generally, however, you will find in these cases that the glass has been under a strain. If a new glass is installed without correcting the cause of the breakage, the new glass also will crack. This might occur while you are making the installation. In other cases, the glass might break after a few days. In still other cases, the glass might not crack for several months. It is part of your responsibility to see that whatever glass you install is not under a strain that may cause it to break later. Make sure that body flanges and glass channels are not distorted or out of position before the new glass is installed.

a. Windshield and Rear Window. The windshield and rear window glass are quite similar in construction. For this reason, all service procedures involving windshields can be easily applied to rear

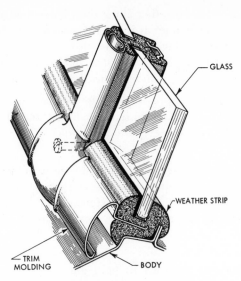

Fig. 36. Cross Section through Two-
Piece Windshield Weather Strip

windows. Fig. 36 shows a typical cross section through a two-piece
windshield and weather strip. A cross-sectional view of a one-piece windshield installation is shown in Fig. 37.

Most windshields and rear windows are held in place by a rubber
weather strip, whether they are single-piece or multiple-piece installations. Both the glass and the outside trim molding are recessed in the

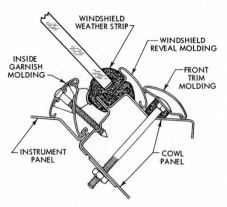

Fig. 37. Cross Section through One-Piece
Windshield Installation

weather strip. The weather strip also has a recess which fits over the body flange all around the opening for the glass. It is this portion of the weather strip that holds the entire assembly in place.

Some windshields and rear windows are sealant-bonded directly to recesses in the car body.

Replacement procedures for both one-piece and two-piece windshields with rubber weather stripping are given here. With a few minor exceptions which will be quite obvious, these same methods can be applied to replacement of rear windows.

In some cars, all of the windows including windshields and rear windows are tempered curved glass. Improved tempering and forming techniques have made this possible. All of the replacement procedures given here can be applied in these cases. A flexible tempered glass has also been developed for use in rear windows of convertibles.

(1) *TWO-PIECE WINDSHIELD REPLACEMENT.* If it is necessary to replace half of a two-piece windshield, only the broken half will have to be removed.

(a) REMOVAL. Working inside the car, remove all of the garnish molding from around the windshield. The most common types of windshield installations are shown in Fig. 38. Remove the inner and outer center strips.

Remove the outside trim molding. This can be done by starting at the center of the car and working toward the outside, loosening the molding with an awl. Working from the center will eliminate the danger of kinking the molding.

Loosen the rubber lip from the body flange all around the inside and the outside. This can also be done with an awl or a screwdriver. The glass and weather strip can then be removed from the opening. If the installation is of the type shown in (C), Fig. 38, it is necessary to remove it toward the inside of the car. This is accomplished by using a screwdriver as a lever. Beginning at the top of the windshield, insert the screwdriver under the lip of the weather strip, and prying with a block of wood between the screwdriver and the glass, work the weather strip off the body flange all around the windshield opening (Fig. 39). The windshield can then be pushed out toward the inside of the car. The glass can then be taken out of the weather strip.

If the windshield is of the type where the rubber lip over the body flange is from the outside, then the windshield is pushed outward to remove it. Gloves should be worn for this operation. With the flat of your hand, push against the upper inside corner of the glass until it

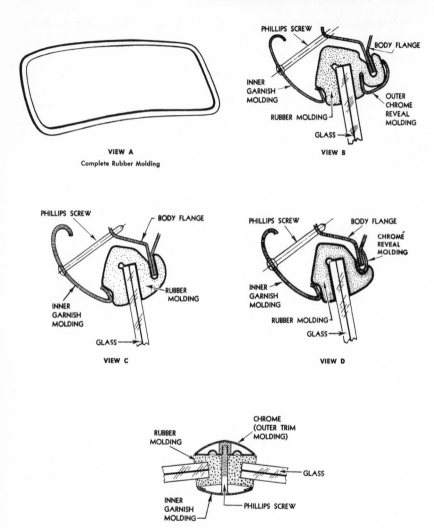

VIEW A
Complete Rubber Molding

VIEW B

VIEW C

VIEW D

VIEW E
Center sections of body types in
Views B, C, D.

Fig. 38. Typical Windshield Installations
(*Courtesy Pittsburgh Plate Glass Company*)

is loosened from the opening. Continue all around the windshield opening until the entire glass assembly is loose, then remove it from the body. The glass can then be removed from the weather strip.

(b) INSTALLATION. Installation of the glass begins with inserting the glass in the weather strip. Be sure the rubber channel is free from all foreign material. Insert a good grade of glass sealer in the rubber channel around the weather strip. Work the glass into the channel and be sure that it is properly seated all the way around. Then install a heavy cord in the rubber lip which fits over the body flange, and leave the ends of the cord overlapped at the center of the windshield. Fill the rubber lip with a good grade of sealer to prevent water leaks.

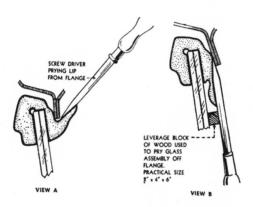

SCREW DRIVER PRYING LIP FROM FLANGE

LEVERAGE BLOCK OF WOOD USED TO PRY GLASS ASSEMBLY OFF FLANGE. PRACTICAL SIZE 2" x 4" x 6"

VIEW A   VIEW B

Fig. 39. Prying Glass from Opening
(*Courtesy Pittsburgh Plate Glass Company*)

Place the entire unit in the opening as close to the body flange as possible. Remember that on certain bodies you will be working from the inside, while on others you will be working from the outside. Press the glass against the body flange with one hand. With the other, slowly pull the cord out of the rubber lip. This will pull the lip of the weather strip over the body flange. Work all around the opening until the rubber lip is firmly in place over the body flange. Smear the trim molding opening in the weather strip with a soap solution. Then, working from the center to the ends, install the trim molding. Install the inside garnish molding, wipe off all excessive sealer, and wash the glass.

(2) *ONE-PIECE WINDSHIELD REPLACEMENT.* The information given here applies to both straight and curved glass in either the windshield or back window. Most one-piece windshields can be re-

moved from the outside of the vehicle and have a cross section similar to the one shown at (*A*), Fig. 40.

In other vehicles, the windshield is removed from the inside. These windshields have a section similar to that shown at (*B*), Fig. 40.

The procedure given here is for removing a windshield which comes out toward the outside of the car (Fig. 41). If it is necessary to remove a windshield which comes out toward the inside, the same procedure can be used, except that instead of prying off the rubber weather strip from the inside, it is done from the outside.

(a) REMOVAL. Cover the hood and cowl to protect the finish. Working inside the car, remove any instrument panel moldings which interfere with removing the inner garnish molding. In this respect, it might be well to note that on some makes of cars, the radio grille extends above the garnish molding. Remove the inner garnish molding from around the windshield. Working from the outside, remove any windshield chrome trim molding.

Again working from the inside, pry the rubber weather strip off the body flange with a screwdriver. Press firmly against the glass with your hand, adjacent to the portion of the rubber lip being removed. This will force the entire assembly out of the opening and the windshield can then be removed.

To remove sealant-bonded windshields, first remove the window moldings and then saw through the sealant around the glass by means

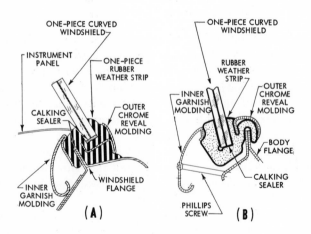

Fig. 40. One-Piece Windshield Installations

(Courtesy Pittsburgh Plate Glass Company)

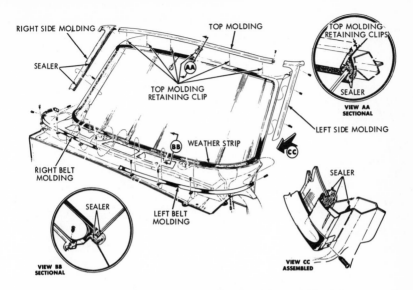

Fig. 41. Exploded View of Windshield Mounted from Outside of Car

(*Courtesy Lincoln-Mercury Division, Ford Motor Company*)

of a fine wire pushed through a hole drilled in the sealant. Then remove the defective glass.

(b) INSTALLATION. Clean the glass channel in the rubber weather strip to be sure all traces of sealer and old glass are removed. Place a bead of new sealer all around the weather strip in the bottom of the glass. See channel in (*A*), Fig. 40. Work the glass into the weather strip and be sure it is properly seated all the way around. Lay the windshield on a bench. If the glass is curved, lay it so the curved ends are up. Install any outside chrome trim molding. Use a soap solution in the groove and a pair of spreading pliers to spread the groove. Start at the center of the windshield and tap the molding in securely with light taps of a rubber mallet. Exercise care to avoid kinking the molding.

Turn the windshield over on the bench so that the curved ends are down. With the windshield in this position, the pull cords used to seat the rubber lip over the body flange can be inserted. Two pull cords, inserted so they can be pulled in opposite directions, will make the installation easier.

Start one cord from the bottom right-hand side of the windshield, leaving an excess of about one foot as shown in Fig. 42. Proceed to the left, and end up at the right top. Start the second cord from the bottom

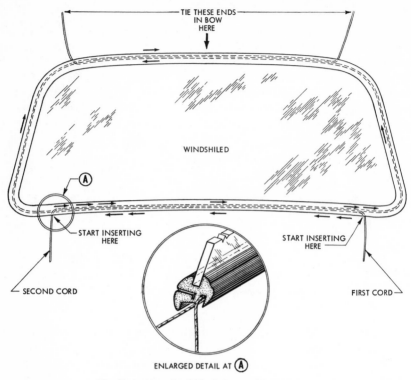

Fig. 42. Position of Pull Cords for Windshield Removal

left and proceed to the right to the top left. Tie the ends in a bow at the top left center of the glass.

Insert a bead of sealer into the same groove occupied by the cord. The location of this calking sealer is shown at (*A*), Fig. 40. Place the entire unit in the windshield opening with the cord ends hanging inside the vehicle. An assistant can be used to press against the glass while you pull each cord slowly out of the groove. As the cord is pulled out, the rubber lip will seat over the body flange. If it is necessary to make the installation by yourself, stand at the side of the body and press the glass in with one hand and pull the cord out with the other.

Be sure the rubber lip is seated firmly over the body flange. A rubber mallet can be used to tap the unit around the outside of the opening. Be careful not to hit the chrome molding too hard, as it is possible to kink the molding or break the glass.

Replace any instrument panel moldings or accessories which were removed. Replace the inside garnish molding and wipe off any excess sealer that has squeezed out. Wash the glass and the job is completed.

To install sealant-bonded glass, use moistened pumice powder to roughen the marginal edges of the new glass and provide a good bonding surface. Use a solvent to remove all old sealant from the mounting recesses in the body. All bonding surfaces must be free of dirt and grease to ensure a watertight seal. Apply new sealant with a caulking gun. Align the new glass using crayon marked center lines and rubber

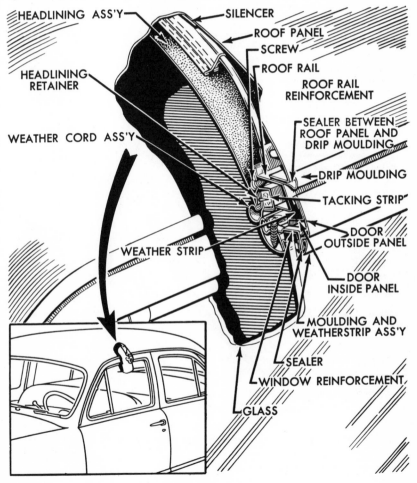

Fig. 43. Typical Cross Section through Door and Roof Rail

(Courtesy Ford Motor Company)

shims. (Do not mark bonding surfaces with crayon.) If possible, use suction cups to handle the glass and avoid contaminating the prepared bonding surfaces. Press the glass into position. Work the seal with a rounded piece of wood to ensure a neat and watertight bond. Then reinstall the window moldings and test the repair job for water leaks.

b. Door Glass. Door glass is fastened along the bottom only in a channel which is connected to the window regulator assembly (raising and lowering mechanism). The glass is held in the door by a channel or reinforcement so that it runs up and down evenly. This channel is

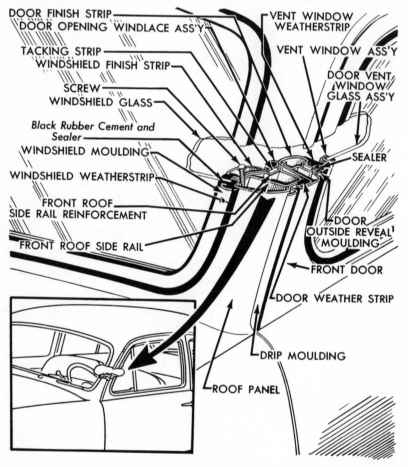

Fig. 44. Typical Cross Section through Windshield Pillar and Door

(*Courtesy Ford Motor Company*)

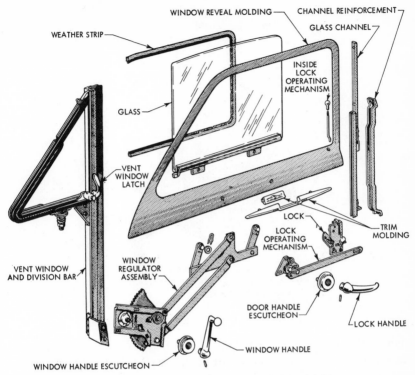

Fig. 45. An Exploded Front Door Window and Lock Assembly

secured in the opening between the outer and inner door panel. The channel is usually provided with a weather strip which not only seals the glass against the weather, but also keeps the window from rattling.

A typical section through an upper door is shown in Fig. 43. In this illustration, the position of the glass is clearly shown in relation to the other door parts in this area. Another section through the windshield pillar and door is shown in Fig. 44. This section is through the vent window area of the door and shows typical construction in this area.

A complete front door window and lock assembly is shown in Fig. 45. This illustration is typical of manually operated window mechanisms in car front doors. Fig. 46 shows a front door which has an electrically operated curved glass window.

c. Ventilator Windows. In some cars, the vent window is an integral part of the window reveal or garnish molding. A typical installa-

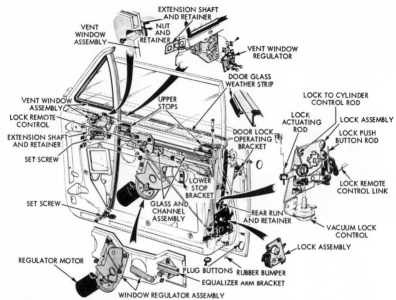

Fig. 46. Exploded View of Front Door with Electrically Operated Curved Glass Window

(Courtesy Lincoln-Mercury Division, Ford Motor Company)

tion of this type is shown in Fig. 47. With this type of vent window arrangement, the vent window can be disassembled easily by removing the reveal or garnish molding.

A division bar is placed between the vent window opening and the large window opening. A weather strip is installed around the ventilator window, constructed in such a way that the vent window is sealed securely against the weather when closed, but is easily opened.

Another type of vent window arrangement is shown in Fig. 45. With this type of construction, the division bar and vent window are considered as a separate unit of the over-all door construction. It can be replaced without removing the large door glass.

d. The Quarter Window. The quarter window is the window in the rear quarter upper side panel. In some types of cars, the quarter window is a stationary installation and no provision is made for raising or lowering it. With this type of construction, the installation is similar to a windshield or rear window. The glass is secured in a molding which is channeled to fit over the body.

In other types of cars, the quarter window is constructed in such a way as to allow it to be raised or lowered. In this case, the quarter

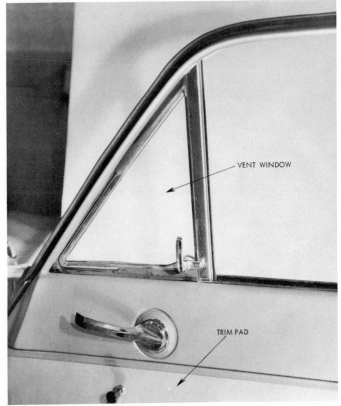

Fig. 47. This vent window is an integral part of the window molding.

(Courtesy Lincoln-Mercury Division, Ford Motor Company)

window construction is similar to door window construction. Some quarter windows of this type have small vent windows similar to front door vents. When this is the case, the same principles apply as for door vent windows.

In some cars, the quarter window consists entirely of a ventilation window which is similar in construction to front door vent windows except that it is larger. These windows usually hinge at the top and bottom near the front. Consequently, they actually pivot around a point ahead of the center of the opening. In most cases, they are fastened in the closed position at the rear with thumb latches. As with front vent windows, quarter vent windows are mounted in weather stripping so that a perfect weather seal is obtained.

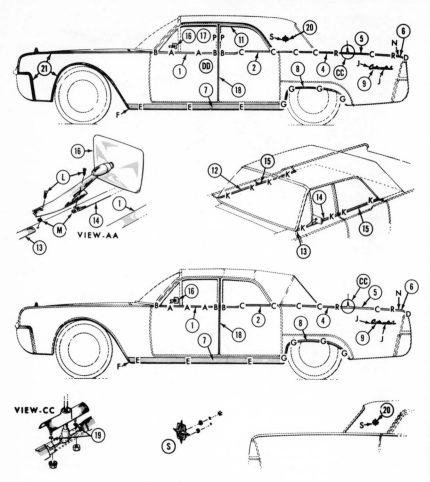

1. FRONT DOOR OUTSIDE MOLDING

2. REAR DOOR OUTSIDE MOLDING

3. QUARTER OUTSIDE UPPER FRONT MOLDING, RIGHT HAND

4. QUARTER OUTSIDE UPPER FRONT MOLDING, LEFT HAND

5. QUARTER OUTSIDE UPPER CENTER MOLDING, LEFT HAND

6. QUARTER OUTSIDE UPPER REAR MOLDING

7. BODY ROCKER PANEL MOLDING

8. QUARTER WHEEL OPENING MOLDING

9. BODY SIDE NAME PLATE

10. ROOF DRIP SIDE FINISH MOLDING EXTENSION

Fig. 48A. Exterior Hardware and Trim Parts

(Courtesy Lincoln-Mercury Division, Ford Motor Company)

VIEW-BB

SECTIONAL VIEW-DD

11. ROOF DRIP SIDE FINISH MOLDING

12. FRONT DOOR OUTSIDE BELT MOLDING, RIGHT HAND

13. FRONT DOOR OUTSIDE BELT MOLDING, LEFT HAND

14. FRONT DOOR OUTSIDE REAR BELT MOLDING, LEFT HAND

15. REAR DOOR OUTSIDE BELT MOLDING

16. OUTSIDE REAR VIEW MIRROR, LEFT HAND

17. CENTER BODY PILLAR OUTSIDE UPPER MOLDING

18. CENTER BODY PILLAR OUTSIDE STRIP FINISH

19. SEALER

20. ROOF SIDE ORNAMENT

Fig. 48B. Exterior Hardware and Trim Parts

(Courtesy Lincoln-Mercury Division, Ford Motor Company)

VII. HARDWARE AND TRIM

The preceding sections of this chapter have set forth in some detail the basic construction of automobile bodies and cabs. Bodies need hardware and trim to complete them just as a house with floors, walls, ceilings, roofs, doors, and windows needs hardware and trim. In the automobile body, as in the house, the doors need handles and locks. The window openings are unsightly when viewed from the inside and require decorative trim to give them a finished appearance. In the body, as in the house, these finishing touches, which are put on the outside as well as the inside of the body, are called either hardware or trim.

The car illustrated in Fig. 48 has all of the exterior hardware and trim parts labeled, and the method of attaching some of the items is shown. Both a sedan and a convertible are illustrated.

In addition to providing eye appeal, some trim parts are functional as well as decorative. However, they all contribute to the comfort and convenience of the passenger. Parts which are termed hardware are similar to items in a house which are called hardware. Door handles, window handles, locks, latches, etc., are all hardware parts. Trim parts, on the other hand, include moldings and some of the soft trim inside the car, and the bumpers, grille, and moldings on the outside of the car.

A typical car interior, with the hardware and trim parts labeled, is shown in Fig. 49.

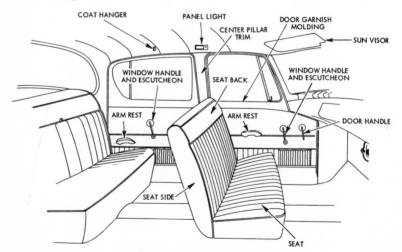

Fig. 49. Interior Hardware and Trim Parts

The location of all hardware and trim parts is described in this section. How these parts are held in place is also described and illustrated. These discussions on trim and hardware are given under headings which are descriptive of the parts involved.

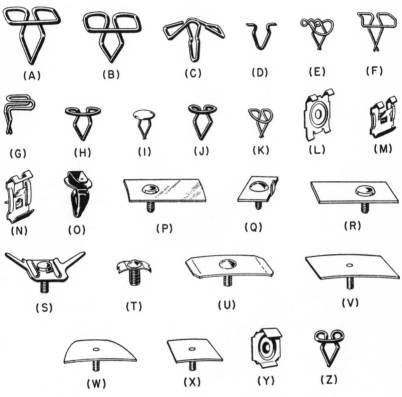

Fig. 50. Trim Fasteners and Retainers

Standard methods for fastening trim parts in place are used throughout the automotive industry. The devices employed are designed for use in specific locations, and they are made so that hardware and trim parts can be easily and quickly removed. A variety of trim fasteners and retainers is shown in Fig. 50. In this illustration, each retainer is labeled with a letter from the alphabet. In subsequent discussions of various moldings and trim parts, reference to this illustration will be made by letter designation.

a. **Grille.** The grille is usually the largest single unit of trim. Grilles are usually made from several pieces of steel which are fastened to one another by nuts and bolts or by welding. In some cases, the grille is made from cast aluminum or a white metal alloy, and is one single piece. Some grilles are made from heavy steel stampings and are made to look like part of the front bumper.

A typical grille arrangement is shown in Fig. 51, with all the component parts labeled. Grilles are usually fastened in place by bolts which attach it to the front splash pan and front fenders. Some grilles are fastened with soft expandable rivets made of an alloy with a low melting point. The rivets can be softened with a torch so that the grille can be removed without damage to the decorative plating. Brackets and supports which fasten to the front-end sheet metal forward of the radiator are also provided. It is these brackets which give a grille its rigidity and strength.

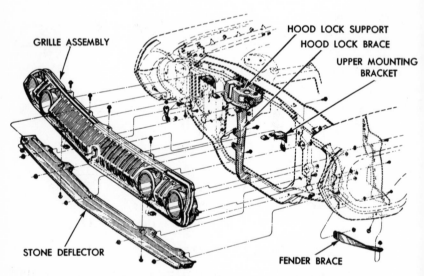

Fig. 51. Exploded View of Typical Grill Arrangement

(*Courtesy Lincoln-Mercury Division, Ford Motor Company*)

b. **Moldings.** Moldings generally are used freely both inside and outside on automobiles. Some moldings are strictly decorative, while others are functional. Moldings differ in type and style, depending on where they are used. A typical molding arrangement is shown in Fig. 52. The moldings illustrated in Fig. 52 are secured in place by re-

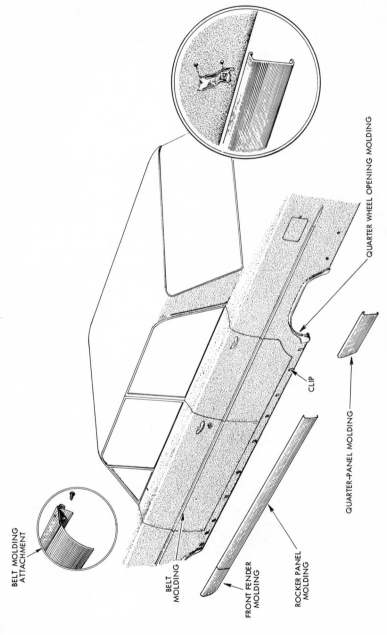

BELT MOLDING ATTACHMENT

QUARTER WHEEL OPENING MOLDING

CLIP

QUARTER-PANEL MOLDING

BELT MOLDING

FRONT FENDER MOLDING

ROCKER PANEL MOLDING

Fig. 52. Molding Arrangement

tainers *N* and *R,* Fig. 50, and by special clips designed for the particular model shown. These special clips, however, are typical of those you will find on many different cars. The clips usually fasten to the molding and extend through the body to be secured on the inside by speed nuts which fit the clip studs.

The moldings used around the windshield and rear windows on most cars are held in place in an entirely different manner. All of the moldings generally used in a windshield installation are shown in Fig. 53.

The weather strip which is used to secure the windshield glass is also channeled to receive the outside reveal molding. The molding is held by its own "spring back" to a great extent after it is inserted into the weather strip. The inside garnish molding which fits across the top of the instrument panel and around the windshield opening is fastened in place with sheet metal screws. The sheet metal screws have bright metal on the heads so that they present an attractive appearance. Generally, the screws used are of the Phillips-head type (cross-slotted head) which require a special screwdriver.

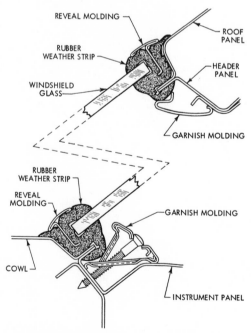

Fig. 53. Windshield Installation Showing Moldings

Another arrangement of windshield molding is shown in Fig. 54.

The moldings used around rear windows usually are installed in the same manner as the windshield on the particular model involved. Before moldings installed in this manner can be removed, it is necessary to break the seal between the weather strip and the body. This can be done easily in most cases by inserting a thin knife blade between the weather strip and the body, then running it along the length of the molding.

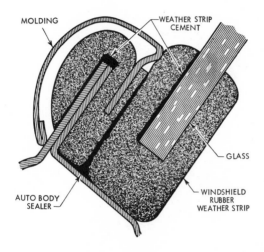

Fig. 54. Section through Windshield Weather Strip and Molding

A different type of molding is used around the window openings in the doors. This molding, called *door garnish molding*, is held in place by sheet metal screws. The screws may or may not show to the eye when the molding is in place with the door closed. If they do not show, it is because they are covered by the upholstery on the lower part of the door. Typical door garnish moldings are shown in Figs. 49 and 57.

Most of the moldings are held in place by screws through the molding into the door inner panel. A spring clip is usually mounted on the door inner panel behind the lower portion of the molding. This engages the molding and holds it firmly against the door trim pad.

To remove a garnish molding, remove the screws and the door inside locking rod knob, if any. Lift the molding out and upward to disengage it from the lower portion of the window opening and the spring retainer, if any.

c. Bumpers. Bumpers may or may not be considered as trim. In any event, they are a necessary and functional part of the vehicle. Bumpers protect the car from damage due to minor collision bumps.

Most bumpers are held in place by heavy steel strips which are bolted at one end to the bumper, the other end to the frame. Bumpers vary, of course, in size and shape depending on the make of car. Some bumpers are quite massive.

d. Handles. All of the doors on a vehicle have handles with which the latch is operated. Handles are used both inside and outside on the doors leading into the passenger compartment. A complete outside door handle assembly is shown in Fig. 55. Another type of outside door handle is shown in Fig. 56.

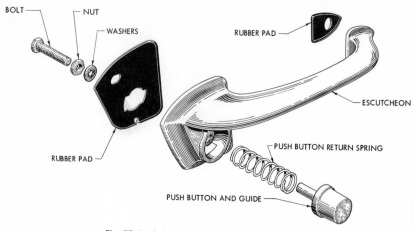

Fig. 55. Exploded View of Door Handle Assembly

Only the front doors on a vehicle usually can be locked with a key, although some models have been produced with facilities for locking all four doors with a key.

In some cars, the lock on the front doors is constructed integrally with the door handle push button. In this case, the key opening is in the push button. On other cars, the locking mechanism is separate from the handle. A separate opening is provided in the door for the lock.

All outside door handles extend through the outer panel so that the necessary linkage can be connected to operate the latch mechanism.

They are given ornate but functional designs to blend with the trim pattern of the vehicle. Door handles are usually fastened in place by means of a machine screw through the door inner panel. This screw is accessible when the door is opened.

The deck lid door lock is usually an integral part of the handle. One type of deck lid handle and lock arrangement is shown in Fig. 35. With this arrangement, the handle is actually a decorative molding with a functional purpose.

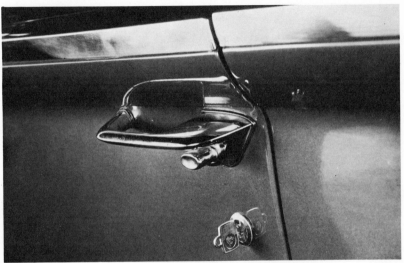

Fig. 56. Assembled and Mounted Door Handle Assembly
(Courtesy Lincoln-Mercury Division, Ford Motor Company)

Other arrangements have an integral deck lid handle and lock which is similar in appearance and operation to the passenger compartment door handle and lock. In some cars, the deck lid handle and lock are separate units, an opening being provided in the door for each.

All deck lid handles are secured from the inside with machine screws which are accessible when the deck lid is opened.

Inside door handles are used only on the doors which open into the passenger compartment. In most cases, an escutcheon plate, held in place by the handle, fits over the handle shaft and covers the hole where the handle comes through the door trim pad. This gives the handle a surface to ride on when the door or window is operated. See Figs. 57 and 58.

The handle is held in place by a push fit pin which is concealed under the escutcheon when it is in place. A spring inside the escutcheon allows the escutcheon to be depressed for access to this retaining pin.

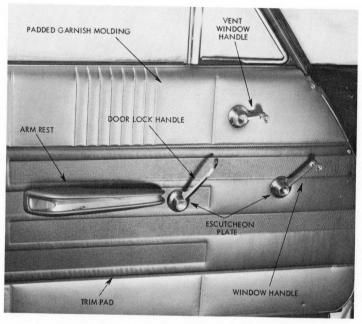

Fig. 57. Handle Arrangement on Interior Trim Pad
(*Courtesy Lincoln-Mercury Division, Ford Motor Company*)

Another type of door handle which is used on some cars has an integral handle and escutcheon held in place by a spring retainer or "horseshoe clip," as shown in Fig. 58. It is necessary to use a special pair of thin pliers to remove the spring retainer before the handle can be removed. When the retainer is removed, the handle can be pulled off the shaft easily.

e. Door Trim Pads. Door trim pads are the coverings used to conceal the lower portion of the inside panel of the doors. The pads are usually prefabricated and assembled on the door as one unit. These pads are held in place by sheet metal screws and spring clips such as those illustrated at *A, B, C, E, F, H, J, K, O, and Z*, **Fig. 50.** Typical

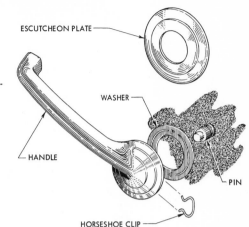

trim pads are illustrated in Figs. 47 and 57. These door trim pads are held firmly at each corner by sheet metal screws.

Door arm rests are provided on most cars (Fig. 57). They are sometimes considered as a part of the door trim pad. Arm rests are usually held in place by sheet metal screws which extend through the arm rest and trim pad into the door inner construction.

f. Seats and Upholstery. The seats and upholstery must be considered by themselves when trim is mentioned because of the difference in the construction of the seats and other parts of the car.

Rear seats are stationary. That is, no provision is made for moving them. Front seats, on the other hand, are made so they can be moved forward or backward. Front seat mounting and adjusting mechanisms are shown in Figs. 59 and 60.

All seat mechanisms are held in place by bolts through the floor pan. Most mechanisms provide a means for raising and lowering the seat, and some provide a means for tipping either the seat cushion or seat back, or both. The actual construction of a seat is shown in Figs. 61 and 62.

These seats are typical of seat construction. Fig. 61 is a seat construction using what is known as zigzag springs. The arrangement in Fig. 62 is a type of construction employing coil springs.

VIII. SEALING AGAINST DUST AND WATER

It is important to remember that as an automobile is traveling down the highway, a vacuum is created behind every rear surface. If a

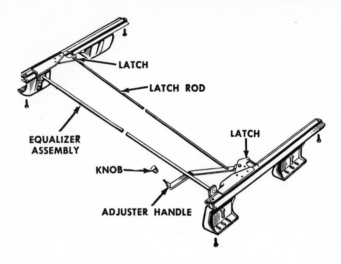

Fig. 59. Front Seat Adjusting Mechanism

window ventilator is opened, air in the body is drawn out, creating a vacuum in the body. When a vacuum exists in the body as a result of either or both of these conditions, it will cause air to be drawn into the body through even the smallest openings. Since the air is being drawn

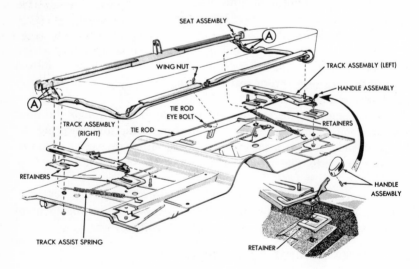

Fig. 60. Spring-Loaded Front Seat Adjusting Mechanism
(*Courtesy Lincoln-Mercury Division, Ford Motor Company*)

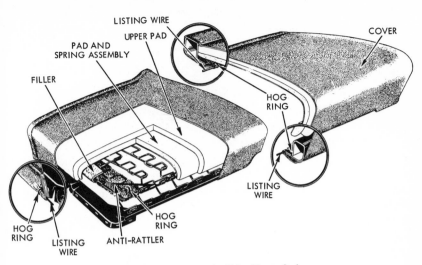

Fig. 61. Seat Construction Using Zigzag Springs

(Courtesy Lincoln-Mercury Division, Ford Motor Company)

Fig. 62. Seat Construction with Coil Springs

in by vacuum, it can go around corners, up through the center of a lock pillar, or a hundred other places that you might not ordinarily consider as points of leakage. If this incoming air is dust-laden, the dust will be carried into the car. If water gets in the way of this in-rushing air, it too will be carried in.

Many cars now have a ventilating system which forces air into the body. With such a body, if the ventilators are open and the windows are closed, the body becomes pressurized just as are some airplanes. When the body is thus pressurized, air is forced out of all of these minute openings instead of being drawn in. However, no one can expect a car owner to drive with all of the windows closed all of the time, so it is necessary to effectively seal all points of possible dust or water entry.

At the time of assembly, all panel joints are sealed. In some cases, a $\frac{1}{2}$ to $\frac{3}{4}$ in. diameter stream of mastic is laid in the joint where two panels come together. The mastic adheres to both surfaces, and its own surface hardens slightly. This mastic remains elastic enough so that it can absorb the flexing between the panels without breaking away from the panels.

It would be impossible to point out all of the possible points of dust and water entry even for one model of car. Nevertheless, if you remember that dust or water, or both, can enter at any point where two metal panels are joined, an appreciation of the importance of proper sealing is possible. Since both dust and water leave unmistakable evidence, the point of entry usually can be quickly located after the leakage occurs. This, in one sense, is like locking the door after the horse is stolen. It is much better and costs much less in the long run to reseal all joints that have been disturbed as a result of collision work.

Protecting the interior of the car from the elements has long been a problem. However, most of the automobile manufacturers have been successful in designing sealing methods which make a car tight against either dust or water leaks.

In addition to the general discussion of leakage just presented, this section describes the places where dust leaks are probable and the steps which are taken to prevent them from occurring.

a. Dust. Dust leaks most usually occur around the underbody. The door openings are another spot where dust can enter.

At the front of the underbody, holes are provided in the floor pan for the control pedals. Seals are placed around the openings so that dust cannot enter. If these seals become worn, it is necessary to replace them.

Weather strips are provided around the doors and along the bottom of the door. If any of the doors do not fit properly, dust can enter between the weather strip and the body. Sometimes the weather strip along the bottom of the door becomes loosened. When this is the case, the weather strip should either be recemented or replaced.

If there are any openings in the cowl panel for wiring or tubing to enter into the engine compartment, felt or rubber seals must be used to prevent dust leaks. Fumes which might originate in the engine compartment are by this means kept from entering the passenger compartment.

b. Water. It is usually considered possible for water to enter an automobile body at any point where dust can enter. The points discussed under dust, therefore, should be considered whenever water leaks are encountered. In addition to these points of possible leakage, water can enter at several points which are rarely or never points of dust entry.

(1) *DECK LID HINGES.* Some sports cars have externally mounted deck lid hinges (Fig. 63) which necessitate holes through the deck lid. Sealer is used around the holes between the hinge and the deck lid to prevent water entry.

(2) *REVEAL MOLDINGS.* A sealer is used between all the reveal moldings and the body proper. If this sealer becomes defective, it is necessary to replace it.

(3) *WINDSHIELD WEATHER STRIP.* Sealer is used all around

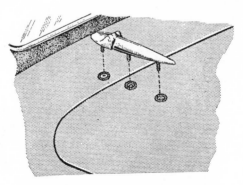

Fig. 63. Externally Mounted Deck Lid Hinge

the windshield weather strip. The same procedure applies to the windshield as to window reveal moldings in case a water leak occurs.

(4) *THE DECK LID.* The deck lid is provided with a weather strip just as the doors are. If this weather strip becomes loosened or worn, it should be replaced.

IX. FENDERS, SHIELDS, AND HOODS

This section explains and illustrates all body panels which are not considered as an integral part of an automobile body. These are the fenders, shields, and hoods, and the deck lid, which is really only a door of slightly different construction than regular doors. It is these panels which most often become misaligned or otherwise damaged. Therefore, it is necessary for you to understand the different types of construction which you will be apt to encounter when you start doing collision work.

Each of these panels is discussed individually under one of the following headings which are descriptive of the material covered.

a. Fenders. A fender is that part of the body which covers the wheels. Each car is equipped with four fenders, one for each wheel.

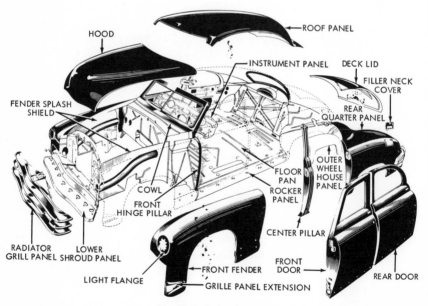

Fig. 64. Typical Body Panels

Aside from covering the suspension construction, the fender prevents water, mud, etc., from being thrown up onto the body by the wheels. The fender is particularly necessary when wet roads are encountered.

(1) *FRONT FENDERS.* A typical type of front fender is shown in Fig. 64. The front fender is usually bolted to the inner construction of the main part of the body, where it is held in place firmly. This is accomplished by having a flange turned downward or inward from the outside surface through which the bolts can pass (Fig. 65). To add greater strength and to prevent vibration of unsupported edges, fender brackets are incorporated. Sometimes a mudguard is incorporated as part of the fender bracket. A mudguard protects the underside of the fender from being struck by road dirt, etc.

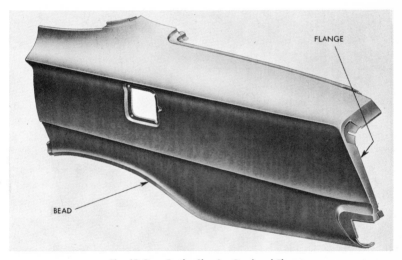

FLANGE

BEAD

Fig. 65. Rear Fender Showing Bead and Flange
(*Courtesy Buick Division, General Motors Corporation*)

Adjustment of the front fenders is usually provided for at the fender attaching points. The fender can be moved either forward or rearward by loosening the attaching bolts.

In most late model automobiles, the headlights, and sometimes the parking lights, are recessed in the front fender. Flanges are provided (Fig. 64) on the fender so the light assembly can be fastened in place. To cover the outline of the opening and the inner construction for accommodating the light, trim rings are used on the outside of the fender. These headlight trim rings are held in place by sheet metal screws.

Any trim or chrome which appears on the side of a fender is usually held in place by specially designed clips or fasteners which allow easy removal of the trim.

The unsupported edges of the fenders are formed into what is called a bead (Fig. 65). This bead is merely a flange which is turned inward on some cars. On others, however, the flange is turned in and then up to form a **U** section. The bead not only gives strength, but prevents cracks from developing in the edge of the fender due to vibration, and provides a smooth finished appearance to the edge of the fender.

(2) *REAR FENDERS.* Rear fender construction differs greatly among the various makes of cars. In general, the rear fender is bolted to the body in the same manner as the front fender. However, many cars have no rear fender as such. Instead, the fender is an integral part of the rear quarter panel.

When the fender is bolted to the body proper, it is considered as an independent type fender. This illustration shows both a rear and front fender with connecting running board and associated parts.

The rear fender has a bead around the unsupported edge similar to that on a front fender. Fender brackets are also used as well as mudguards. These parts are easily recognized, and the method of removal is usually obvious.

When the fender is an integral part of the quarter panel, the inner construction is utilized to form part of a housing around the wheel which is called the wheelhouse (Fig. 64). The outer half of the wheelhouse is a separate panel which is welded to the underbody to complete the housing. This housing is totally concealed by the rear quarter panel, and damage done to it is sometimes difficult to detect. This wheel housing prevents road dirt from being thrown upward between the outer panel and inner body construction. The outer side of the wheelhouse usually is attached to the quarter panel around the wheel opening. The bottom edge of the quarter panel is flanged inward and upward around the lower edge of the outer wheelhouse.

b. Shields. Panels called shields (Fig. 64) are mounted between the bumpers and the body proper. In some areas, these shields are called "stone deflectors." The functional purpose of such a panel is to keep as much road dirt, etc., as possible from flying up between the bumpers and the body.

Sometimes fender skirts are used on the rear fenders of cars. These skirts cover the wheel opening and are attached to the fender by clamps. A shield of this type is used more for decorative purposes than any other reason.

Another type of shield is that used behind the front fender and under the grille assembly on some cars. The shield used behind the front fender, between the fender and the engine compartment, is called a fender apron or splash shield (Fig. 66).

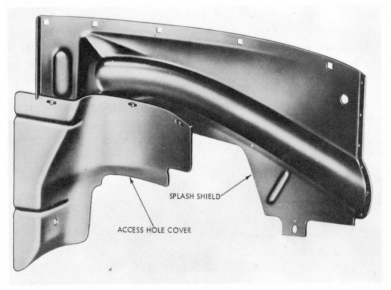

SPLASH SHIELD

ACCESS HOLE COVER

Fig. 66. Front Fender Apron

The purpose of the fender apron is to keep road dirt and mud from entering the engine compartment. The apron is generally bolted into place with bolts through the frame and body cowl panel.

The shield which is used under the grille and radiator is called a splash pan or lower shroud (Fig. 64). The purpose of this panel is just as the name suggests; it keeps mud and water from splashing into the front of the engine compartment. In some cases, these shields have the function of directing air through the radiator core. Other shields are designed to prevent the recirculation of warm air from the engine compartment back through the radiator core.

Different makes of cars employ different types of sheet metal panels under the engine. These are considered as shields. They are either bolted in place or else are held by sheet metal screws.

c. Hoods. The hood is the panel which covers the engine compartment. Several kinds of hoods are in use on different makes of automobiles.

Early model cars used a jointed, hinged type of hood. This type of hood was held in place by bolts through the center section of the top of the hood into the body cowl and into the radiator bracket. A piano type hinge was used, both where the hood hinged at the center and at the joint between the top of the hood and the panel which formed the side of the hood. Different types of latch mechanisms were used. However, they were all of simple design and operated externally.

The most commonly used hood on later automobiles is the one-piece type (Fig. 64). A one-piece hood can be opened in different ways. On some cars, the hood is hinged at the front so that the rear end of

Fig. 67. "Alligator" Type Hood
(*Courtesy Ford Motor Company*)

the hood swings up when the hood is opened. Several makes of cars have the hood designed so that it can be opened from either side, or unlatched at both sides and removed altogether without further disassembly. Most one-piece type hoods, however, are of the "alligator" type. The hood is hinged at the rear. When opened, the front end swings up (Fig. 67).

The type of hood latching mechanism depends, of course, upon the type of hood. When a hood opens from the rear, it is latched at the rear. When the hood opens from either side, a combination hinge and latch are provided at each side. "Alligator" type hoods are latched at the front. In many cars, the latch mechanism is controlled remotely from the driver's seat. One good reason for this arrangement is because the battery is contained in the engine compartment. By having the hood latch control inside the car, theft of the battery can be made difficult.

One-piece type hoods are quite large. To make opening the hood an easier task, the hinges are usually counterbalanced. In instances where the hood is smaller, it is not necessary to use counterbalanced hinges. Adjustment of the hood position is possible by moving the hinges. Hood alignment and adjustment are discussed in a subsequent chapter of this volume.

X. PRINCIPLES OF MEASUREMENT

Damage to the body inner construction or to the frame of a car or truck might be quite severe and yet not be apparent. In some cases, the damage to the skin or sheet metal of the body can be repaired, and the original damage will appear to have been corrected. The job, however, is not done unless the frame or body inner construction is either known to have been undamaged or has been corrected.

Failure to check for and correct such damage can result in poor fitting doors, hood, or fenders; faulty steering control; and a multitude of other faults. The possibility of these faults makes necessary a number of measurements throughout the correction of collision damage. The measurements taken generally are not made in inches or feet as might be expected, but rather are comparative measurements in which one distance is compared by means of a trammel to another that should be equal.

This section gives the principles on which the standard for measurement in collision work is based. Methods of measuring specific units of bodies and frames are given in subsequent chapters of this volume where the correction of damage to those particular units is discussed. Comparative measurements are universally used by body and frame repairmen and are generally regarded as the simplest, speediest method for measurement in collision work.

Automobile bodies are generally regarded as having two sides which are exactly the same. Therefore, if one side only is damaged, it can be compared with comparable measurements taken on the undamaged side. There is more to comparative measurement, however, than merely comparing a damaged panel with a similar but undamaged panel. The occasion will arise when both sides of a vehicle are damaged so that it will be impossible to compare one side with the other. This is when the true meaning of comparative measurements comes to light. Fig. 68, at (*A*), shows a metal picture frame with sides *A* and *C*, and *B* and *D* of equal length respectively. Therefore, the diagonals *X* and *Y* are also equal. If the square is distorted as at (*B*), Fig. 68, the diagonals are no longer the same length. If you visualize this picture frame as being

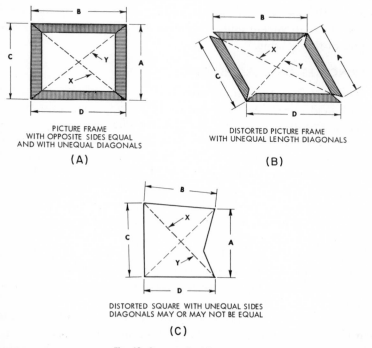

PICTURE FRAME
WITH OPPOSITE SIDES EQUAL
AND WITH UNEQUAL DIAGONALS

(A)

DISTORTED PICTURE FRAME
WITH UNEQUAL LENGTH DIAGONALS

(B)

DISTORTED SQUARE WITH UNEQUAL SIDES
DIAGONALS MAY OR MAY NOT BE EQUAL

(C)

Fig. 68. Comparative Measurement

movable at the corners, you can readily see where pressure must be applied to make it square once more. You do not need to know the original length of either the sides or the diagonals. By making comparative measurements of the diagonals, you can tell when they are again equal and at which time the frame is again perfect, as it was at *(A)*.

If the frame is distorted as at *(C)*, Fig. 68, it is possible for the diagonals to be the same if the distortion is exactly at the mid-point of side *A*. Therefore, a comparison of sides *C* and *A* will reveal the difference, and side *A* can be straightened until both side *C* and side *A* are the same length. A quick check will show that the diagonals are also the same length.

These illustrations show how it is possible to align a body or frame by measuring from nothing but the body or frame itself.

The comparison of diagonals is commonly called **X** checking. Some occasions will arise, however, when it will be impossible to determine the original shape of a unit by **X** checking or measuring the diagonals. An example of such a case is shown in Fig. 69.

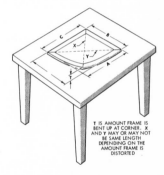

Fig. 69. Picture Frame with Corner Bent Up

T IS AMOUNT FRAME IS BENT UP AT CORNER. **X** AND **Y** MAY OR MAY NOT BE SAME LENGTH DEPENDING ON THE AMOUNT FRAME IS DISTORTED

In this case, the frame is bent up at one corner. The diagonals *X* and *Y* may or may not be equal, although it is more likely they will not. However, a sure method of determining whether the frame has been restored to its original shape is to measure from some surface (such as the table illustrated) to each corner of the frame. When the frame is perfectly flat again, the distance from each corner to the table will also be the same.

This type of measurement is used a great deal in frame straightening. When four points on a frame should be in the same plane, the four points, if placed on four blocks of the same height, all should touch the blocks. If all do not, either the point that does not touch the block is bent up, or one of the points that does touch the block is bent down. The floor from which you make such a measurement must be flat and should be as near level as possible.

It is, of course, possible for four points to be in the same plane and yet have a member connecting these points bent up or down. An example of this is illustrated by the picture frame in Fig. 70.

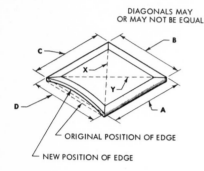

Fig. 70. Edge of Picture Frame Bent Up between Corners

By measuring first from the opposite, undamaged side of the frame to a surface, then from the bent portion to the same surface, you can determine how much and which way the frame is bent. By making these comparative measurements during the correction, you can determine when the frame is again flat.

On an automobile, this type of measurement is used to determine if one side of a frame is bent up or down. When the two sides of the frame are again the same, they will be the same distance from the floor or surface from which the measurements are made.

When an entire section of the vehicle is knocked out of alignment, another aspect of **X** checking measurement must be considered. The body proper can be considered as a cube. Any section of the body can also be considered as a cube. It is a simple matter to determine whether or not a cube is square by checking the diagonals from opposite corners (Fig. 71). The diagonals checked should be from one corner of the box to another so that they cross in the exact center of the cube.

This same principle can be applied to measuring the cubelike sections of an automobile body. It can also be applied to checking one section with another section. Examples of this type of measurement are explained and illustrated in subsequent chapters of this volume.

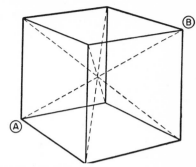

Fig. 71. Diagonals of Cube Are always of Equal Length

TRADE COMPETENCY TESTS

The following questions, while they represent only a small portion of the material in this chapter, may be used to determine the percentage of the information retained.

1. What is the term applied to the curved surface formation of metal in automobile bodies and fenders? (p. 2)

2. How is the strength of large metal sheets or panels affected by angles or flanges formed along their edges? (p. 3)

3. What is the construction of a **U** channel? (p. 4)

4. How is box section construction in connection with frames obtained? (p. 4)

5. Where is the heaviest frame cross member mounted with regard to the chassis? (p. 5)

6. What quality is imparted to the vehicle by lowering the center of the frame between the wheels? (p. 6)

7. Why are heavy commercial vehicle frames made flat behind the cab? (p. 6)

8. Is it usually possible to see inner construction from the outside of a vehicle? (p. 7)

9. Does an automobile body derive most of its strength from the panel or the inner construction? (p. 7)

10. What major panel is the instrument panel considered part of? (p. 9)

11. Is the center body pillar always visible from the outside of the car? (p. 17)

12. How are major body panels held in place for assembly at the time of original manufacture? (p. 22)

13. What is the function of the weather strip on windshield and rear window glass other than to keep out the weather? (p. 33)

14. How is a door glass held in place so that it can be run up and down evenly? (p. 40)

15. What is the small triangular window incorporated in the front doors of some cars called? (p. 41)

16. How are bumpers held in place on automotive vehicles? (p. 52)

17. How are the steel strips attached which are used to hold bumpers in place? (p. 52)

18. What is an escutcheon plate? Where are they used? (p. 53)

19. How is an integral door handle and escutcheon assembly held in place? (p. 54)

20. What is the panel on which the rear of the hood rests? Do the front fenders connect to this panel? (p. 60)

21. What is the formed edge of a fender called? (p. 61)

22. What is the common name for the shield which goes between the bumper and the body proper? (p. 63)

23. What is the panel called which is used behind the front bumper and under the grille? (p. 63)

24. What is the most commonly used type of hood on automobiles? (p. 65)

25. Is it necessary to know the original dimensions of a panel before it can be restored to its original shape? (p. 65)

26. What are the simplest, speediest measurements that can be made by collision men? (p. 66)

CHAPTER 2

METAL BUMPING AND DINGING

The restoring of automotive body panels of sheet metal, such as fenders, hoods, doors, etc., to their normal contour after they have been damaged is referred to as metal "bumping" or "dinging." Dinging is a highly skilled trade, and in areas where automobiles are manufactured, "dingmen" are in constant demand.

In retail establishments, the term dinging is rarely used. When it is used, it has a different meaning than it has in automotive manufacturing plants. In garages, car dealerships, and collision shops, dinging is accepted as meaning the same thing as bumping. In this field, the interpretation of the term bumping generally presumes that damage to the paint will result. In automotive factories, however, dinging presumes that no damage to the paint will result and involves the highly skilled use of hand tools. These tools are the hammer, dolly, and spoon, the employment of which, along with exercises that will help you develop skill in their use, is presented in this chapter. In general, these are the same tools as used by the metal bumper in retail establishments.

The chief difference between dinging, as the term is understood in automotive factories, and metal bumping in the retail field is that the dingman must do his work without damaging the paint. The usual course of development for these men is from metal finishers to dingmen. Metal finishers in automotive plants bump, file, grind, and weld surfaces and build up contours with solder. It is generally felt that this background of experience is a necessary part of the development of a dingman.

All of the practices employed by dingmen are presented in this chapter. Other skills not employed by dingmen, but considered as a necessary background for them, are presented elsewhere in this volume. Regardless of whether you want to become a collision expert, a metal finisher, a metal bumper in a retail establishment, or a dingman in an automotive plant, it will be necessary for you to learn all of the principles presented in this chapter and to acquire skill in the use of each of the hand tools. Learning the proper use of these hand tools is the first and most important step in becoming a body repairman. Even though power tools (discussed in later chapters) are available for use in collision work today, the bulk of the jobs is done with hand tools, and hand tools are used exclusively for the finer finishing work.

Collision work involves both metal bumping and straightening. Every job you encounter will require the fine handwork involved in metal bumping to finish the job. Much of the minor damage that you encounter will require dinging only. As a metal bumper, you will be able to restore the normal contour to most automobile bodies and fenders damaged in minor collisions.

To become a metal bumper, you must apply yourself to the thorough mastery of each phase of the work. Practice is the only means by which the mastery of the necessary skills can be made possible.

I. BASIC REQUIREMENTS OF METAL BUMPER

Body bumping and dinging are highly paid trades which anyone with a mechanical aptitude can learn by practice.

Certain tools of the trade are required. You should obtain these tools before you start the exercises outlined in this chapter. However, before you invest in these tools, it may be advisable to evaluate your aptitude for this work.

In collision work, the use of the hammer is one of the most important factors. You must learn to strike an object squarely and to have complete control of the hammer at all times. If, from your past experience with a good hammer, you have found that you can drive nails without bending them, you can develop the skill necessary as a metal bumper and you can omit the following exercise.

If you have had trouble driving nails, the following exercise will permit you to judge whether or not you should attempt to master this trade.

Drive some ¾–1 in. nails in a board. Lath nails are a good size for this test. The board selected should be one without hard grain. White pine is very good.

Place the board on a bench. Grasp a good hammer about three-fourths of the handle length from the hammer head. Hold the hammer so that the face of the hammer head rests squarely on the board and your forearm is parallel to the board.

Bending your arm at the wrist, raise the hammer head about nine inches, then hit the board lightly. Remember to confine the movement to bending the wrist only. Do not bend your arm at the elbow. Increase the strength of your blows until the hammer head starts to mark the board.

If the marks indicate that you are hitting with one edge of the hammer face, either turn the hammer handle in your hand or raise or lower your elbow, whichever is required, until you hit the board squarely. Now, try driving the lath nails into the board, using the same arm and hammer movement just described. Hit the nail lightly at first, then gradually increase the strength of your blows until you drive a lath nail in with one blow.

Continue until you can drive ten nails without bending any of them. If you can do this, you have the co-ordination necessary to master this trade. If, however, after much practice you are still unable to control the hammer, examine it. If the hammer face is not parallel and square with the handle, get another one and practice with it. If, with a good hammer, even after much practice, you cannot drive nails, you lack the co-ordination necessary to master this trade. Anyone who can drive nails all the way into the board and have an evenly shaped hammer mark on the board, however, should not experience any difficulty in achieving the co-ordination necessary in learning the metal bumping trade.

As previously mentioned, a minimum number of tools will be required to start on minor repairs such as dings in fenders. It is necessary that you thoroughly understand just what these tools are and how to use them. Ten separate tools are considered as the minimum number with which you should start. These ten tools are described and illustrated in Section II of this chapter. Later in this chapter, other tools and their use will be explained. However, you can develop the necessary skills with this minimum kit of tools. As you grow to be more and more proficient, you will gradually become aware of the need for additional tools.

II. MINIMUM KIT OF TOOLS

A great variety of hand tools is available to the metal bumper, and you will no doubt acquire many of them eventually. The minimum kit of tools necessary, however, takes into account a wide variation of forces. Force, of course, is necessary to form metal. With a given hammer, you can vary the force of a blow. The difference between the strongest blow you can control and the lightest blow you can strike, however, is not great enough to do all of the things you will have to do. For this reason, a vastly greater range is provided in these tools by differences in the areas through which the force is applied. An appreciation of this is a necessary part of learning the trade.

If a force of 100 lbs. is applied through the face of a hammer head $1\frac{1}{4}$ in. in diameter (1.2284 sq. in.), the resultant force amounts to 80 psi (pounds per square inch). If the same 100 lbs. is applied through a hammer only $\frac{1}{16}$ in. in diameter (0.0031 sq. in.), the resultant force amounts to 31,680 psi (nearly 16 tons). The $\frac{1}{16}$ in. diameter approximates the size of the end of a "pick" hammer which is one of the ten tools in the minimum kit.

If a flat piece of steel having an area of 4 sq. in. is placed on the surface on which you are working, and is hit with a 100-lb. force, the effect of the blow will be distributed over the 4 sq. in. and the resultant pressure will amount to but 25 psi. Of course if your hammer blow only has a force of 4 lbs., the resultant force would only amount to 1 psi. A piece of steel to place between your hammer and the surface on which you are working is included in this minimum kit of tools and is called a "spoon." Thus we see that not only is it necessary to apply force exactly where it is needed, but it is also necessary to vary the intensity of the force by having the right selection of tools.

With the tools just discussed, the force in the examples given varied from 25 to 31,680 psi with the same hammer blow.

With the ten tools in this minimum kit, you can do most of the minor repairs which you will encounter in body work. Each of these tools is described and illustrated in the following, under a heading which agrees with the name of the tool.

a. Mallet. A mallet (Fig. 1) having a face diameter of about two inches permits a good distribution of force. The mallet head is *lignum vitae,* a hard, heavy wood from a tropical American tree found in the West Indies. Its light weight (as compared to metal hammers) permits soft blows. Since it is made of material softer than the metal being formed, hammer marks are not made on the surface. With such a mallet, you will be able to correct some minor damage without injuring the paint.

b. Pick Hammer. As shown in Fig. 2, the pick hammer selected as a part of your minimum kit of tools has a round face which can be

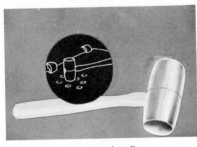

Fig. 1. Wood Mallet
(*Courtesy H. K. Porter*)

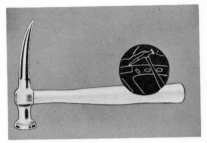

Fig. 2. Pick Hammer
(*Courtesy H. K. Porter*)

used for most hammering operations. The pick portion of the hammer is round for its entire length (about six inches) and tapered to a point. The forces possible in terms of pounds per square inch were discussed at the beginning of this section. It should be noted that the pick is slightly curved so that, when properly held in your hand, the point of the pick is approximately the same distance from your wrist as the center of the face on the other end of the hammer. This assists you in hitting exactly where you want.

c. The Square Face and Taper Shank Bead and Molding Hammer. The hammer shown in Fig. 3 will be required for those jobs where it is necessary to form the metal up to a corner. This ham-

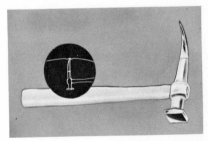

Fig. 3. Square Face and Taper Shank Bead and Molding Hammer
(*Courtesy H. K. Porter*)

mer, under some circumstances, is used in the same way as the round shanked pick hammer previously described.

In the various exercises described in the following pages, this hammer can be used for most of the exercises where a hammer is used in conjunction with a dolly. The sharp corners of the square head may result in marking the metal with the edge or corner of the hammer face if you do not hold the hammer properly.

d. Low-Crown Dolly. As pointed out in Chapter 1, most surfaces on an automobile body are curved. Dollies are made to fit these contours to provide the necessary backing for the hammer. A low-crown dolly (Fig. 4) is used in conjunction with bumping hammers primarily in places where a slight contour is encountered, such as fender skirts,

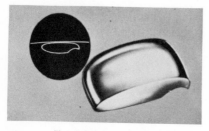

Fig. 4. Low-Crown Dolly
(*Courtesy H. K. Porter*)

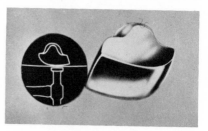

Fig. 5. High-Crown Dolly
(*Courtesy H. K. Porter*)

doors, tops of hoods, etc. It can also be used as a hammer for roughing out minor damage.

e. High-Crown Dolly. A high-crown dolly is also used in conjunction with bumping hammers. It is required for use whenever a high-crown radius is encountered (Fig. 5). This dolly has a rounded corner which is useful for bringing up low spots as is done with a pick hammer.

Fig. 6. Roughing Dolly
(*Courtesy H. K. Porter*)

f. Roughing Dolly. The roughing dolly, which is shown in Fig. 6, is one of the most versatile tools in the group. This dolly weighs about four and one-half pounds and is heavy enough to force out a high percentage of the damage you will encounter when used as a hammer. Being formed in the shape of a **U**, it provides a variety of surfaces that can be used as either a dolly or as a hammer. One edge of the dolly is formed so it can be used for forming a bead on a fender.

g. Surfacing Spoon. The surfacing spoon shown in Fig. 7 is used with a bumping hammer. The main purpose is for driving high spots back to their normal positions without disturbing or denting the surrounding surfaces. The broad face of the spoon distributes the force of the hammer blow over a larger area.

h. **Body File and Holder.** A body file and holder is necessary for smoothing the work after the hammering is finished. The body file is also used for other operations which will be explained in subsequent sections of this chapter. The file can be adjusted to fit the contour of the area being worked on by means of an adjustment screw or turn-

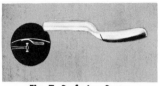

Fig. 7. Surfacing Spoon
(*Courtesy H. K. Porter*)

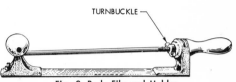

TURNBUCKLE

Fig. 8. Body File and Holder
(*Courtesy H. K. Porter*)

buckle provided on the file holder (Fig. 8). Sometimes the blade is adjustable merely by turning the handle of the holder.

III. ACQUIRING SKILLS

The only method of learning any trade is by continual practice with the tools of that trade. Constant practice is the only means of attaining skill in the use of the hand tools used in body repair work. Your degree of success depends upon your diligence in practicing with each tool and each piece of equipment until you have mastered them all.

This section presents a discussion of co-ordination and the care and maintenance of hand tools to get the best possible use from them.

a. Co-ordination. Perfect co-ordination between the hammer and dolly is necessary if you are going to become a good body repairman. The first step toward achieving this perfect co-ordination is to become complete master of the hammer. To master the hammer, you have to be able to control the force as well as the accuracy of the blow. Many light blows with the hammer are better than a few hard blows which may look like they are doing the trick, but which actually are stretching the metal, making your job much more difficult in the end.

How to handle the hammer is explained in the following paragraphs. As soon as you have become proficient in the use of the hammer alone, you can start practicing using the hammer and a dolly together.

(1) *PRELIMINARY HAMMER EXERCISES.* Before you actually start to work on metal with the hammers used in body repair work, you should practice several different exercises to learn your hammering mannerisms and to acquire some new techniques. In carpentry and in

other trades employing a hammer, hammer blows are usually struck with a combination of wrist, elbow, and shoulder movement. In collision work, however, a much wider variation in the force of the blow to be struck is required, and an additional way of striking a hammer blow should be learned.

What to you will probably be a new way of swinging a hammer is presented here and involves finger and finger and wrist movement. This method of swinging the hammer is actually unnatural and will become normal to you only after much practice. This, however, should not discourage you inasmuch as most of the skills are not natural, but are learned only through practice. The daily papers, for example, print columns on how to hold and swing a golf club and how to roll a bowling ball. These things do not come naturally, otherwise we would all bowl in the 200's and go around the golf course in the 70's. The same is true in the control of the bumping hammer.

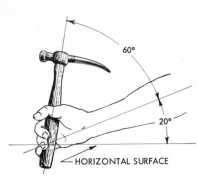

Fig. 9. Hammer at the Top of the Stroke

(a) FINGER MOVEMENT. In most other trades involving the use of a hammer, very little use of the strength of the fingers is employed. In metal bumping, you often will be required to use finger strength. The ability to throw the hammer head at the surface on which you are working merely by finger movement will be found to be of considerable advantage to you when working from underneath surfaces where you can see neither the hammer nor the surface on which you are hammering.

In this exercise, you must remember that the hammer is held loosely in the hand. In fact, in all of the exercises and in the actual work with these hand tools, you will find that all tools are held rather loosely. This makes the work less tiring and permits the achievement of a much higher degree of accuracy. Moreover, the loose holding of dollies and hammers permits them to bounce back naturally, thus assuming a position that permits you to strike an additional blow in the same place without conscious effort. Grasp the hammer as shown in Fig. 9.

You will note that in this illustration the hammer handle is at about a 60° angle to the forearm, and that the forearm is about 20° out of parallel with the surface on which you will be hammering. The hammer handle is resting against the base of the thumb and is some distance from the heel of your palm. The fingers of your hand are hooked over the hammer handle as shown. With the hammer in this position, by merely closing the fingers you will be throwing the hammer head forward by finger strength. With practice, a high degree of accuracy can be achieved by this method. Though it may be surprising to you at first, a considerable amount of force can be developed.

Practice this method of swinging the hammer without bending either the elbow or wrist. Generally, you will find that the hammer at the end of its movement will be in the attitude shown in Fig. 10, which shows the hammer about 20° out of parallel with the forearm. In other words, the hammer has moved about 100° by finger movement alone, neither the wrist nor the elbow contributing directly.

Practice the swinging of the hammer with no wrist movement against the palm of your other hand until you have mastered the technique of throwing the hammer head by closing your fingers. When you feel that you have mastered this method of throwing the hammer head at your other hand,

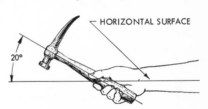

Fig. 10. Position of Hammer at End of Finger Movement

try striking a board or some other surface with the hammer head. Hold the hammer as shown in Fig. 9, and position your arm at a 20° angle from the board. The bottom of your hand should be about three inches above the surface, as shown. Now raise the hammer until it assumes the attitude shown in Fig. 9. The fingers should be extended but hooked around the hammer handle. Now start striking this surface without moving your forearm. Continue to practice this exercise until you feel you are hitting the surface squarely.

The next step in this exercise involves the driving of lath nails into a soft board or plank. White pine is ideal. Drive the lath nails into the board using the hammer movement you have been practicing. Don't be concerned if you are unable to drive the nail all the way in at first. Just continue to hit each nail until it has been driven all the way in.

After you have driven a few nails into the board, examine the marks the hammer has left in the board. These marks left in the board by the hammer tell you a story. If you understand what they mean, you can easily correct any small errors which you are making before you actually start practicing on metal. If, for example, the mark is heavy on the left side or the right side of the nail as you face the board, you are not holding the hammer straight in your hand. Merely turn the hammer slightly, whichever way is required to raise the side of the hammer which is leaving the deepest mark.

If the mark in the board is deepest on the side of the nail which is farthest away from you as you face the board, you are holding your elbow too high. Lowering your elbow slightly will bring the hammer head so it strikes the board squarely.

If the hammer mark in the board is deepest on the side of the nail nearest to you as you face the board, you are holding your elbow too low. Raising your elbow slightly will square the hammer head with the board.

After you have closely examined your hammer marks and made the necessary corrections in the method of hammering, practice driving nails until you can leave the same kind of mark in the board every time.

In driving the nails all the way into the board with one blow, you

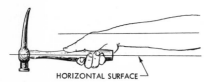

HORIZONTAL SURFACE ⟶

Fig. 11. Combination Finger and Wrist Movement

may have the tendency to hit the nail too hard. After you have mastered the technique of leaving the same kind of mark in the board every time, try hitting the nail with lighter taps. By trial and error, you will find that you can drive the nail all the way into the board with a surprisingly light hammer blow. You will also find that the hammer will leave a mark which is barely discernible.

(b) FINGER AND WRIST MOVEMENT. Once you have mastered the throwing of the hammer by finger movement, learn to complete the swing with a slight wrist movement. In this exercise, at the instant the hammer head strikes the surface on which you are hammering, the hammer handle and your forearm should be parallel as shown in Fig. 11.

Hold the hammer as shown in Fig. 9. Your forearm, however, should be parallel to the surface you are to strike (as in Fig. 11). The hammer handle will be at about a 60° angle to the forearm. Close the fingers as you did in the previous exercise. This time the hammer will not strike the surface, but will stop at about a 20° angle from the board. The blow is completed by a slight bending of the wrist so that the hammer strikes the surface on which you are working. The hammer, your hand, wrist, and forearm will be similar to the arrangement shown in Fig. 11.

Go through all of the exercises you performed with finger movement alone. The swing of the hammer is completed this time, however, by wrist movement. Drive nails and study the marks you make on the board. Continue these exercises until you feel that you have complete control of both where you hit and the force with which the blow strikes.

(2) *EXERCISES WITH HAMMER AND DOLLY.* Assuming that you have now mastered the basic principles of hammering by driving nails in a board, you are now ready for another exercise. Before you can actually start hammering on metal, you must further improve your control of the hammer, then learn to use the hammer in conjunction with the dolly block in perfect co-ordination.

Using the bumping hammer is like batting a baseball or driving a golf ball. The best results are obtained when you are perfectly at ease and as near as possible in a natural position. After you have faithfully practiced the finger and wrist movement in the use of the bumping hammer, you will find this method of swinging the hammer will come to you quite naturally and you will find you have a high degree of control of the force with which the hammer lands.

The force of the hammer blow is extremely important. In order to develop complete control of the force of the hammer blow, perfect finger and wrist action is necessary. As you develop this finger and wrist action, your accuracy with the hammer will also improve.

You became familiar with the pick hammer while driving nails into a board, so you can again use the pick hammer for the next exercises.

Grasp the pick hammer about three-quarters of the way down the handle from the head (Fig. 10). Hold the hammer easily in your hand. Do not grip it tightly. By grasping the handle in this fashion, the hammer will assume an almost naturally balanced position when you swing it.

Practice different strokes with the hammer—both full swings, involving both finger and wrist movement, and short swings, using the power of your fingers only, allowing the flat side or face of the hammer head to land lightly in the palm of your free hand. Limit your movement to finger and wrist action. Allow your wrist to flex naturally with each swing you make. Wrist action multiplies the force of the hammer blow and permits hard blows where required with a short swing and a minimum of exertion on your part.

Now practice swinging the hammer with a medium stroke until the force of the blows seems to be the same on your free hand each time, and until the hammer feels as though it has assumed a natural position in your hand.

So far, you have merely been swinging the hammer into your free hand with your free hand always in the same relative position. It is now necessary to learn to swing the hammer and attain accuracy of the blows while moving your arm about. At the same time you are becoming proficient at this, you can also get the feel of using two tools at once. For the next exercise you can again use the pick hammer. Instead of swinging against your free hand, however, you can hold the high crown dolly in your free hand and practice hitting it with the face of the hammer (Fig. 12).

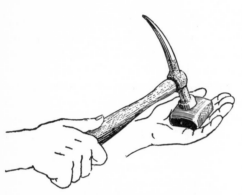

Fig. 12. Striking Dolly Block with Pick Hammer

How you hold the dolly block for this exercise is important. It should lie naturally in your hand with the high crown side up. Different ways of holding the dolly blocks will be explained later in this chapter where different kinds of hammering are explained in detail.

The important thing to learn now is to strike the dolly squarely and with the same force with each blow of the hammer. Swing the hammer against the dolly block, moving both of your arms to different positions. Without changing the way you are facing, practice this exercise to the left so one arm passes in front of you, then to the right. Now hold the dolly at eye level and continue to exercise. Next, practice with the dolly on a level with your belt buckle. Continue to practice in each position until the blows seem to fall against the dolly with no conscious effort. Don't grip either the hammer or the dolly tightly. Don't try to stop the hammer from bounding back, and don't let the hand holding the dolly become rigid. Let it move naturally as the hammer strikes it.

This bounding back of the dolly is one of the important factors in straightening metal.

Each time the hammer strikes the dolly block it will have a certain metallic ring, and will impart an impact to the hand in which you are holding the dolly. Practice swinging the hammer against the dolly until the metallic ring is nearly the same with each impact and the shock to the hand holding the dolly feels the same with each hammer blow.

After you have practiced striking the dolly in different positions, move the hand holding the dolly after each two or three strokes. This exercise will help you to develop co-ordination of your two hands. Continue this exercise until you can bring the hammer and dolly together in any position just as naturally as you can bring your two hands together.

After you have mastered the use of the hammer and dolly without actually hammering on anything, you are ready to start exercises with the hand tools on a metal body part.

b. Use of Hand Tools. The previous exercises have given you a good deal of practice with the hammer. You have been able during these exercises to get the "feel" of the basic hand tools while you can see both tools. In actual metal bumping, the metal to be worked will be between the hammer and the dolly, and you will be able to see only one of these tools at a time.

When a fender or body panel is formed, the shape of the die is imparted to the sheet metal. Later, if the panel becomes bent, creases in the panel hold it out of shape. Nevertheless, the stresses imparted to the metal when it was formed on the body die are mostly still in the panel, and when the stress of the crease is relieved, the panel will return to this original shape by itself.

Since the metal will try to return to its original contour of its own accord, the secret of dinging is to determine just what is preventing it from returning. It will be found usually that a crease has been formed by the impact causing the damage. This crease may exist either in the panel itself, or it may be a bend or a crease in the inner construction which is holding the panel from returning to its original contour. By undoing this crease, you will restore the original contour.

If, on the other hand, in trying to hammer or drive the damaged area back into shape the metal is hammered excessively, it will be stretched. The stretched portion of the metal will lose its tendency to return to the original contour. For these reasons, it is of the utmost importance that you approach each job with the object in mind of relieving the strain which is holding the damaged area out of position.

Since each hammer blow displaces some metal, it is important that you acquire skill in being able to hit exactly where you want to, and with exactly the right force. Light blows will not displace the metal as much as heavy blows, and several well-placed light blows are far more effective than one or two hard blows. Each well-directed blow of exactly the right force is a move toward permitting the metal to come back to its original contour. Each misplaced blow, and each blow that is harder than is required, may create additional damage which you will eventually have to correct.

You will have to acquire a high degree of skill in the use of each of the hand tools just described. Until such time as you have developed skill, it is not advisable to work on an automobile. As a means of acquiring these skills, obtain an old fender from a body shop, car dealership, or garage on which to practice the use of these hand tools. During this part of your learning period, you are going to develop skills in doing a number of separate operations, all of which are used in restoring metal to its original contour. The exercises given will not represent any procedure that you will ever follow on any particular body or fender repair job. These exercises are merely intended to permit you to develop the skill you will need with each of the tools. Don't be impatient to work on actual damage. Follow these exercises faithfully, and you will be able to step up to your first actual bumping job, confident that you can do it.

(1) *BODY FILE AND HOLDER.* The body file is a simple tool. Being simple, however, does not mean that it is unimportant. Metal finishing with the file is one of the most important phases of sheet metal repair.

A body file is used for many things—to remove paint, to smooth metal, to find low spots, and to form the correct contour of areas that have been built up with solder. No doubt you have seen body men doing these same operations with a grinder, and you may wonder why you must learn the laborious method of hand filing. Several sound reasons exist which will become apparent to you as you master the separate techniques presented in this volume. By hammering alone, you will never make any surface perfectly smooth. Nevertheless, you will have to achieve near perfection. Otherwise, in filing or grinding to remove the high spots, you will cut through or weaken the part.

The gauge of metal on automobile bodies is as light as practical, and every precaution must be taken not to file (or grind) away any metal unnecessarily. Like all of the other hand tools used in bumping or dinging, you will have to develop skill in the use of the file. Many jobs do not lend themselves to grinding.

(a) CONSTRUCTION OF BODY FILE HOLDER. The file blade is the most important part of this tool because it is the part that does the work. The file blade is detachable from the holder (Fig. 13), and is different from any other type of file. These blades are accurately machined with unbroken cutting edges about ⅛ in. apart.

The holder is a flexible frame with some form of turnbuckle (Fig. 13) which makes it possible to adjust the blade to fit the different contours encountered (Fig. 14). The blade fits into the holder snugly and positively, yet is quickly replaceable.

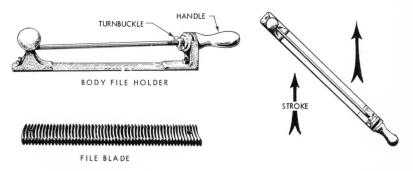

Fig. 13. (Left) Body File Holder and File Blade. (Right) Position of File to Produce Shearing Action

Examine the file blade closely and notice the curvature of the individual cutting edges. The curvature makes it possible to position the file as shown in Fig. 13 so that a larger area is covered with each stroke of the file. The file is pushed straight away from you, but the angle of the file produces a shearing action which produces a smoother surface.

(b) FILING METAL. Fasten the file blade to the file holder with the cutting edges of the teeth facing away from the handle. Adjust the contour of the file holder so that it almost, but not quite, matches the contour of the surface on which you intend to work. One hand is used to hold the file handle. The other is used to grasp the file around the saddle at the opposite end.

For your first exercise, adjust the file blade so that it is concave, its center touching the surface on which you will be working and the ends clearing by $\frac{1}{16}$ to $\frac{1}{8}$ in. (Fig. 15). This illustration shows the file adjusted for use on a high-crown surface. Secure the fender in some manner so that it will not move as you attempt to file it. Place the file on the fender. With a straight stroke, push the file away from you so that

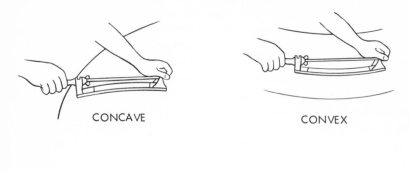

CONCAVE   CONVEX

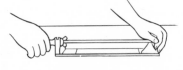

FLAT

Fig. 14. The Body File Is Adjustable to Contours

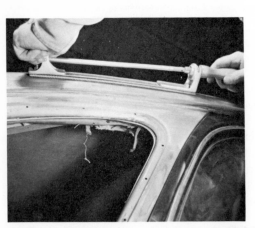

Fig. 15. File Adjusted to Contour of Surface To Be Filed (Left) and File Adjusted for Use on a High-Crown Surface (Right)

(Courtesy H. K. Porter)

it is traveling in the same direction its length runs. If the file digs in, you are putting too much pressure on it. Lessen the pressure. At the end of the first stroke, raise the file and bring it back to where you started, and make a second stroke. Repeat this until you have removed all of the paint from the area on which you are working, remembering to raise the file at the end of each stroke. It should not be dragged back over the metal. Dragging the file back over the metal will tend to dull the file blade, thereby shortening its life. (These blades are expensive.)

You will find that all of your file marks are parallel to each other and that you have removed all of the paint and probably some of the

metal from the fender in the area on which you have been filing. This type of filing is referred to as *line filing*. The term "line filing" merely means that all the strokes, and consequently all of the file marks, are in the same direction.

Now change the direction of your file strokes so that the file is moving at about a 45° angle from the previous direction. This is referred to in the trade as **X** filing.

Fig. 16 File Position for Cross Filing
(Courtesy H. K. Porter)

You may find that the contour of the area differs slightly when you change the file stroke 45°. If this is true, adjust the file holder again to nearly but not quite match the contour, then go over the entire area once lightly. You will now find that the new file marks cross the original file marks at a 45° angle, and that these two sets of file marks form a series of innumerable **X**'s from which the term **X** filing is derived. Continue to file in this direction until you have completely removed all of the original in-line file marks. You are now again filing in-line. In other words, all of your file marks are in one direction.

Now turn your file so that it is 90° from these file marks. You probably will again find that your file holder no longer matches the fender contour. As you proceed to file in this new direction, you will find that the new file marks imposed on the previous ones form crosses. This is referred to as cross filing (Fig. 16).

Of course, when cross filing or **X** filing in actual practice, you make a few strokes in one direction, then a few strokes in the second direction, after which you go back to the first position, and so on to maintain the cross or **X** pattern in the file marks. **X** filing and cross filing are necessary to maintain or establish a contour which curves in more than one direction, whereas line filing is used on more simple surfaces. When filing, it is always a good plan to make a few cross or **X** strokes occasionally to make sure that you are not destroying a secondary contour in the metal. This is particularly important when filing areas that have been built up of solder or other soft material.

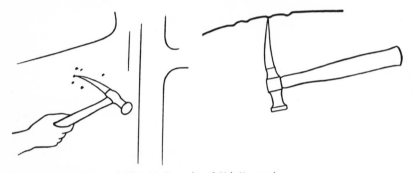

Fig. 17. Examples of Pick Hammering

You should continue to practice on the fender until you have succeeded in setting up the various filing patterns over several differently crowned areas.

(2) *PICK HAMMERING*. In this, the second hand-tool exercise on metal, you are going to create damage to the fender and at the same time gain valuable experience and practice. Using the pick hammer on an undamaged surface will create the damage. You will need this type of damage for a later exercise. While you are actually damaging the fender, you are at the same time developing skill in pick hammering. Pick hammering is one of the most difficult jobs to master, and you will need a lot of practice before you can make competent use of this tool.

A pick hammer is used to bring up low spots, particularly in areas which have been badly creased or stretched and have lost their tendency to return to their normal contour. Fig. 17 illustrates examples of pick hammering employed to raise low spots. As a rule, the pick hammer, working from the underside of the metal, is used to hit the center of low spots $\frac{3}{8}$ in. or less in diameter. The pick, being sharp, stretches the metal, forming a pimple on the surface. At the same time this pimple is formed, the metal immediately surrounding it, while not displaced or stretched, is raised. From the foregoing, it is obvious that accuracy in the use of the pick is of the utmost importance.

Place a small cross on the outside surface of the practice fender skirt, and try to hit the center of this mark with the pick from underneath. Try a light blow, at the same time watching the surface of the fender to see if you are raising a pimple. If not, increase the force of the blow until you see a pimple raised by the pick. Determine the distance and the direction that you will have to move the hammer in order to hit in the center of the cross mark, and continue to hit the underside of the fender until you actually hit under the center of the cross. Don't be discouraged if you find that you raise thirty or forty pimples on the metal before you hit exactly where you want. This is one of the most difficult techniques in dinging, and you will need a lot of practice before you can master it. Form the habit of noting quickly where a hammer blow strikes and judging the distance you have to move your hand in order that following hammer blows will be where you want them.

A more simple exercise, but one which will help if you encounter difficulty in hitting the chalk marks with the hammer, is to practice hitting a point under your finger. Place the index finger of one hand against the outside surface of the fender, then try to hit the inside surface of the fender with the pick hammer so as to raise a pimple directly under the index finger. It is usually easier to hit a point under your finger because your other hand will bring the hammer to your finger quite naturally. Practice doing this until you can raise a pimple directly under your finger every time. Then try hitting under the chalk marks again.

The chief aim of this exercise is to give you a method whereby you can achieve skill in the accuracy of your blows with the pick hammer. Continue practicing with the pick until you can hit the mark every time. After you feel you have become proficient in the use of the pick hammer, you can move along to the next exercise.

(3) *DIRECT HAMMERING.* As a result of the exercise with the pick hammer, you will have an area of the fender skirt on which you have a number of small pimples. These can be removed by a method referred to as direct hammering. Figs. 18 and 19 show how you should hold the dolly for this operation, as well as the relationship of the hammer to the dolly. As mentioned in the discussion of basic hand tools, you will find that you have a low-crown dolly and a high-crown dolly.

Before using the hammer and dolly together, it will be necessary to clean the underside of that portion of the fender on which you will be working. This will be true on all subsequent exercises and in actual practice when you are working on collision jobs. Body panels and some fenders will be covered with sound-deadening material which must be removed. Deadening material may be pads or mats of a felt-like material glued in place, or a heavy, tarlike, black material which has been applied in a semifluid state. This material may have been brushed or sprayed on the panel and later dried. In addition, the underside of fenders, hoods, and bodies may be undercoated.

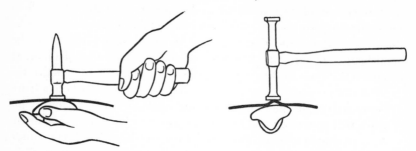

Fig. 18. How To Hold the Dolly when Direct Hammering   Fig. 19. Hammer and Dolly in Direct Hammering

Regardless of whether the metal to be reworked is covered with undercoating, tarlike, sound-deadening material, or a silencing pad, or is just dirty, it will have to be cleaned before you start with the hammer and dolly. Use a putty knife, wire brush, or whatever it takes to remove this material.

If you fail to clean the surface, deadening material or road tar will not only gum up your dolly but will, to a large degree, destroy its effectiveness. Sand and gravel embedded either in the undercoating or in road tar just sticking to the body metal may nick your dolly block.

Dolly blocks are important tools in body and fender repairing. Regardless of what your first impression of these tools might be, they are precision instruments, each scientifically designed for a particular type of job. Later in this section you will learn how to care for these tools, and how to correct damage that may occur to them.

Of first importance is the selection of the correct dolly block for the job you are going to do. The different dolly blocks which were introduced to you in the minimum kit of tools represent the basic kinds of dollies. Eventually, you may accumulate a wider selection. The main difference in the dolly blocks is in the radius or crown provided on the anvil side of the block, and in the weight of the block itself. In some of the additional dollies you may later acquire, further variations in shape might be practical. However, you will be able to follow each of the exercises presented here with the three dollies included with the minimum kit of tools previously described.

In repairing a high-crown radius of a fender, you will have to use a dolly block with a high-crown radius. Fig. 20 illustrates how a high-crown dolly is used in conjunction with a bumping hammer on a high-crown radius.

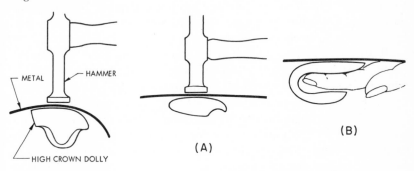

METAL — HAMMER

HIGH CROWN DOLLY

Fig. 20. Using a High-
Crown Dolly

(A)

(B)

Fig. 21. Using a Low-Crown Dolly

In repairing larger body panels and on door panels, front parts of quarter panels, tops of hoods, and centers of metal tops, it is necessary to use a dolly block with a low-crown radius. How the low-crown dolly you will be using in your primary operations is used in conjunction with a bumping hammer is illustrated in (A), Fig. 21. Another type of low-crown dolly is shown in (B), Fig. 21.

In all cases, a dolly should nearly but not quite match the original contour of the metal being straightened. If this damage were in a high-crown area, a high-crown dolly would be used.

In direct hammering, by having a dolly that matches the original contour under the damage and striking the damage with a hammer, you are pushing the displaced metal back to its original contour. The dolly provides support and prevents the undamaged areas (between the pimples) from being pushed out of place. Here, again, accuracy is important. If you don't strike squarely over the dolly, you will be hitting an unsupported area of the sheet metal and will displace the metal, creating damage that you will later have to undo. Direct hammering requires skill in directing the hammer blow. It requires close observation of what you are doing so as not to hit the metal too hard, thereby displacing it. Perfect co-ordination between your two hands is necessary to enable you to move the dolly around under the damaged area and still continue to hit squarely over it with the hammer. The following few exercises are designed to assist you in developing this skill and co-ordination.

If you find you cannot hit directly over the dolly, practice swinging the hammer again. First, practice swinging the hammer against your palm, then against the dolly block held loosely in the other hand. Move the dolly to different positions, striking it during the movement. Continue these exercises until you have no difficulty striking the dolly squarely every time.

Return to the damaged area of the fender, and hammer the pimples down. Start by using light blows that won't do the job but will show you whether or not you are hitting squarely over the dolly. Don't forget to let the dolly just lie in your hand and to grip the hammer loosely. Use the finger movement described in your first exercise.

With the dolly directly under the pimple to be flattened, using finger movement only, tap the top of the pimple. A true ring will be heard if you are directly over the dolly. Otherwise, the sound will be dull. When you are sure you are directly over the dolly, increase the force of the blow gradually until you have found just the right force to push the pimple back without flattening the surrounding metal.

When the first pimple has been eliminated, move to the next one, and so on, until all have been removed. You will find that, with each hammer blow, two additional things occur. The hammer bounds back of its own accord so that it is ready for the next stroke. Likewise, the dolly will spring away from the surface, and the normal resiliency of your arm will bring it back, striking a blow on the metal from underneath. These things will occur normally only if you hold both hammer and dolly loosely. The importance of this spring-back of the dolly becomes apparent as you begin your exercises of indirect hammering.

(4) *INDIRECT HAMMERING.* As previously mentioned, metal that has not been excessively hammered, displaced, or stretched, will have a tendency to return to its original contour of its own accord. This is due to the internal strain imparted to the metal by the forming dies. If the metal is prevented from springing back by other strains imparted to it by additional bends or creases that have been formed, the metal is restored to normal contour by relieving whatever new strain is holding it out of position. In bumping or dinging, this is

accomplished by indirect hammering. Fig. 22 represents a cross section of a damaged area in which sharp creases have been formed all around an area and another sharp crease has been formed in the low spot or center of the damaged area.

The procedure employed in indirect hammering is to hold a dolly having the correct contour to match the original contour of the metal at the low spot and to strike a series of light blows around the outer crease. Fig. 22 illustrates how the dolly is held and where the blow is struck in indirect hammering.

The corrective action is as follows: A light blow will not displace the surrounding undamaged area, but the force of the blow will be transferred to the dolly block. In effect, this will be like pushing the bent portion downward to straighten it out.

As a result of receiving the hammer blow indirectly, the dolly

Fig. 22. How the Dolly Is Held in Indirect Hammering

will be pushed away from the low part of the damage. However, in doing this, it imparts a light push upward on this area. Being knocked away from the fender, your hand will automatically bring it back in place, imparting a second light blow to the area. As you progress, using light hammer blows around the outer edge of the damage, you will find that the center of the damaged area slowly but surely rises until the original contour is restored. To gain practice in this, use the roughing dolly to strike a sharp blow on the outside of a high-crown area of the fender to create damage ranging from 1½ to 3 in. in diameter.

Select a dolly that matches the contour (high crown). Using the round head of the pick hammer, hold the matching contour of the dolly on the low spot of the damage (you can feel this with your fingers). Gently tap around the creased outside edge of the damaged area, going around and around progressively with light blows until the contour is restored. Don't strike hard blows, or you will create secondary damage which may be harder to correct than the original damage.

If, during this process, due to inaccuracy in handling the hammer, you have created indentations with the edge of the hammer head, repeat the first exercises (driving lath nails into a board) until you have perfected your control of the hammer. Whatever hammer marks you may have inadvertently created should be hammered smooth by direct hammering to complete this exercise.

Select a new area of the fender and continue practicing spring hammering until you have mastered the technique. In one of these additional exercises, substitute the mallet for the hammer.

(5) *SPRING HAMMERING.* When a crown is formed in metal, it becomes strong in that it resists any change to its shape. In one sense it can be compared to an arch used in the construction of a building or bridge. The strength of this arch or crown can, in many instances, be used to support the surface being hammered without the use of a dolly. This type of hammering is called spring hammering.

Creases in metal at points where it is impossible to back up the hammer often can be corrected by this method. To take advantage of a greater amount of the natural support provided by the crown of the metal, the force of the hammer blow is spread over a larger area through a spoon. The spoon is placed lengthwise over the ridge of the crease or other high spot and then struck a series of light blows with the hammer until the unwanted stress is relieved and the raised portion is back to its original shape or position.

In this method of hammering, no hammer marks are formed on the metal since all of the blows are on the spoon rather than on the metal. Once the metal is back to its original crown, additional hammering will cause the surface to sink below its original contour line, and you may not be able to bring it back readily.

Always start with light blows, and as you near completion of the job, inspect the contour after each blow. This will reduce the possibility of sinking the hammered surface too low.

Keep the surface of your spoon clean and highly polished. Any irregularities in the surface of the spoon will be transferred to the surface of the metal on which you are working and will create additional work for you. Dingmen using a spoon to correct damage without injuring the paint often pass the surface of the spoon over their cheek before using it. This accomplishes several things. Any irregularities are felt by the sensitive skin of the face. At the same time, a light film of oil is spread over the surface of the spoon.

Strike your practice fender from underneath with the pick hammer to raise a pimple in a high-crown area. Then without using a dolly, push back the raised metal by spring hammering with a hammer and spoon. Repeat this practice exercise a number of times. Spring hammering a crease in a door panel is illustrated in Fig. 23.

Delivering the hammer blow to the spoon when it is held directly over high spots drives the high spots back to their normal positions without disturbing or denting surrounding surfaces.

Next, strike several blows in a high-crown area of your practice fender with a pick hammer from the outside. This will create depressions that can be brought back up by spring hammering from underneath.

In addition to fine finish work where the paint is to be preserved, spring hammering is effective in roughing out damaged areas, and is used in straightening high spots as they appear on either side of the metal.

(6) *USING DOLLY TO ROUGH OUT DAMAGE.* In the previous exercises, damaged areas have been brought up to original contour by direct hammering, indirect hammering, and spring hammering. Again

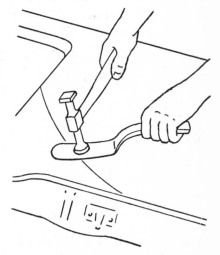

Fig. 23. Spring Hammering, Using a Spoon

create damage in your discarded fender. Strike a sharp blow at a point where the fender skirt starts to blend into the high-crown area of the fender. Use the rounded edge of the roughing dolly, and control your blow so it travels approximately two feet. Swing the dolly as hard as you can. This should cave in the fender at this point.

It probably is well to point out that in all dinging and straightening methods used in collision work, the damage is corrected by reversing the process whereby the damage was created. In this case, the damage you have just created was caused by a single direct blow. The place where the blow was struck is now the lowest part of the damage. To reverse the process whereby the damage occurred, you would hit the underside of the fender with approximately the same force directed against the low part of the damage (Fig. 24). If you can accurately hit this low spot with the roughing dolly with the same force that you hit it when you formed the damage, you will find that the fender will spring back almost to the contour it had prior to its damage.

You will find that in many instances you will be able to correct fender damage with a single blow of a dolly in this manner. In most cases, however, for one reason or another, the damaged area will not be completely restored to its original contour. However, it will be "roughed out" and the balance of the correction is easily accomplished by either direct or indirect hammering.

It will be noted that in the preceding exercise, and in previous exercises and discussions of hand tools, no mention has been made of a roughing hammer. This has been deliberate. While, in the hands of an accomplished metal bumper, a roughing hammer might be considered by some as an essential tool, it has no place in your tool kit at this time. There is some doubt as to whether or not a roughing hammer is ever advisable. A roughing hammer permits heavy blows which are concentrated in a small area and

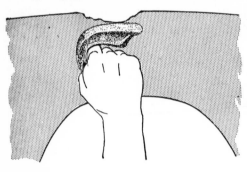

Fig. 24. How Roughing Dolly Is Used

invariably result in stretching or otherwise distorting the metal. In other words, a roughing hammer creates damage which you will later have to correct, and in thus stretching the metal, the metal involved loses its natural tendency to return to its original shape. A well-directed blow with a dolly that matches or nearly matches the original contour of the damaged material spreads the blow over a larger area and results in very little distortion or stretching of the metal. Of course you will encounter complex damage later where a series of accordion pleats and folds have been formed in the metal which will require straightening. However, hammering with either a roughing hammer or dolly is not the way to rough out these jobs. Here, the use of power tools is called for. The use of power tools is covered in a subsequent chapter of this volume.

A more difficult exercise with the roughing dolly is to create a more complex ding in the fender, then to straighten it with the roughing dolly. This exercise will serve to introduce you to performing more than one type of hammering in a logical sequence until the damaged area has been returned to its normal position.

Use a sharp corner of the roughing dolly block and strike the fender hard enough to make a deep ding. Then strike the fender a second time adjacent to where you struck it the first time. This will give you a complex type of damage similar to that shown in Fig. 25. You now have damage that resulted from a series of events. In correcting this damage, you will correct, first, the damage that occurred last.

Strike the underside of the damaged area directly on the low spot that resulted from the second blow, trying to duplicate as nearly as possible the force with which the damage was created. Then strike a second blow on the low spot created by the first blow.

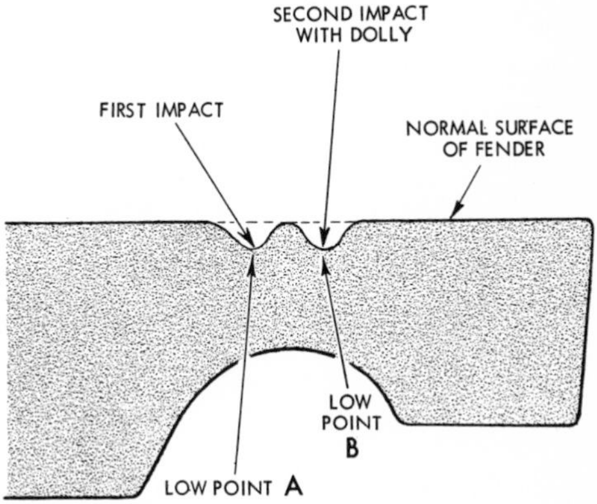

In a complex type of damage like this, you will have more than one low spot and more than one ridge and valley effect. Naturally, the more complex the damage, the more difficult it will be to straighten.

Again look at Fig. 25

Fig. 25. Complex Type of Fender Ding

and notice the two low points labeled A and B. The damage that occurred first caused the deeper ding at A.

Grasp the roughing dolly lightly in your hand, then strike the center of what appears to be the lowest point in the damaged area caused last. Strike the other low spot as near the center as you can. Then strike each low spot alternately with the roughing dolly until the low spots are pushed back to near normal. Be sure that you are using the crown of the roughing dolly that matches as nearly as possible the crown of the surface which you are trying to restore.

You may have noticed on your first exercise with the roughing dolly that when you had succeeded in forcing the damaged area back to normal, the surface was still not smooth. The roughing dolly is, of course, only to be used as a hammer for the first operation in straightening a damaged area. For the second operation, you may use either direct or indirect hammering.

In the type of damage which you set up from the example in Fig. 25, you will be able to finish bringing the surface back to normal by direct hammering. However, in this example, you only had two low spots, and the dings were not very deep. If you had a larger area of damage, you would still have ridges and valleys existing after you had used the roughing dolly to the limit of its efficiency. In this case, you would use indirect hammering to finish roughing out the damage.

Fig. 26 illustrates the conditions which may still exist after the damage has been roughed out with a roughing dolly. These small indentations will not be very deep, but they will be of such a nature that they will not easily lend themselves to straightening with a roughing dolly. An attempt to do more work with the roughing dolly than is possible will result in the metal becoming stretched. How to correct a stretched metal condition will be explained in later exercises.

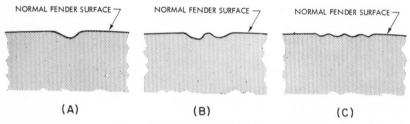

Fig. 26. Conditions after Roughing Dolly Is Used

(7) *LOW SPOTS.* Select one of the areas on the practice fender on which you have been working, and by means of direct hammering, go over the surface again and make it as smooth as you can. Don't hit the surface any harder than you have to, as more force than is necessary will merely stretch the metal.

Either cross or **X** file this surface just enough so that the tops of the high spots are removed by the filing. If, after a few file strokes in each direction, the high spots appear as little islands, you have not done a good enough job with your hammering. Continue with the direct hammering until a few strokes in each direction with the file make the low spots instead of the high ones appear as little islands on the surface.

These low spots are eliminated by pounding from underneath, which brings them up to the level of the surrounding surface. This can be accomplished in several ways. You will note that one corner of the high-crown dolly is rounded, having a radius slightly smaller than that of a golf ball. Hold the dolly so that you can strike the underside of the fender with this rounded corner. Start with the low spot having the largest diameter, and hit it from underneath with the rounded corner of the dolly. It must be remembered that if you do not hit exactly in the center of the low spot, it will raise metal in some place where you do not want it to be raised. Accuracy in this can be accomplished by holding a finger in the low spot and lightly tapping the underside of the fender with the rounded corner of the dolly until you feel that it is exactly underneath your finger. Then strike a sharp blow to raise the metal at this point. Since the corner of the dolly represents a fairly large area, the low spot is raised with a minimum of distortion of the metal. After you have raised each low spot in this manner, again cross or **X** file the damaged area to again show up the low spots. You will now find that most of the low spots have been reduced in size. Continue to raise the low spots in this manner, concentrating on low spots of $\frac{3}{8}$ in. or more in diameter and again cross or **X** file, repeating this process until all low spots have been reduced to $\frac{3}{8}$ in. or less diameter.

After you have practiced with the dolly block for some time and have become successful at removing low spots with it, you are ready to try removing the smaller low spots with the pick hammer.

(a) REMOVING LOW SPOTS WITH A PICK HAMMER. Bringing up low spots by pick hammering is more difficult than by the use of the rounded corner of a dolly block. With the pick hammer, more accuracy in placing the blow will be required. Likewise, greater control of the force of the blow is necessary. However, many low spots can only be brought up by pick hammering.

You can start using the pick hammer in a manner similar to the way you started with the dolly. Hold the end of your finger in the low spot. Tap the under surface of the fender lightly with the pick until you feel that the pick is directly below your fingers. Then strike a light blow from beneath the fender, of sufficient strength to form a pimple in the low spot. This pimple represents stretched metal, but, in being formed, the immediately surrounding metal was also raised. When all of the low spots have been raised with the pick hammer in this manner, use a dolly that matches the contour of the fender, and hammer down these pimples by direct hammering. Here, extreme accuracy is required in hitting directly over the dolly block with each blow, as any blow that does not hit directly over the dolly will cause the surrounding surface to be displaced and this surface will have to be raised again.

After hammering down these pimples by direct hammering, again

X or cross file the damaged area, repeating the raising of low spots until you have a smooth surface with no low spots.

In the preceding exercise, it will be noted that the body file was used exclusively for revealing low spots. This was done deliberately to provide you with experience in the use of the file and to permit you to develop skill in its use. It is suggested that this exercise be repeated a number of times. If necessary, obtain additional discarded fenders on which to practice. After you feel that you have acquired sufficient skill with the file, you will want to try several other methods for locating low spots.

Skill in the raising of the low spots will permit you to do this job in a mere fraction of the time you would use if you did not acquire mastery of the direction and force of the blows you strike, whether you use a hammer or dolly. To give yourself every advantage in locating these low spots, several things can be done.

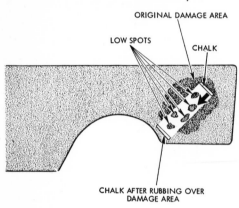

Fig. 27. Rubbing Chalk on Fender

(b) LOCATING LOW SPOTS WITH CHALK. During one of the exercises, substitute a piece of chalk for the file in detecting low spots.

Using the side of the chalk, draw it over the damaged area in several directions (Fig. 27). Form **X**'s or crosses until you have gone over the entire damaged area at least twice. As you rub the chalk over the damaged area, it will rub off on the metal on the high spots only, and will leave the low spots clearly revealed to you. This means much less physical effort on your part as well as a great saving in time, as compared to locating the low spots by filing. It is, however, necessary to finish the job with the file, because only by filing on the last operation can the metal surface be made as smooth as it was originally.

(c) LOCATING LOW SPOTS WITH A LIGHT. Another method for locating low spots is by the use of a bright light. A portable shop light which you can raise or lower and move around a vehicle is almost indispensable when doing body repair work. When working on fenders or other near vertical panels, you will find that a light on the floor will help you in locating low spots. Use a sheet of white paper for a reflector.

Hang the practice fender up so that it is in approximately the same position with relation to the floor as it would be if it were on a car. Place a large sheet of white paper on the floor with one edge extending under the outside edge of the fender. Place a light on the white paper so that the reflection of the light is upward past the fender. Reflecting the light from a white sheet, a newspaper, or some other suitable dull reflecting surface will cause the shadows and the slight depressions to be on the same side of the high spots as your eyes, thereby making the low spots more readily seen. Probably the most relaxing position for

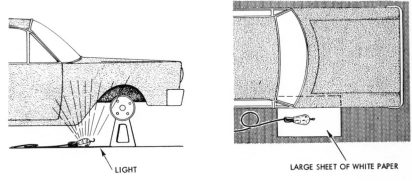

LIGHT

LARGE SHEET OF WHITE PAPER

Fig. 28. Locating Low Spots with a Light

this operation will be for you to sit right on the floor in front of the fender. Move the light around until it is in the one best position to show up the imperfections in the surface of the work (Fig. 28). By sitting on the floor and manipulating the light, you will easily be able to reach up under or behind the fender surface on which you are working, once you get the light in the best position. As the low spots are shown up, you can remove them in the ways which have just been described.

You can easily see that there will be several areas of an automobile body that do not readily lend themselves to working with a light reflected from a paper. Whenever you encounter damage in any surface other than a vertical or near vertical plane, it will be necessary to suspend the light or otherwise locate it to get the best possible reflection.

(d) LOCATING LOW SPOTS WITH GLOVES. You will notice that you can feel irregularities in the surface by rubbing your bare hand over it. However, you will notice immediately that by wearing an ordinary, loose-fitting cotton glove (Fig. 29), your hands will be more sensitive.

Without the glove, your hand is registering both the contour of the metal and its temperature. With the glove, your hand is insulated from the metal, and needs to be sensitive only to the irregularities.

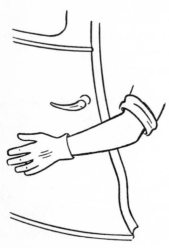

Fig. 29. Feeling Irregularities in the Metal with Gloves

c. Care and Maintenance of Hand Tools. Quality work depends a great deal on the condition of the tools used to do the work. Any irregularities in the working surface of the hand tool will be imparted to the surface being worked. Your pride in your craftsmanship is reflected in the way you maintain your tools. If your tools are allowed to become rusty, nicked, or dirty, it generally will be assumed that you do sloppy work.

When tools are left unused for a period of time, such as over a week end, etc., they should be coated with a light film of engine oil or similar substance. This film of oil will prevent rust formation. Rust, if allowed to form, is not only unsightly, but is detrimental to the working surfaces of the tools.

On occasion, hand tools will become marred slightly during use. These marks should be removed before the tool is used again. An effective, simple method of removing such marks is by the use of emery cloth. Hold a piece of No. 100 emery cloth in the palm of one hand and stroke the working surface of the tool over it in one direction only. The emery cloth, when held in the hand, will conform to the surface of the tool and will not change its contour. Also, the edges of the emery cloth will have a tendency to curl around the edge of the tool, leaving a small radius instead of sharp edges which are difficult to work with.

Never allow a hammer head to remain loose on its handle. This will noticeably affect your control over the accuracy and force of hammer blows.

Remember the body file blade is an expensive tool. Avoid practices that will nick the cutting edges. Keep the file clean.

IV. FORMING FENDER FLANGES AND BEADS

Automobile fenders are constructed in such a way that one side is rigidly held in place while the other is virtually unsupported. One side, of course, is fastened to the body with either screws or bolts or by welding. The outside of the fender is supported mainly by the crown put in the fender itself. The metal all around the bottom edge of the outside of the fender is flanged, or formed into a bead, to give the fender more rigidity. In some cases, the bead is merely a flange with a small radius turned toward the inside of the fender (Fig. 30). In other cases, the bead is formed by turning the flange toward the inside of the fender, then turning it up. This forms a **U** shaped section (Fig. 31).

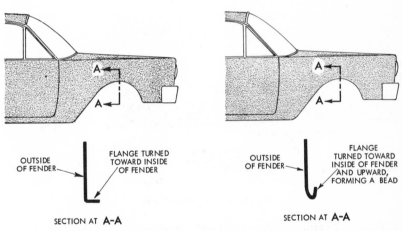

SECTION AT **A-A**   SECTION AT **A-A**

Fig. 30. Flange with Small Radius   Fig. 31. U Shaped Section Fender Bead

In any case where fender damage involves the bead, the bead will require re-forming after the fender is straightened. The bead is always formed last, because it would be impossible to reshape the edge of the fender before the fender proper has been drawn into shape.

In cases where the fender has been damaged so badly that the flange or bead has been torn, it will be necessary to repair the tear by welding, even though the tear might not show from the outside. The edges of fenders are subject to much vibration. For this reason, any small break in the edge would gradually grow larger.

The tools generally used to re-form flanges and beads are a dolly block and a bumping hammer.

With a dolly block, create damage to the flange or bead of the same practice fender you have been using. After you have smoothed the surface of the damaged area the way you have learned, find the surface of the low-crown dolly that most nearly matches the contour of the fender just above the flange.

On one end or side of each dolly block there is an anvil which can be used to form the flange. Place the dolly block against the inside surface of the fender with the projecting anvil against the flange at the edge of the damaged area. The flange will be easier to re-form if you start at the edge of the damage area where the flange is undamaged.

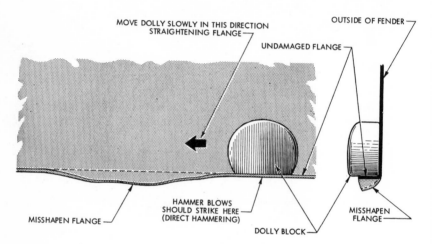

Fig. 32. Forming Fender Flange

By direct hammering, re-form the flange by moving the dolly block along slowly across the damaged area, forming the flange as you go (Fig. 32). The radius of the fender flange toward the outside surface of the fender will automatically be shaped by the radius on the anvil of the dolly block.

Use short, even strokes with the hammer, and do not strike the metal too hard, as there is danger that the flange might split. Also, be sure that the hammer blow falls squarely in the center of the anvil area of the dolly block. This will prevent the flange from being split over the edge of the dolly.

In cases of re-forming a **U** shaped fender bead, make a second pass along the damaged area after the flange is turned toward the inside of the fender, and turn the edge up as required. Use the same anvil on the dolly block. Use direct hammering, as you did to form the flange.

Practice forming the edge of your practice fender. It may have either a bead or just a plain flange turned toward the inside of the fender. Whichever it has, you can practice forming it until you are able to end up with a smooth contour on the edge that shows to the outside.

If the fender originally had a **U** shaped bead, form a straight angle bead at one portion of the fender. If the fender originally had a straight flange, re-form it to a **U** shape. Repeat this exercise until you feel that you will have no difficulty with it when you start working on an actual fender.

Whenever a flange or a fender bead is torn, it will be necessary to weld the two sides of the split metal together again. How this is done is explained in Chapter 3 of this volume.

V. OTHER HAND TOOLS

In preceding sections of this chapter, you learned of the basic hand tools required for body repair work and how they are used. However, there are many more hand tools used in body repair work than the ones which have been described to you so far.

In many instances, even though it is possible to do a job with the basic kit of tools, a tool developed especially for a particular job will do that job better. The tools which will be described and illustrated to you in the subsequent paragraphs of this section are variations of the basic kit of tools which have been designed for use with special contours, or which have been designed for reaching otherwise inaccessible places. An example of an inaccessible place is the inside of a door panel when all of the inside trim has not been removed. Certain minor repair jobs on doors make it impractical to remove the inside trim. Consequently, if it is not desired to remove the trim, it is necessary to have the proper tools to do the job. These tools perform the same function as any of the tools in the basic kit; they are merely designed for special applications.

Two additional operations not practical with the basic kit of tools will be used in connection with welding and shrinking of metal as covered in Chapter 4. The two tools involved in these two operations, and a practice exercise whereby you can learn how to use them, are presented in the following paragraphs.

a. **Tools for Shrinking Metal and Sinking Welds.** The dolly block shown in Fig. 33 is called a shrinking dolly. This dolly is formed so that two sides of it have a low-crown radius, the two ends being concave.

The hammer is similar to other bumping hammers except that one end of the head is shaped to exactly fit the concave contour of the dolly block after an allowance for the thickness of body metal has been taken into consideration (Fig. 33).

After a fender or panel is welded, the dolly block is placed against the inside surface so that the concave portion of the dolly is directly under the seam of the weld (Fig. 33). A blow is then struck with the hammer directly against the seam. The seam, being unsupported, will be depressed in a neat fashion. This operation is continued for the full length of the weld, leaving what might be referred to as a valley. This

 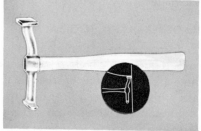

Fig. 33. Special Dolly Block and Hammer Used for Sinking Welds
(*Courtesy H. K. Porter*)

depression is later filled with solder and smoothed off. How this is done is explained in a subsequent chapter.

The main benefit derived from this procedure is the strength that is achieved by not filing or grinding the weld smooth. The weld is further strengthened when the valley made by the hammer and dolly is filled with solder.

In Chapter 4 you will learn how to shrink stretched metal with an acetylene torch and the shrinking dolly. Lacking a torch, the same effect can be accomplished with the dolly and hammer alone. This method is not too practical in actual collision work, but you can gain some experience in the use of these tools by performing this operation on your practice fender.

Whether the skirt of your practice fender is actually stretched or not makes little difference. For the purpose of this exercise, assume that the skirt of the fender is stretched so that it bulges outward slightly.

Place the dolly under the "high spot" and form a concave bead or valley as shown in Fig. 34. Move the dolly along slowly in a straight line beneath the "high spot" and strike the outside surface with the hammer. When working with actual damage, do not make the bead any longer or deeper than necessary to draw the stretched metal back to its normal contour. It may be necessary to make an **X** shaped bead as shown in the right-hand illustration in Fig. 34 if the metal is badly stretched.

An **X** shaped valley is made in the same way as a single valley except that a second one is made at right angles to the first one. Form the second bead so that it intersects the other one near the center of the stretched area. This gives an **X** shaped appearance.

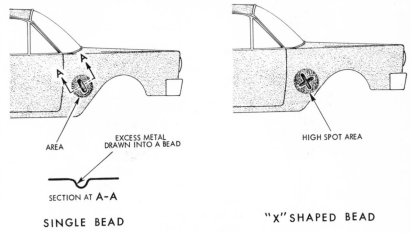

EXCESS METAL
DRAWN INTO A BEAD

AREA

HIGH SPOT AREA

SECTION AT **A-A**

SINGLE BEAD

"X" SHAPED BEAD

Fig. 34. Bead Formed To Remove a High Spot

Viewed from the other side, you will see that you have formed a rib that could be used to stiffen a panel to give it strength or to prevent "oil-canning" (the tendency of a panel to act like the bottom of an oil can).

Do this operation several times until you can sink a neat valley in the metal each time.

b. Body and Fender Hammers. Eventually you will want to add tools to the basic kit described earlier in the chapter. Several different hammers and their use, therefore, are presented here. Don't be in too much of a hurry to buy these extra hammers; you may never really need some of them.

The hammer shown in (*A*), Fig. 35, is a general-purpose hammer for use on any body panel.

A serrated face hammer is shown in (*B*), Fig. 35. This type of ham-

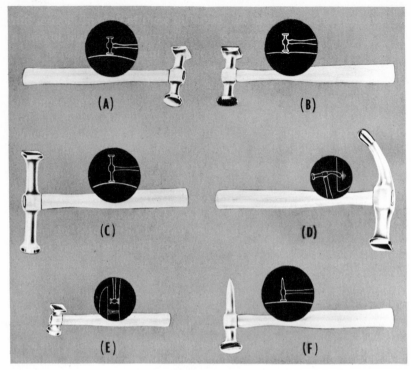

Fig. 35. Bumping Hammers
(Courtesy H. K. Porter)

mer is preferred by some for roughing out either high- or low-crown surfaces where the metal has been badly creased. The two hammers shown in (C) and (D) of Fig. 35 are other variations of bumping hammers. The heavy hammer with the long, curved end shown at (D) in Fig. 35 is a roughing hammer. Don't use a roughing hammer until you have completely mastered your other tools. By that time you will probably find you don't need one. You cannot hammer out metal with a heavy hammer without stretching the metal.

A short-shanked, square- and round-face hammer for use when working where the space is restricted (such as between the bumper bar and the fender) is shown at (E), Fig. 35. The hammer shown in (F), Fig. 35, is a bullet-type, short pick hammer.

A hammer which is ideally suited for fine finishing work by dingmen who repair damage without injuring the paint is the high- and low-crown finishing hammer shown in Fig. 36. This hammer is used for fine finish hammering on either low- or high-crown surfaces. Both ends of this hammer are crowned, one slightly more than the other.

Two styles of offset hammers are shown in Fig. 37. The combination offset cross and straight peen hammer, shown in (*A*), Fig. 37, has a triple purpose. It has a high-crown face for all narrow concave surfaces. The other, or cross-peen face, has a high crown, and is used for wide concave surfaces. The hammer head, having one end offset from the other, not only gives this type of hammer its name, but also allows the user to work close to beads and seams without damaging the surrounding area.

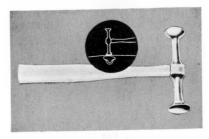

Hammer

Fig. 36. High- and Low-Crown Finishing
(Courtesy H. K. Porter)

The hammer in (*B*), Fig. 37, is a combination offset square face and cross peen bumping hammer. The offset square face is used for general work where an offset hammer is required. It affords ample clearance for adjoining panels. The high-crown, cross-peen face is designed for deep and narrow panel surfaces and return contours.

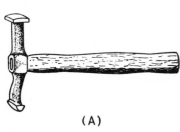

(A)

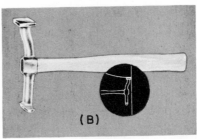

(B)

Fig. 37. Combination Offset Cross- and Straight-Peen Hammer (A), and Combination Offset Square Face and Cross-Peen Bumping Hammer (B)

c. Spoons. You are acquainted with the surfacing spoon included in the minimum kit of tools. Many other spoons are available for use in body repair work. Each of these spoons is designed for some specific use on certain body panels or fenders.

The double-end, lower back panel and quarter panel spoon (Fig. 38) is used for removing bumps on quarter panels around rear pillars. It is also used for getting behind inner construction and behind back panel strainers, center sills, and lower sills.

Another double-end spoon is the heavy-duty driving spoon shown in Fig. 39. This is a general purpose utility spoon which has a variety of uses. It is employed for setting the inside seams of front fenders, bumping top rail moldings, calking quarter panel moldings, etc. It is also used extensively in beading work. It is sometimes used for raising low spots in fender finishing and around cowl ventilator openings.

Fig. 38. Double-End, Lower Back Panel and
Quarter Panel Spoon
(Courtesy H. K. Porter)

Spoons which are developed especially for work on certain contours are shown in Fig. 40. The spoon in (*A*), Fig. 40, is a high-crown, concave finishing spoon. This type of spoon is used for spring hammering with a mallet or bumping hammer on all concave surfaces. The spoon shown in (*B*), Fig. 40, is a low-crown, concave surfacing spoon which is used in the same way on low-crown surfaces.

Fig. 39. Double-End, Heavy-Duty Driving
Spoon
(Courtesy H. K. Porter)

Two types of spoons designed especially for work on fenders are shown in Fig. 41. The fender and cowl bracket spoon in (*A*) of Fig.

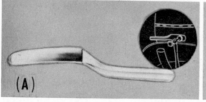
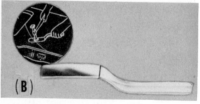

Fig. 40. Low-Crown Concave Surfacing Spoon (A), and High-Crown Concave
Finishing Spoon (B)
(Courtesy H. K. Porter)

41 is used to hook over a fender bracket. It may also be used as a dolly which sometimes makes unnecessary the removal of the wheels on jobs involving the fender brackets. It is also a handy tool when working over cowl strainers and cowl brackets from post to dash.

The tool in (*B*), Fig. 41, is a specially designed fender beading tool for use with the latest style fenders. It may also be used for flanges on one-piece hoods and for aligning inner body panel construction. Some manufacturers provide hammer pads on this type of spoon for use in hammering operations. This tool, when hooked into the flange of the fender or hood as shown in the insert of the illustration, provides a surface on which you can pound with a hammer to bring the metal back in place.

When you are working on door panels, it is necessary, in order to hold the amount of disassembly required to a minimum, to have tools that you can use to reach far behind inner construction. The spoons shown in Fig. 42 are designed for use especially on door and side panels. The function of these two spoons is very nearly the same, except that they are for use on slightly different

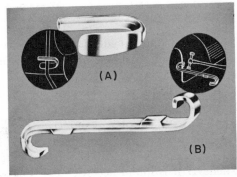

Fig. 41. Fender and Cowl Bracket Spoon (A), and Fender Beading Tool (B)
(*Courtesy H. K. Porter*)

contours and in slightly different cases. When you have the need for one of these tools, it will immediately become apparent to you which one you should use for the particular job on which you happen to be working.

Another tool which is usually considered to be of the spoon family is the wide calking iron (Fig. 43). This tool is designed for use in calking all straight-line surfaces along the center pillar door panels.

d. Dolly Blocks. Much money can be wasted in buying dolly blocks if you do not utilitze each block you buy on all of the jobs for which it can be used. Besides the dollies with which you have already become familiar, there are other types, some of which you will want when you round out your kit of tools.

The finger dolly (*A*), Fig. 44, is especially useful because its unique shape allows it to be used for bump hammering where inner construction or adjoining metal makes the use of the ordinary dolly difficult. Its design permits working in close quarters without danger of injury to the back of your hand on the back stroke.

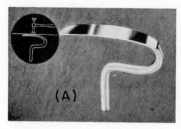
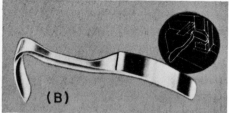

Fig. 42. Door and Side Panel Spoon (A), and Double-End Door and Side Panel Spoon
(Courtesy H. K. Porter)

You may want an additional high-crown dolly heavier than the one included in the basic kit previously discussed. Such a dolly is shown at (*B*), Fig. 44.

e. Pick Tools. Pick tools have the same function as a pick hammer. However, many places are inaccessible with a pick hammer.
For this reason, pick tools have
been developed which can be used
whenever it is found necessary to
work in one of these places. Two
pick tools (Fig. 45) which have
similar uses are the long curved
pick and the short curved pick.

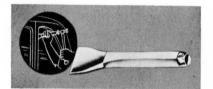

Fig. 43. Wide Calking Iron
(Courtesy H. K. Porter)

These pick tools are used where a long reach is required, either through inner construction or through the lower part of the frame. Both tools are curved so that when they are turned by the handle, when they are between an outside panel and the inner construction, small bumps

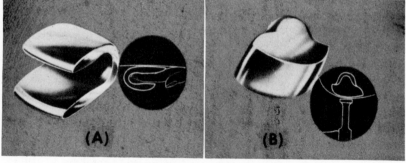

Fig. 44. Finger Dolly Block (A), and High-Crown Dolly Block (B)
(Courtesy H. K. Porter)

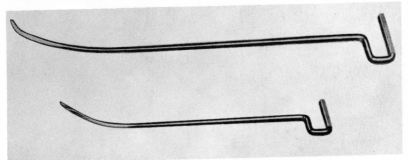

Fig. 45. Curved Long Pick (Top), and Curved Short Pick (Bottom)
(Courtesy H. K. Porter)

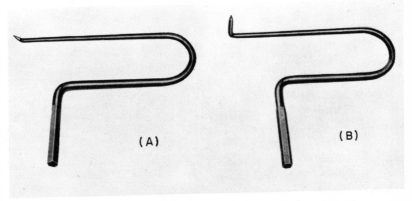

(A)   (B)

Fig. 46. Deep Throat Straight Pick (A), and Deep Throat Curved Pick (B)
(Courtesy H. K. Porter)

in the metal will be forced back to its approximate original position.

Pick tools designed especially for use around door panels and rear deck lids are shown in Fig. 46.

The deep throat straight pick in (*A*), Fig. 46, is used for raising low spots in the center section of rear deck lids, or in the center sections of door panels, where it is necessary to get behind inner construction.

The deep throat curved pick (*B*), Fig. 46, is similar

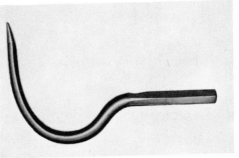

Fig. 47. Top Rail Pick Tool
(Courtesy H. K. Porter)

in design to the deep throat straight pick and it is used in a similar fashion. Where the straight throat is used for working on center sections of door panels, the curved pick is used for working around the edges of door panels, rear deck lids, and also around quarter panels where a tool is needed to reach around some inner construction.

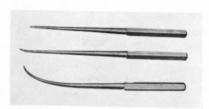

Fig. 48. Straight Finishing Punch (Top), Curved Finishing Punch (Center), and Hooked Finishing Punch (Bottom)
(Courtesy H. K. Porter)

Another type of pick tool is shown in Fig. 47. This is a top rail pick tool designed for fitting over the top rail inner construction so that fine finishing work may be done on the top rail panel above the drip molding.

The three other pick tools which will round out the complete set of pick tools you may eventually want are shown in Fig. 48. These pick tools are really punches which, because of their design and intended use, are called pick tools.

These tools are particularly useful when you are working around reveal moldings or where it is necessary to reach inside doors through door handle holes. They are also useful where offset blows are necessary, and when working around the rear deck lid. Of all the pick tools available, these are the ones which you will want to procure first.

f. Miscellaneous Tools. Several tools are available which will make certain jobs easier and which will save you much time. One of these is a pair of drip molding pliers (Fig. 49). The pliers are used for pulling out crushed drip moldings. Another

Fig. 49. Drip Molding Pliers
(Courtesy H. K. Porter)

tool which will be helpful to you is a leverage dolly. A leverage dolly is shown in use in Fig. 50.

VI. STRAIGHTENING TYPICAL DAMAGE

As has been emphasized throughout this discussion, skill in the use of the hand tools is of prime importance in body repair work. This skill can only be acquired through much practice. Of equal importance is the ability of the body repairman to apply his knowledge of the tools to the job at hand.

On any repair job, no matter how minor the damage might be, you should analyze the damage before you even consider starting to bump. By analyzing the damage, you can determine what it was caused by, the sequence in which it occurred, and what tools will be required to correct it. This should be the procedure on every repair job you encounter. When you actually become employed in a body shop, it will immediately come to your attention that analyzing the job has another value. By analyzing the job, you can make an estimate of the cost of the repairs. Estimating is a subject in itself, and it will be covered in a subsequent chapter of this volume. For the present you are concerned with analyzing or studying the damage merely to determine what must be done to restore the damaged portions of the body to normal.

Fig. 50. Leverage Dolly
(*Courtesy H. K. Porter*)

Of the several reasons for studying the damage, the most important one is to determine the sequence in which the damage occurred. In complex types of damage (damage resulting from a series of events), it is necessary to reverse the process by which the damage occurred in order to straighten the damaged area with a minimum amount of effort. Another factor involved is the danger of stretching the metal or causing cracks or breaks where otherwise none would occur if the damage were removed in the reverse order of occurrence.

a. **Straightening Metal Without Damaging the Paint.** In some simple types of damage, it is possible to remove the dent without damaging the paint. When the damage is slight and no sharp creases are involved, you should always consider the possibility of straightening the damage without damaging the paint.

Many fender repairs can be accomplished without disturbing the paint if the inside and outside surfaces have been thoroughly cleaned and properly prepared. A typical instance of straightening a minor damage without injuring the paint is illustrated in Figs. 51, 52, and 53. In this example, a "ding" has occurred in the outside lower front corner of a front fender. The metal is merely caved in and is not torn or severely creased.

Hit the deepest portion of the dent from underneath with a heavy dolly such as that (roughing dolly) shown in Fig. 51. Use a surface of

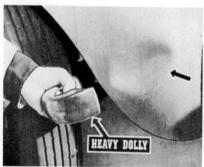 

Fig. 51. Hammer from Underneath with a Heavy Dolly

Fig. 52. Cover the Outside Surface of the Fender with Oil

(Courtesy Ford Motor Company)

the dolly which conforms with the original contour of the metal. With practice, you will find that in many instances you can push the metal back with one blow. This is what you should strive for. However, if you need to, hit the number of blows necessary. Be careful not to hit the metal with the corner or edge of the dolly. If this happens, the metal will be stretched and the paint will become damaged.

After the dent has been pushed back, clean the outside surface, then cover it with oil (Fig. 52). The oil will prevent the mallet from damaging the paint when you remove the small irregularities in the surface left by the dolly block.

Remove the irregularities or low spots by direct hammering with a wooden mallet and a dolly block of the proper contour. Hit the high spots (Fig. 53) with the mallet. At each blow, the dolly underneath leaves the fender. As it comes back up, it will force up low spots, evening the surface.

If you exercise a reasonable amount of care in performing the straightening operations for damage of this type, you will save yourself and your customers much cost and inconvenience.

b. Straightening Damage by the Reverse Process. The first step in straightening metal is to get it back as nearly as possible to its original

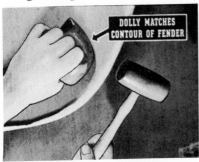

Fig. 53. Dolly under Low Portion, Hit High Spots

Fig. 54. Typical Example of Complex Fender Damage

(Courtesy Ford Motor Company)

shape or contour. In cases of complex damage, this is accomplished by reversing the process by which the damage occurred.

Fig. 54 illustrates a fender which has been damaged by a series of events. By studying the fender, you will be able to determine which damage occurred first. In this fender, the corner of the skirt was hooked

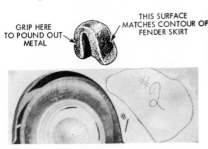

Fig. 55. Last Damage Should Be Corrected First

Fig. 56. Pushing the Fender Skirt Back into Position

(Courtesy Ford Motor Company)

first, then pulled back. The area marked *1* in Fig. 54 was pulled until the fender bracket bent, at which time the crown in the area marked *2* was reversed, leaving a concave surface.

To straighten the fender, this process must be reversed. First, loosen the fender bracket and push the metal in the area marked *2* back to the original contour. Don't use a roughing hammer. Use a heavy dolly as shown in Fig. 55. Be sure the contour of the dolly conforms with the original contour of the fender as nearly as possible. When using the dolly, be careful not to hit the metal with the corners of the dolly. To do so will stretch the metal.

After the low portion is removed, push the corner of the fender skirt back to its original position (Fig. 56). You will notice that the dingman pictured in Fig. 56 is using his hands and feet to push the fender skirt back into position. In a case such as this, where the damage is in an easily accessible portion of a panel, you can save much time by just push-ing the damaged portion into place by hand. If you are able to do this, you have, in effect, succeeded in accomplishing the same re-sult you would have achieved by indirect hammering.

Fig. 57. Restoring Contour of Fender Skirt
(Courtesy Ford Motor Company)

It will be necessary for you to restore the original contour of the fender skirt by direct hammering. See Fig. 57.

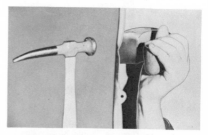

Fig. 58. Showing Up Low Spots   **Fig. 59. Reforming the Fender Bead**
(Courtesy Ford Motor Company)

After the contour of the fender has been restored, it will be neces-sary to bring up the low spots (Fig. 58). If you do a thorough job of bringing up the low spots, it will save a lot of filing or grinding, making the job much easier.

Re-form the fender bead (Fig. 59). The fender bead stiffens the skirt, thereby strengthening the entire fender. The bead and the curved surface of the skirt will then hold the metal in position. Get the metal as smooth as possible with a hammer and dolly, using care not to stretch the metal.

File the repaired area, and use the high-crown dolly and pick hammer to bring up low spots. By direct hammering with a hammer and dolly, flatten the metal raised with the pick. File as required until the metal is completely smooth. Straighten and reattach the fender bracket.

At this point the metal bumping operation is complete, and the job is ready for the metal finisher.

You can easily see that the job just described was complex damage of a simple type. You are probably wondering what happens when you encounter a job with the roof caved in and all the windows and doors smashed. Several subsequent chapters of this volume are devoted to straightening these more serious types of complex damage. However, before you move on to a study of straightening complex damages, you will require a knowledge of the power tools used in collision work. Power tools are available from several manufacturers, and are used by all progressive body shops throughout the country.

TRADE COMPETENCY TESTS

The following questions, while they represent only a small portion of the material in this chapter, may be used to determine the percentage of the material retained.

1. What are the duties of a dingman in an automobile manufacturing plant? (p. 71)

2. What pressure variation in psi is possible with the two sides of the pick hammer if a blow of 100 pounds force is struck in both instances? (p. 74)

3. Why should you have a wood mallet in your kit of hand tools? (p. 75)

4. Why must your kit of tools contain both low-crown and high-crown dollies? (p. 76)

5. How is adjustment of a body file obtained so that the file can be used on surfaces with a contour? (p. 77)

6. What is meant by the term *line filing?* (p. 87)

7. At what angle are the file strokes to one another if you are doing **X** filing? Cross filing? (p. 87)

8. What is meant by the term *direct hammering?* (p. 89)

9. Why is the use of a heavy roughing hammer usually inadvisable? (p. 96)

10. Which hammer is most generally used for bringing up small low spots? (p. 99)

11. When a light is used for locating low spots, how is it reflected to the body panel? (p. 100)

12. How does using a glove on one hand aid in locating low spots? (p. 101)

13. When your hand tools are to be left unused for a period of time, what should you do? (p. 102)

14. How can the working surfaces of hand tools be kept smooth? (p. 102)

15. Why must a hammer head be kept tight on the handle? (p. 102)

16. What hand tools are most generally used for reforming fender flanges and beads? (p. 103)

17. What is the name of the dolly block used for shrinking welds? (p. 105)

18. What hand tool is used with a shrinking dolly? (p. 105)

19. Is it possible to shrink metal by any other method than with a hammer and shrinking dolly? (p. 106)

20. Under what circumstances is a serrated face hammer used by some collision men? (p. 108)

21. Under what circumstances is a short shanked, square and round face hammer a valuable tool? (p. 108)

22. When is a long curved pick tool or a short curved pick tool used? (p. 112)

23. What tool is used to restore a smashed drip molding? (p. 114)

24. Why is oil sometimes applied to a painted surface before straightening it? (p. 116)

CHAPTER 3

WELDING AND CUTTING

Welding is the process of joining two or more pieces of metal together by the application of heat and, sometimes, of pressure. Welding is usually accomplished by heating the metal until it becomes molten and flows or fuses together.

A casual inspection of a modern car reveals little evidence of welding, yet all modern cars are welded from bumper to bumper. In fact, today's automobile could not be assembled at its present low cost without welding.

In body and frame straightening, and in all forms of collision work, it is often necessary to use welding techniques to reinforce frame members, and to weld in place whole new body panels and patches in old panels. These operations can be performed with oxyacetylene gas welding equipment, and most collision men have found it necessary to develop skill in the use of oxyacetylene equipment.

An oxyacetylene torch may also be used to melt and apply solder to body panels, to heat parts to permit bending, and to cut through body panels, inner body construction, and frame members.

An electric arc welder can also be used to cut metal or fuse two separate pieces or two edges together although no satisfactory method has been developed whereby the electric welder can be used for applying solder or heating parts prior to bending or shrinking.

If gas welding equipment is not available, a small blowtorch can be used almost as effectively for applying solder as the acetylene torch. A gasoline or alcohol blowtorch costs but a few dollars.

In shrinking metal (discussed in Chapter 4 of this volume), it is necessary to heat small areas to a cherry red, then to pound the heated portions down. Here again, oxyacetylene equipment possesses a distinct advantage over any other. Some manufacturers of arc welding equipment, however, have developed a two-carbon torch that results in a flame which can be used for metal shrinking. However, a disadvantage exists in that during the application of the heat to the metal, the eyes and face must be protected, and the operator is, to a degree, working blind.

Arc welding, on the other hand, is generally conceded to be much faster and less costly than oxyacetylene welding. Electric welding equipment, satisfactory for most body panel jobs, can be purchased for as little as you may charge for a single job.

Any collision expert should be thoroughly familiar with both types of equipment, for as he goes from shop to shop, he must be able to use whatever equipment is placed at his disposal.

The purpose of this chapter is not to take sides as to which of these two methods of welding is preferable or which type equipment is the better for a shop to select, but to provide you with the necessary instructions so that you will be able to operate satisfactorily either type of equipment. Actually, most shops probably should have both kinds of equipment, and many of them do.

Neither is it the intention of this chapter to teach you how to do all kinds of welding. You will be instructed only in those things you will be required to do as a collision expert. No one can truly qualify as a collision man who is unfamiliar with, and unable to use, both kinds of equipment.

In collision work, it is often necessary to repair places where the metal has become rusted through, torn, or otherwise broken. The only process by which this can be done involves raising the temperature of the metal to the point where two pieces of metal or two edges of the same piece of metal are fused together. This process is called welding. Both gas welding and electric (arc) welding are explained and illustrated in this chapter.

Sometimes it is necessary to cut out badly damaged portions of body panels or fenders and replace them with new ones. In other instances, it is necessary to cut inner construction in order to gain access to the inner surface of the outer panels. Metal can be cut in several ways, and Section III of this chapter deals with a number of methods of cutting both sheet metal and the inner construction.

Welding or cutting with welding equipment leaves an uneven edge and surface. Regardless of this, it is necessary for the welder to leave the surface as smooth as possible. A discussion of the welder's responsibility in preparing the surface for metal finishing is given in Section V of this chapter.

A problem confronting a welder using either gas or arc is achieving good *fusion*. Many times fusion and *adhesion* are confused in people's minds. In welding, the prime objective is to achieve good fusion of the two edges being welded. Fusion is the condition which exists when two materials actually flow together in a molten state and form one piece when they become hard. Adhesion is the condition which exists when two different materials are made to stick tightly to one another. This is especially true of soldering which is discussed in a subsequent chapter of this volume.

A process often confused with welding which utilizes the principle of adhesion is *brazing*. Brazing does not provide the same degree of strength as welding, and is actually a form of soldering. Never substitute brazing for welding in automotive sheet metal welding. It not only is an inferior method, but is usually considered as the mark of an amateur.

A material known as *flux* enables a welder to achieve either fusion or adhesion. The use of flux effectively eliminates the formation of oxide in the weld. If oxide does form, flux will reduce and remove it from the weld. If oxide is not removed from the weld, the molten metal will be enclosed in a thin film of nonmetallic material, and any additional metal that may be added will adhere to this film rather than to break through it and fuse homogeneously with the other metal. However, flux is not used solely to dissolve the oxide, but also to float off other impurities such as sand, scale, and dirt.

Several good brands of flux are commercially available. Be sure to use the proper flux for the type of welding you are doing. It is advisable to follow the manufacturer's recommendations on this.

I. GAS WELDING

An oxygen acetylene flame can be used for fusing practically any kind of metal. Because oxygen and acetylene are both gases, the process is commonly called "gas" or "torch" welding.

Two tanks, one filled with oxygen and the other with acetylene, are used to contain the gases which are metered to a torch through hoses. The operator controls the metering by means of valves on the tanks and on the torch (Fig. 1).

The actual welding is done with the torch tip. A different type tip can also be used with the same equipment for cutting. Both of these processes are explained in the following pages. First, however, you should understand why the gases at the end of the torch burn.

The standard oxygen tank is a seamless steel bottle about 5 feet high with walls about ½ in. in thickness. The tank, when full, contains approximately 220 cubic feet of oxygen compressed to 1½ cubic feet. The oxygen, when compressed to this degree, exerts a pressure on the walls of the tank of 2,000 psi (pounds per square inch). Smaller tanks having a lower capacity also are available.

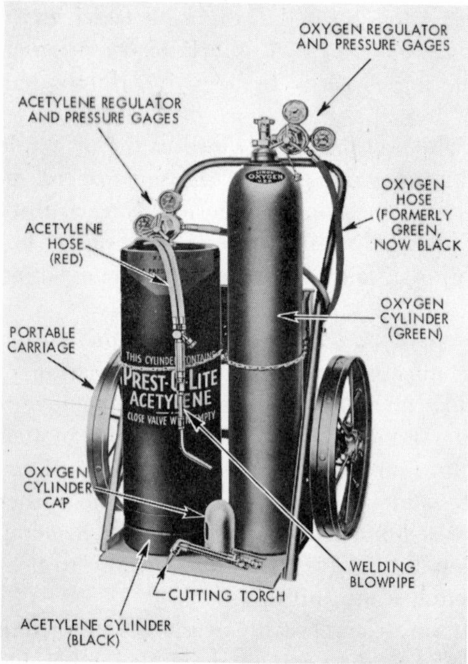

Oxygen alone is noninflammable, but it will actively support combustion. If no flame is in the torch tip and oxygen is allowed to escape, a film of ice will form around the tip. If oil or grease, which are forms of carbon, are brought into contact with oxygen under pressure, the mixture becomes highly inflammable, and even explosive at times.

The acetylene tank or cylinder is similar in construction to the oxygen tank except that it is filled with a porous filler similar to a sponge. This filler may

Fig. 1. Welding Outfit and Nomenclature
(*Courtesy Linde Air Products Company*)

be made of either asbestos, corn pith, charcoal, or other material, depending upon the manufacturer. This filler is completely soaked with acetone, which dissolves and absorbs the acetylene, allowing more acetylene to be carried in a tank. Acetylene in a free state not dissolved can be safely compressed to a pressure of 14.7 psi. The acetylene in the cylinder is compressed until it exerts a pressure of 250 to 275 psi on the cylinder. Acetylene is sold by weight, not pressure, as is oxygen.

The flame at the torch tip is a result of combustion of pure oxygen and pure acetylene. Two and one-half parts of oxygen are needed to consume one part of acetylene. It is not necessary to supply all of the oxygen through the torch. The torch is designed to supply one part each of oxygen and acetylene. The air surrounding the flame will supply the other one and one-half parts of oxygen necessary for perfect combustion and the creation of a neutral flame necessary for a perfect weld.

a. **Equipment.** The following items are the necessary components of a gas welding outfit. You will also need some metal to practice welding: (1) an oxygen tank, reducing valve, hose and connections; (2) an acetylene tank, reducing valve, hose and connections; (3) a welding torch and an assortment of tips—usually numbers 1, 2, 3, 4, and 5; (4) a set of welder's goggles with double glass for each eye (outer glass clear, inner glass smoke colored); (5) assorted welding rods; (6) a brick- or metal-top table or bench; (7) some thumb clamps and a vise; and (8) several pieces of 20- to 14-gauge sheet metal.

Before you start assembling and setting up the equipment, there are several rules concerning its proper use which you should learn and always remember.

(1) *Don't* use oil or any greasy substance on any connections on a welding outfit.

(2) *Don't* connect the oxygen hose on the acetylene valve.

(3) *Don't* turn the oxygen torch valve on first.

(4) *Don't* leave a welding outfit without closing the tank valves.

(5) *Don't* leave the torch burning when it is not in use.

(6) *Don't* smoke or otherwise bring fire into the area where you are working with an oxygen tank.

Observing these basic rules will prevent you from having accidents with your equipment.

(1) *SETTING UP EQUIPMENT.* The first procedure in assembling a gas welding outfit is to remove the valve caps from the oxygen and acetylene tanks. Open and close each valve quickly to blow out any dust or dirt which might be carried to the regulators. This is known as "cracking the tank." When "cracking the tank," do not direct the high-pressure stream of gas toward anyone or toward an open flame.

Next, connect the oxygen regulator (Fig. 2) to the oxygen tank. When you are tightening the connection, do not hold the regulator in a fixed position. Allow it to come into position freely as the collar is tightened. This will eliminate any strain on the regulator and will reduce the wear on the valve seat.

Connect the oxygen hose (now black, but formerly green) to the regulator tightly. Be careful not to tighten the connections excessively. If you suspect that the connection is leaking, paint it with a solution of soap and water with the pressure at the tank turned on. Any leakage will show up in the form of a soap bubble.

The acetylene tank is hooked up in the same manner as the oxygen tank with a few exceptions. The acetylene hose is red and has left-hand threads which must be turned counterclockwise to tighten.

Fig. 2. Gas Welding Tanks Mounted on Portable Truck
(Courtesy Linde Air Products Company)

(a) CONNECTING THE TORCH. Once the hoses are connected to the tanks, the torch can be connected to the hoses. On most equipment, there is no danger of interchanging hose connections because of the left-hand thread on the acetylene hose. However, a few older torches have right-hand threads on both the oxygen and acetylene connections, so it is advisable to exercise care if this type of equipment is encountered.

(b) SELECTION OF TIP. After the torch is connected, it is necessary to select the correct size tip for the job at hand. The selection of tips is based on the thickness of the stock to be welded. Since the numbering of tips has never been standardized, it is difficult to set up a specific rule. However, Table 1 will be helpful. Such a table, however, cannot be followed rigidly because the size of the tip used also depends on several variables such as the skill of the operator, the volume of the surrounding metal, the position in which the welding is done, and the kind of metal being welded. If a tip is too small for a job, much time will be wasted and poor fusion will result. If a tip is too large for a job, it is likely to produce poor metal in the weld due to overoxidation, and a rough job due to the lack of control of the flowing metal.

After the correct size tip has been selected, install it in the nozzle. Adjust the nozzle at the union joint (Fig. 3) so that the tip will point correctly when the torch is held conveniently for operation and adjustment.

TABLE 1. TORCH TIP SIZES AND PRESSURES FOR WELDING

Metal Thickness		Welding Head Size Number for Blowpipe				Pressures* (Psi) for Both Oxygen and Acetylene
(Inches)	(Gauge)	00–D	33	34	35	
....	28	1	....	....	....	1
		....	1	....	....	1–3
		....	....	1	1	1–2
....	26	....	1	....	....	2–4
		....	....	1	....	1.5–3
		....	....	....	1	1–2
....	24	2	....	....	....	2
		....	2	....	2	1–4
		....	....	2	....	1–4.5
		....	3	....	....	2–3
¹⁄₁₆	16	3	....	....	....	3
		....	3	....	....	2–4
		....	4	4	....	2–3
		....	....	....	3	2–5
³⁄₃₂	13	4	....	....	....	4
		....	4	....	....	2–5
		....	....	4	....	2.5–4
		....	....	....	3	4–6
¹⁄₈	11	5	....	....	....	5
		....	4, 5	....	....	3–5
		....	....	4	....	3–6
		....	....	....	5	2–4
³⁄₁₆	....	....	5	....	5	4–6
		....	....	6	....	4–6.5
		....	6	....	....	3–5
¹⁄₄	....	....	6	....	....	5–8
		....	....	6	....	6–10.5
		....	....	....	7	4–6
		....	7	....	....	4–7

* Regulator setting with twenty-five-foot hose lengths.
(Courtesy Linde Air Products Company)

(c) ADJUSTING REGULATORS. To adjust the oxygen regulator, make sure that the adjusting screw (Fig. 3) is turned all the way out and is free of spring tension so that when the oxygen pressure is released from the tank, it will not bang against the diaphragm and damage the nozzle.

TABLE 2. TORCH TIP SIZES AND PRESSURES FOR CUTTING

Metal Thickness (in Inches)	Nozzle Size Number for Cutting Attachment or Blowpipe				Pressures* (Psi)		
						Acetylene	
	33	34	35	Type "E"	Oxygen	Four-Flame Nozzle	Six-Flame Nozzle
1/16	0	....	....	....	10–15	3–5	....
1/8	0	....	....	....	15–20	4–6	....
	....	1	1	1	10–13	2–3	1–2
1/4	0	....	....	....	30–38	4–8	....
	....	1	1	....	17–24	2–5	1–3
	....	....	....	1	17–22	2–4	

* Regulator setting with twenty-five-foot hose lengths.

Courtesy Linde Air Products Company

Open the oxygen tank valve fully. Open the oxygen valve on the torch handle one-quarter turn, then turn the adjusting screw on the regulator clockwise until the proper pressure for the tip being used on the torch is registered on the pressure gauge. Close the oxygen valve on the torch handle when the correct pressure is established according to the gauge.

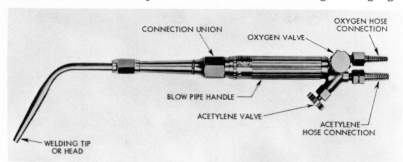

Fig. 3. Welding Torch with Nozzle in Place
(Courtesy Linde Air Products Company)

The acetylene regulator can now be adjusted in the same manner with the exception that the tank valve need be opened only a quarter to one-half turn, or until the tank pressure registers on the tank pressure gauge.

(d) LIGHTING THE TORCH. A flint lighter (Fig. 4) is generally used for lighting the torch because it will produce a good-sized spark quickly.

To light the torch, open the acetylene valve on the torch handle about one-quarter turn and immediately spark the flint lighter at the end of the torch tip. If too much time elapses before the lighter is sparked, there is danger of a small explosion which may burn your hands. When the gas is lit, turn the acetylene valve on the torch handle until the proper flame is established. For general purposes, you can consider the torch correctly adjusted when a yellow flame is produced which is just ready to break away from the tip

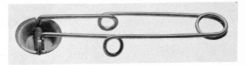

Fig. 4. Flint Lighter
(Courtesy Linde Air Products Company)

and burns approximately ⅛ in. away from the end of the tip. After the correct acetylene flame is established, open the oxygen valve on the torch slowly until the flame changes from a ragged yellow flame to a perfectly formed bluish tone. This is known as a neutral flame and is the proper flame for most welding.

(e) WELDING FLAMES. Unless the oxygen and acetylene are combined in the proper amounts to produce a neutral flame (Fig. 5 at top),

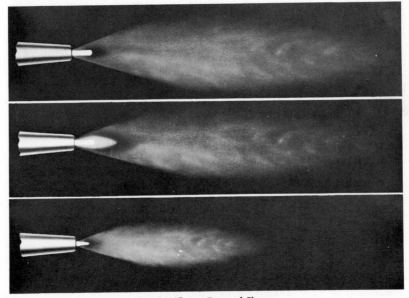

Fig. 5. Different Types of Flames
Neutral Flame (Top), Reducing Flame (Center), and Oxidizing Flame (Bottom)
(Courtesy Linde Air Products Company)

the release of unburned carbon or oxygen will occur, and lower temperatures will result. The different types of flames which you will encounter in welding when the torch is not properly adjusted are illustrated in Fig. 5, center and bottom.

Free carbon in the welding flame will result in what is called a reducing flame (Fig. 5 at center) and will cause carbonization of the metal. This will cause slag and brittleness and will result in loss of heat, porosity of the metal, and you will have a difficult time fusing the two pieces of metal.

An excess of oxygen will result in a purplish colored flame, commonly called an oxidizing flame (Fig. 5 at bottom). This type of flame will cause rapid oxidation, slag inclusion, porosity, and again you will have difficulty in fusing the two pieces.

For combustion purposes, the acetylene obtains about one and one-half parts of oxygen from the atmosphere and one part provided by the oxygen supply. If more or less is furnished due to improper adjustment of the regulator or torch valves, the effects are noticeable at once by the appearance of the flame, by the sound of the combustion, and by the appearance of the weld metal. Proper adjustment of the welding flame is a vital factor of welding. It must be studied continuously if you expect to obtain good welds.

The sound of combustion is the sound made by the torch in the process of burning the acetylene and oxygen. When the flame is properly adjusted, it will burn softly and evenly. If too much oxygen is being delivered to the torch, the flame will burn with a sharp hissing sound.

If the pressure of both the acetylene and the oxygen is too great, the flame will burn with a harsh blowing sound, and the vertical cone will be too long. This type of flame will cause "blowing of the metal." The force of the oxygen and gas is so great as it leaves the nozzles that it actually blows holes in the molten metal.

If too low a pressure is being used, it will permit the flame to burn within the tip. This condition will soon cause overheating of the tip. When the tip becomes hot enough to ignite the gases within it, backfiring or popping will result, spattering the metal, whereupon the continuity of the weld will be interrupted.

(1) CARBONIZING FLAME. When an excess of acetylene is used, the flame will be ragged. Certain welding operations make it desirable to have a slightly carbonizing flame. When welding aluminum, a carbonizing flame is desirable because it will prevent the formation of an

excess of aluminum oxide, which interferes in the fusing of the metal. A carbonizing flame is also desirable when welding monel metal, stainless steel, and white or die-cast metal.

(2) OXIDIZING FLAME. An oxidizing flame, as mentioned before, is injurious to the metal. An oxidizing flame can easily be recognized by the size of the flame cone (small and pointed) and by the brilliant blue color.

The use of too much oxygen will cause the metal to burn rapidly. This is a prime factor in cutting metal, so it can be seen readily that an excess of oxygen should not be used when you are trying to make a weld.

(2) *MANIPULATION OF TORCH AND WELDING ROD.* Before you actually do any welding, you should become familiar with holding and moving the torch correctly. You will also have to familiarize yourself with adding welding rod to the weld. The welding rod provides the additional material needed for fusing two edges of metal together. The exercises given in this chapter will give you an opportunity to practice the movement of both the torch and welding rod.

Fig. 6. Correct Method of Holding Welding Torch
(Courtesy Smith Welding and Cutting Equipment Company)

(a) MOVEMENT OF THE TORCH. In these first exercises, it will not be necessary to light the torch because you are going to practice moving and holding the torch only.

In order to obtain the best weld, it is necessary to incline the torch at an angle of about 60° to the plane of the work. Fig. 6 shows the proper way of holding the torch with the tip or blow pipe inclined correctly.

The torch should not be inclined too much. Otherwise, the molten metal will be blown ahead of the weld area. Neither should it be held in a near vertical position, for then the flame will not be utilized to its full value in heating the metal ahead of the weld area.

Whenever possible, move the torch from left to right rather than toward and away from yourself. It is much easier to observe the work when the torch is moved back and forth.

To make a proper weld, it is necessary to make a simultaneous fusion of the edges to be joined and the welding rod. This is accomplished by the movement of the torch, depending on the thickness of the stock being welded.

With thick stock, it is necessary to bevel or *chamfer* the edges to be joined, then butt them together and fill the bevel with molten welding rod. The proper movement to impart to the torch for this type of welding is illustrated by the lines in Fig. 7. The torch is oscillated in

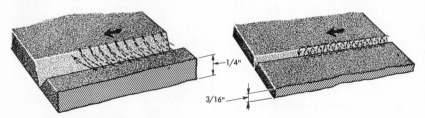

Fig. 7. Oscillation Motion of Torch for Welding Heavy Stock

Fig. 8. Circular Motion of Torch for Welding Light-Gauge Metals

arcs large enough to contact both edges of the bevel. The welding rod is held in the center of the bevel so the torch also contacts the rod. This movement allows the edges of the stock and the welding rod to be heated to the molten stage simultaneously.

When you are welding light-gauge metals, you should impart a circular motion to the torch (Fig. 8). This circular motion should be in the direction of the welding. Experience will soon show you how large the circles should be for the different gauges of metal which you will encounter.

Any motion of the torch, whether it be for either light or heavy stock, should be made in a constant and regular manner to produce a good appearance on the finished weld.

(b) ADDING WELDING ROD. The welding rod plays an important part in welding. It must be held correctly and added to the weld at the proper time. Otherwise, a poor weld will result. Moreover, the rod should be inclined in a fashion similar to the torch. Fig. 9 shows how to hold the welding rod and torch in their proper relationship.

When the edges to be joined are heated to the molten stage, the welding rod should be brought into contact with them. As soon as the bead or crater, as it is sometimes called, is filled, the rod should be removed and the torch advanced slightly along the weld line. The rod can again be introduced into the weld as soon as the metal is ready to receive it. If the welding rod is added to the weld before the edges to be joined are sufficiently heated, poor fusion will result.

(3) *EXERCISES*. You should perform each one of the exercises described here several times. By doing so, you will become quite proficient in the use of the welding equipment. All of these operations or exercises are a necessary part of the practice necessary to become a good sheet metal welder.

The only materials you will require are an old fender, some $\frac{1}{4}$, $\frac{1}{8}$, and $\frac{3}{32}$ in. steel plate, and some welding rod.

(a) WELDING OF HEAVY STOCK. For your first attempt at welding, it is

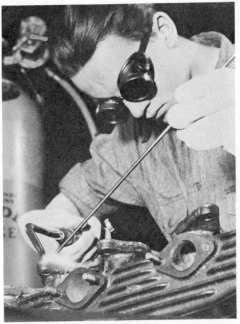

Fig. 9. Correct Method for Holding Torch and Welding Rod
(Courtesy Linde Air Products Company)

best for you to work with thick stock. Obtain some $\frac{1}{4}$ in. thick steel plates, and either file or grind a bevel on one edge of each so that when the plates are butted to one another, a **V** shaped valley is created by the bevels. Be sure the bevel extends entirely through the section to be welded. A 45° bevel usually will provide sufficient depth and width.

It is best to lay the plates on some noninflammable surface. Concrete is generally considered the best. Be sure that the plates are properly aligned and in the same plane so that after the two are welded together, an absolutely flat surface results with the exception of the bead left by the weld.

After the plates are properly prepared, light the torch and adjust the flame correctly. Use the oscillating motion required when welding heavy sections and apply the flame to the work. Preheat a section of the beveled edges. When they are sufficiently molten to fuse with the welding rod, add the welding rod. This forms what is known as a *tack*. A complete weld is commonly called a continuous tack. As you complete a tack, move along the line of the weld making more tacks so that when you have completely traversed the seam, you have a continuous tack.

Enough welding rod should be added to completely fill the bevel. There should be sufficient excess to form a bead on the finished surface. This bead is important for it reinforces the weld. Fig. 10 illustrates the various conditions you may find when you have completed the weld. A properly made weld is shown at (A), Fig. 10. Improperly made welds are shown at (B), (C), (D), and (E), Fig. 10. Each one of these incorrect welds is due to some fault on the part of the welder. However, careful attention to the details will make certain your obtaining a weld like that shown at (A).

The defect in the weld shown at (B) is caused by not adding enough welding rod. The defect in the weld shown at (C) is caused by the edges being heated to the fusion point too quickly, with the result that a film of oxide forms on the edges which will not allow the welding rod and edges to fuse properly. The defect in the weld shown at (D) is caused by failure of the welder to penetrate completely the stock which is being welded. The defect in the weld shown at (E) is caused by the welding rod and edges of the stock not being in fusion. That is, one is colder than the other. This results in what is known as adhesion rather than fusion. The warm metal merely sticks to the cooler metal and does not fuse with it.

Practice welding two pieces of ¼ in. steel plate together until you can produce a weld similar to that shown at (A), Fig. 10.

(b) WELDING LIGHT STOCK. Perform the same operation with some ⅛ or ³⁄₃₂ in. stock as you did with the ¼ in. stock. Remember that you are now working with lighter material. It will be necessary, therefore, to select a different tip for the torch, according to information given in Table 1 on tip sizes.

Because the stock is lighter, only a short time will be required to heat the metal all the way through. Move the torch in a circular motion, and add the welding rod when the metal is sufficiently molten to receive it. Practice this exercise until you can obtain a good weld every time.

(c) WELDING SHEET METAL. Several things must be taken into consideration when you are welding sheet metal with which you were not concerned while you were welding heavy stock. For example, the spread of heat will be much faster when the torch is applied to sheet metal than it will when heavier stock is being welded. If the weld is in only a small area, you will want to save as much paint on the surrounding

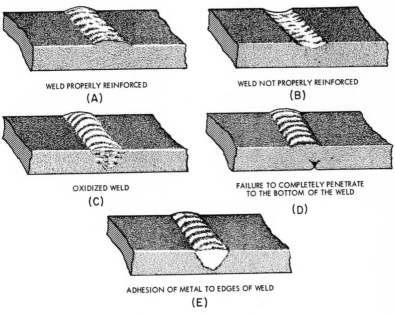

WELD PROPERLY REINFORCED
(A)

WELD NOT PROPERLY REINFORCED
(B)

OXIDIZED WELD
(C)

FAILURE TO COMPLETELY PENETRATE
TO THE BOTTOM OF THE WELD
(D)

ADHESION OF METAL TO EDGES OF WELD
(E)

Fig. 10. Various Weld Conditions

surface as possible. When this is the case, you can place what is known as a heat dam around the area where the welding is to be done. Heat dams are made from asbestos flake and water. Simply mix asbestos flake with water until a stiff paste is formed. Build a little mound 1 to 1½ in. thick and about 8 to 10 in. away from where you are going to weld. Completely surround the area being worked on and the heat will be confined to that area. Asbestos flake is the same substance which was used a few years back to insulate steam pipes in the basements of many houses.

(1) WELDING ON A CROWNED SURFACE. For your first attempt at welding sheet metal you can use an old fender. Fasten the fender in a vise or other suitable clamping device so that it is held rigidly in the

same position it is in when on the car. With a hacksaw, cut into the crown on top of the fender. Make a saw cut approximately 2 in. long. Select the proper torch tip by consulting Table 1. Light the torch and you are ready to begin.

Use the correct movement of the torch, and heat the edges. Then add the welding rod, making a tack from above. As the surrounding crowned surface will rigidly hold the edges being welded, it will not be necessary to use clamps. Continue making tacks the length of the cut until you have a continuous weld.

You will notice that the heat has spread over a large area of the fender. Allow the fender to cool. Make another saw cut, construct a heat dam around it, and weld it up. Practice making welds in the crown of the fender from the top until you can obtain a good-looking weld which is properly reinforced.

Sometimes it is better to make the weld from underneath the fender. After you become proficient at making welds from above in the crowned surface, make another saw cut in the crown of the fender. Sit on the floor and make the weld from underneath. Simply heat the edges of the saw cut until they are in the proper molten state to receive the welding rod. Be sure to sit to one side of the area being welded so that the molten drops of metal which will fall off the weld do not drop on you or your clothing. Asbestos gloves can be purchased and should be worn whenever you are welding from underneath or whenever there is a possibility that the metal may drop on your hands. Practice making welds from underneath the fender until it is as easy for you as welding from above.

(2) WELDING EDGE OF FENDERS. Welding the edges of fenders or other panels is not like welding a cut or tear in the center of a panel. The two edges are free to move back and forth independently of each other. For this reason, it is necessary to use a clamping device to hold the edges in proper alignment with one another until several tacks can be made, at which time the clamp can be removed.

With a hacksaw, cut into the practice fender anywhere along the edge. Make a cut approximately four inches into the fender. With a **C** clamp, secure the two edges together and tighten the clamp (Fig. 11).

Manipulating the torch properly, make a tack as near the clamp as possible. Make several tacks at intervals along the line of the cut. Allow the tacks to cool, then remove the clamp. The edges are rigidly held by the tacks so you can now go ahead and make a continuous weld the length of the entire cut. Practice this exercise several times, then make the same kind of cut in the fender again and weld it from the underside.

It is a good policy, whenever you encounter a job of replacing or repairing fender splash shields, to inspect the edges of the fender to be sure no small cracks have started. Breaks in the edges of fenders are usually caused because a splash shield has been broken or come loose,

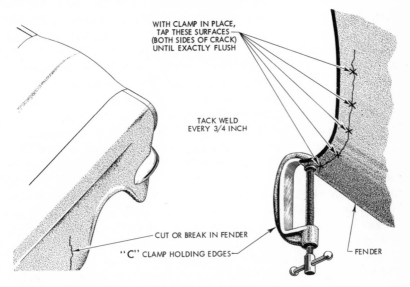

WITH CLAMP IN PLACE, TAP THESE SURFACES (BOTH SIDES OF CRACK) UNTIL EXACTLY FLUSH

TACK WELD EVERY 3/4 INCH

CUT OR BREAK IN FENDER

"C" CLAMP HOLDING EDGES

FENDER

Fig. 11. Edges of Cut in Fender Side Fastened with C Clamps Prior to Welding

allowing the edges of the fender to vibrate. This will cause cracks to start, then to grow with continued vibration.

(d) CUTTING SHEET METAL WITH GAS TORCH. Four sizes of tips or nozzles are furnished for cutting sheet metal. These are graded according to the thickness of the metal to be cut, and are different from those used for welding. Usually, three to six small oxygen-acetylene orifices surround a center orifice which emits pure oxygen. The oxygen and acetylene for the smaller orifices are controlled by an oxygen and an acetylene valve. The pure oxygen from the center orifice is controlled by an oxygen cutting valve. The purpose of the smaller orifices is merely to heat the area surrounding the cut to the point at which it will oxidize (burn) rapidly in the stream of pure oxygen from the center orifice. An attachment is usually provided which screws into the handle of a regular welding torch, enabling it to be used as a cutting torch. This attachment takes the place of the regular torch tip from the handle to the end. A spring-loaded, push-type, oxygen valve (called the "cutting valve") is a part of this attachment.

Working pressures are given by the manufacturers of cutting nozzles. Be sure to use the pressures specified by the manufacturer of the equipment which you are using.

To cut sheet metal with the gas torch, preheat the metal with the torch. As soon as it becomes red hot, open the cutting valve, and move the torch along the surface only as fast as a clean, distinct cut can be obtained. Hold the torch at a constant distance from the work, and move it away from yourself so that you may watch the cut advance.

If at any time the torch is moved too fast and the cut is lost, it will be necessary to restart the cut. In this case, the oxygen supply should be cut off and the heating flames applied to the point where the cut was lost until the metal has been heated enough to start cutting again.

You can practice cutting with a gas torch by obtaining any old body panels which should be available from any body shop. Fix the tip on the torch for the gauge metal with which you are working. Light the torch as you would for welding, preheat the area where you wish to begin your cut, then turn on the oxygen supply and start your cut.

You can mark where you want to cut with chalk so you will have a line to follow. The chalk will burn off near the torch, but it will help to guide you. It is virtually impossible to make any kind of a line which will not be burned off except a scribed line which is scratched into the metal surface.

Always keep the torch the same distance from the metal insofar as is possible. Move the torch only as fast as you can make a clean cut. The edges of the cut will appear ragged, but you should practice making a straight cut with as smooth an edge as is possible.

II. ARC WELDING

Arc welding is a process whereby the heat necessary to bring metal to the molten state is obtained by a continuous arc between a welding rod or a carbon rod and the work.

Arc welding probably is a little more difficult to master than torch welding, since it is necessary to strike an arc and to maintain this arc throughout the time you are welding. Arc welding is not difficult on heavy material in which large size welding rod is used and where high amperages are involved. Such welding, however, will represent only a small portion of the welding you will do in collision work. Most of your work will be on thin fenders and body panels. In working on thin sheet metal as employed in automobile body panels, the amperage used is comparatively low. Likewise, the size of the welding rod is comparatively small. It is more difficult, therefore, for the welder to establish and maintain the position of the welding rod. The distance the welding rod is held from the surface being welded establishes the length of the arc.

In arc welding, the arc is established by scratching the end of the welding rod on the surface to be welded. This is more easily accomplished if the surface is rough, as would be true if you were dragging the welding rod over a broken seam in the metal. As the welding rod is dragged over this roughened surface, an electric spark is generated. The spark ionizes the air immediately surrounding the electrode. This ionized air becomes a conductor for electrical current if the welding rod is not pulled too far away from the surface and current continues to flow through this small air gap. This generates a tremendous amount of heat; both the end of the welding rod and the surface of the metal being welded are brought to a molten state, and fusing of the metal is accomplished.

In arc welding, only coated welding rod should be used. This coating is the flux necessary for the weld. This flux coating, of course, is not an electrical conductor, and it is necessary to remove the coating at the point where the welding rod is clamped into the holder. Sometimes the combination of welding rod holder and the rod itself is referred to as the "torch." This is a carry-over of terms from oxyacetylene welding.

In a measure, the size of the welding rod used controls the amperage flowing into the weld. As a rule, as you are developing skill in arc welding, you will start with a smaller than normal welding rod. This will reduce the possibility of burning holes in the sheet metal. In the early stages of your development as an arc welder, you will want to reduce the amperage as much as possible until you have mastered control of the arc. However, the lower the amperages involved, the more difficult it will be for you to maintain the welding arc.

At one time, motor-generator welding equipment was in common use which delivered direct current to the welding rod. These welders, however, are rather expensive, and it is more difficult to strike and maintain an arc with a D.C. welder than with the comparatively inexpensive A.C. welder. Moreover, these motor-generator sets are heavy and are not as portable as the A.C. welders. For these reasons, the motor-generator D.C. welder outfits are fast disappearing from body shops.

They are still popular, however, in welding shops that do considerable welding of heavy parts.

The purpose of this volume, of course, is to direct you in mastering the skills involved in automotive collision work. The purpose of this section is to show you how, with an arc welder, to do the welding and cutting operations involved in collision work. No attempt is made to show you all of the ramifications of welding that might be employed

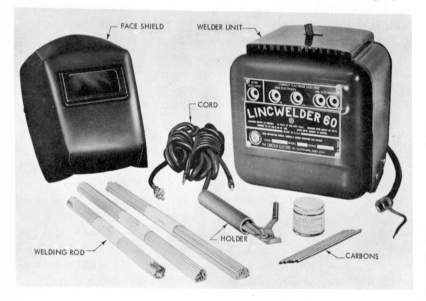

Fig. 12. Small, Portable A.C. Welder
(Courtesy Lincoln Electric Company)

in other kinds of jobs. For this reason, the instructions presented here are written primarily around the A.C. type arc welder which you will find in most shops. The smaller models are so inexpensive (about $50.00) that you may even want to purchase one for your own use so as to develop the skill necessary to master this aspect of collision work.

This small equipment has a means of selecting different amperages that you will be using in the welding of body panels. Larger, more versatile arc welders will be found to have a wider selection of amperages and probably will have some advantages not possessed by these smaller models. Nevertheless, you can learn arc welding such as will be required in collision work with one of these small welders. When at some later date you encounter a larger machine, you will be able to apply the knowledge and technique you have learned with the small welder. The principles involved are identical.

Two different methods of arc welding are possible: carbon arc welding and metallic arc welding. In auto body shop practice, carbon arc welding is used only for aluminum. For this reason, detailed instructions are given here for metallic arc welding only.

a. Equipment. As previously stated, few direct current arc welders are in use today because of the cumbersome equipment necessary to generate direct current.

The most popular electric arc welders are small, inexpensive, portable A.C. welders similar to the one illustrated in Fig. 12. Also shown in this illustration are the necessary pieces of equipment for operating this welder.

Fig. 13. Always wear hand protection when welding
(*Courtesy Lincoln Electric Company*)

Arc welding has an advantage over other kinds of welding in that the heat is concentrated right at the electrode (equivalent to the torch in gas welding). This means that distortion due to heat is minimized.

(1) *PROTECTIVE EQUIPMENT.* When you are working with arc welders, it is necessary to use certain protective measures to guard both your clothing and yourself from injury.

The rays emitted by the arc are similar in character to those given off by the sun and will cause sunburn of the arms and hands unless gloves, mitts, or protective sleeves are worn (Fig. 13). To protect the face and eyes from the harmful rays, protective shields made from pressed fiber and smoked glass are worn (Fig. 14). Some shields are held in the hand, leaving only one hand to operate the torch. Others are made so that they can be worn, leaving both hands free for handling the torch and the work.

On production welding jobs, to protect clothing from hot, spattering metal, leather aprons which extend from the chin to the knee are best. In automotive retail shops, welding is only an intermittent job and, other than gloves and face shields, no special clothing generally is used.

As a final precautionary measure, welding, wherever practical,

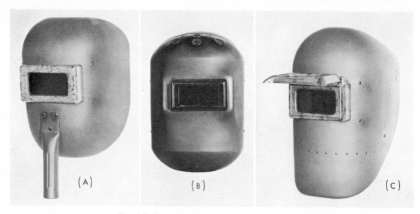

Fig. 14. Protective Face Shields and Hoods
(A) Hand-Held Face Shield, (B) Welding Hood or Helmet, (C) Welding Hood with Hinged Window
(*Courtesy General Electric Company*)

should be done in a closed booth. Any other workers in the immediate area should not expose their eyes to the harmful rays emitted by the torch. These rays are so bright they can cause temporary blindness. In the event of long exposure to them, they can cause permanent injury to the eye.

The welding rod is fastened in a holder similar to those shown in Fig. 15. These holders are so constructed that they allow the op-

Fig. 15. Two Common Insulated Electrode
Holders
(*Courtesy Purity Cylinder Gases Inc.*)

erator to hold the welding rod without receiving an electric shock and to manipulate it freely.

By being its own electrode, the welding rod melts itself down in the heat of its own arc, thereby supplying the necessary additional metal to complete a weld or to fuse together any two edges. With this process of welding, one hand is left free to either hold the work or to manipulate it as the operator desires.

In electric or arc welding, two things govern the quality of the weld. These are the uniformity of the arc and the current (amperage) used. Both, of course, are controlled by the operator.

(2) *ARC LENGTH.* The maintenance of a uniform arc is of the utmost importance in obtaining a good weld. Unless the filler rod fuses perfectly with the base metal or edges being welded, a poor weld will result. In order to bring about this proper fusion, it is necessary to maintain uniform heat during the welding operation. If a short arc is maintained, the welding rod will stick frequently and the edges of the work will not be heated to a molten state to receive the rod. If the arc is too long, the base metal will not be heated to the proper state to fuse with the welding rod. The welding rod will melt, therefore, and will fall on the cold base metal and will stick. Proper fusion will not take place, and a poor weld will result.

The correct length for the arc depends, of course, on the type of welding rod being used and the type of weld being made. For a coated rod, an arc $\frac{1}{16}$ to $\frac{1}{4}$ in. long is best. It is difficult to gauge the length of an arc by sight. However, the sound made by the "torch" will be an even, steady buzz when the arc length is correct. If the arc is too long, the torch will sputter because the arc is being broken and struck again almost instantaneously. This sputtering or popping will cause the metal to spatter. Overhead welding or vertical welding requires a shorter arc than the usual down welding. Welding rod of large diameter needs a longer arc than that necessary with a smaller diameter rod. Fig. 16 shows several examples of what can happen when an incorrect arc is used as well as an example of what a sound weld looks like when properly made.

The weld at (*A*), Fig. 16, has a rough bead and shows evidence of excessive spatter of the weld metal. This type of weld results from the use of an arc which is too long. The weld at (*B*) has a high bead and shows evidence of poor penetration of the weld metal. This type of weld will result from the use of an arc which is too short. The weld shown at (*C*) is the way all welds should look. The proper current was used, the proper arc length maintained, and the welding rod was manipulated correctly.

(3) *CURRENT VALUE.* The current used in arc welding has a direct bearing on both the soundness of the weld and on the ease with which the weld is made.

Most arc welding machines have automatic voltage control. Table 3 gives the current or amperage value for arc welding mild steels with coated rods.

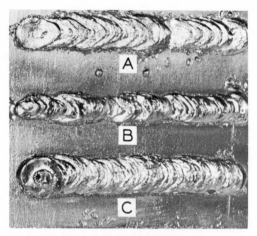

Fig. 16. This is how the welds appear when (A) arc is too long; (B) arc is too short; (C) arc is the correct length.

The welds shown in Fig. 17 are examples of using incorrect welding current. The weld shown at (A) was caused by the use of a welding cur-

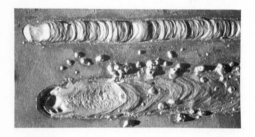

Fig. 17. Examples of Welds where Incorrect Welding Currents Were Used
(*Courtesy Lincoln Electric Company*)

rent that was too low. Poor penetration resulted, and instead of obtaining proper fusion, the weld metal merely adhered to the improperly heated base metal, producing an unsound weld. In the weld shown at (B), too high a current was used and much spattering resulted.

The amperage can be controlled on all arc welding machines. In fact, most small A.C. arc welders have but one amperage adjustment.

TABLE 3. CURRENT VALUES FOR ARC WELDING WITH COATED ROD

Metal Thickness	Rod Size (In Inches)	Amperage Range
Light-Gauge Sheet Metal Up To Approximately $\frac{7}{64}$ In. Thick	$\frac{1}{16}$ $\frac{5}{64}$ $\frac{3}{32}$	10–30 25–45 40–70
Mild Steel Up To Approximately $\frac{3}{16}$ In. Thick	$\frac{1}{8}$ $\frac{5}{32}$ $\frac{3}{16}$	50–130 90–180 130–230
Mild Steel Up To Approximately $\frac{5}{16}$ In. Thick (Frames, Etc.)	$\frac{1}{8}$ $\frac{5}{32}$ $\frac{3}{16}$ $\frac{1}{4}$	60–120 90–160 120–200 190–300

The means of adjusting amperage can be a rheostat providing an infinite variety of available amperages, or it may consist of an assortment of sockets into which a jack on the end of the holder cord is plugged.

All such welders carry an instruction plate which tells you just how to obtain the amperage desired. The small welder in Fig. 12 is provided with five sockets. The left-hand socket is for the cord which is grounded to the material to be welded. The next two sockets are used with $\frac{5}{64}$ in. diameter welding rod. The one socket is for high amperage, the other for low amperage.

The two sockets on the right are for use with $\frac{1}{16}$ in. diameter welding rod. One socket (second from right) is for high amperage. The other is for low amperage.

All such welders have equally simple controls. However, the larger machines capable of delivering high amperages provide, of course, a much greater variety of available amperages. Nevertheless, a few minutes' study of the instruction plate on any of these machines will reveal just how the controls are operated.

To give yourself the best opportunity to control the current you are using, you should pay strict attention to the sound which the arc is making. A good arc will give off a continuous crackling sound and the molten metal will pass across the arc stream in a steady but invisible flow.

b. Exercises in Arc Welding. An inexpensive small A.C. welding unit similar to the one illustrated in Fig. 12 can be used. This welder can be plugged in to any 110-volt A.C. light socket which means you can work in either your own basement or garage. Some welders operate on 220 volts. Be sure to read the rating plate on the equipment. Obtain some ¼ or ⅛ in. steel plates. Prepare and position them for a butt weld. Bevel the edges (45°) and lay them side by side on a non-inflammable surface.

Coated rod is generally used for arc welding. It is much easier to strike and hold an arc with coated rod than with bare rod. You can strike an arc by scratching the welding rod against the work the same

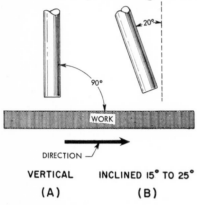

VERTICAL   INCLINED 15° TO 25°

(A)   (B)

Fig. 18. Angles for Holding Welding Rod

as you would if you were striking a match. It is necessary, of course, to hold the welding rod in a holder which is properly connected by cables to the welding machine.

Fig. 18 shows the different angles for holding the welding rod. The metal is more easily directed if the welding rod is inclined as shown at (B), although many welders hold the rod in a vertical position.

After the arc is established, the welding rod is slowly burned away and it is necessary to pay particular attention to the sound the arc is making. If you do this, you will have no difficulty in maintaining the correct arc length.

Move the arc along just fast enough to keep depositing the proper amount of welding rod after a crater has been formed in the base metal to receive it. The smoothness of a weld is dependent upon the uniformity of the arc and the speed with which it is moved. If you should accidentally break the arc, exercise care in restriking it because flaws are apt to occur after such interruptions. If this happens, strike the arc ahead of the weld, then come back and heat the last crater made, then move on again from there.

When you have succeeded in welding the seam between your first practice plates, you will notice that there is a crater at the end of the weld. It is necessary to fill this crater to strengthen the weld. Simply move the rod at right angle to the seam when the end of the weld is reached and at the same time move it away until the arc is broken. If the crater is not filled sufficiently, restrike the arc and go over the same spot again.

(1) *SHEET METAL WELDING.* Welding sheet metal is, of course, more difficult than welding heavy stock. More things must be taken into consideration.

The main point in welding sheet metal is to be certain of the proper current setting on the arc welder. Because of the thinness of the metal, it is possible to burn holes through it quite easily. Use the lowest current setting possible which will still give you the heat necessary to bring the work to a molten state for proper fusion with the welding rod.

For your first exercise in welding sheet metal, you can use an old fender. Fasten the fender in the same position it is in when on a car, and make a saw cut 2 in. long in the crown part of the fender.

After you have made the cut in the fender, obtain some bailing wire, or even a piece of coat hanger will do. Lay the wire lengthwise in the cut, strike an arc with the torch, and fill in around the wire with welding rod. The wire in the cut will help you to keep from burning the metal while you become more familiar with manipulating the torch and moving it with a steady motion.

Try this method of welding several times, then do a weld without the wire in the cut.

After you become proficient at making welds in the crown of the fender, make some cuts in the edge of the fender and weld them. Practice making the welds from underneath. Be sure when you are welding from under the fender that you work so your hands and arms are to one side of the weld. This will eliminate the possibility of any hot metal falling on you.

Practice each of the different exercises several times or until you can produce a sound weld in a minimum of time no matter which way you are doing it.

(2) *CUTTING WITH ARC WELDER.* The same equipment is used for cutting with the arc welder as is used for welding. A welding rod is used which is slightly larger in diameter than those used for welding the same gauge of metal, and the amperage is set higher.

To cut with the arc welder, insert a welding rod in the holder and strike an arc as you would for welding. Instead of moving the torch over an area to preheat the metal, simply hold the torch in one place until a hole is burned through the sheet. As soon as a hole is made, thrust the tip of the welding rod into the hole and move the rod along as the arc burns out the metal along the line which you wish to cut.

To practice cutting with an arc welder, you can use the same panels

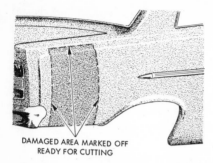

DAMAGED AREA MARKED OFF
READY FOR CUTTING

Fig. 19. Damaged Area Ready for Cutting

on which you have been practicing with the hand tools. Fig. 19
shows a rear fender panel which is
marked in preparation for cutting
out the damaged area. Fig. 20
shows the fender in the process of
being cut away and after the damaged portion has been removed.
Notice (Fig. 20, at left) that the
operator is standing with the
torch tilted at an angle away from
himself.

Practice cutting with the arc welder until you can quickly and
easily make a good clean cut.

Fig. 20. Fender Being Cut Away (Left), and Fender with Damaged Portion Removed (Right)
(*Courtesy Lincoln Electric Company*)

III. CUTTING

As has been pointed out in the preceding pages, it is possible to cut
metal with either a gas torch or an electric torch. However, each of
these methods of cutting leave a ragged edge and are rather slow.

The cutting methods described in this section do not involve the
use of the welding equipment. Cutting is not usually done, however,
except when a welding operation is to follow. The information given
here is for using power saws and hand chisels. Cutting with either hand
chisels or power saws permits a clean cut with only a narrow gap.
These methods permit accurate work, since a drawn or scribed line can
be followed.

a. Cutting with a Chisel. A special chisel which makes a smooth cut
$\frac{1}{16}$ in. wide is available for cutting body panels. The cutting edge of

this chisel is curved so that the shaving which is removed curls neatly out of the way. The chisel is provided with a sharp point so that the cut can usually be started without first drilling a hole. Fig. 21 shows this chisel being used to cut a door panel. It will be noted that the lower part of the panel has had an irregularly shaped piece removed. This irregular cut was merely made to demonstrate the versatility of the chisel. Usually, your cuts will be straight across the panel, since this is the best method for making a patch.

Hold the chisel as shown in Fig. 21. With the chisel tilted in this manner, the hammer boss provided lays at a convenient angle. Hit the boss as indicated in Fig. 21 to pierce the panel. To cut the panel, strike it in the direction of the cut (Fig. 21). By hitting the chisel with hammer blows of medium force, it will cut out and curl up a strip of metal $\frac{1}{16}$ in. wide.

HIT HERE TO PIERCE PANEL

HIT HERE TO CUT

You can scribe a line on an old fender or body panel with a pencil or scriber (scratch awl) and practice cutting along the line. Practice until you are

Fig. 21. Using Chisel To Cut Sheet Metal
(Courtesy Anzich Manufacturing Company)

able to produce a straight, neat cut in a reasonable length of time.

b. **Power Saws.** Two kinds of power operated body panel saws are in common use in body shops. One is a saw having its own motor and constructed expressly for this purpose. It is a machine having a short piece of regular hacksaw blade which is moved in and out at a fast rate in short strokes. The other is an attachment for an electric drill which converts the rotary motion of the drill to reciprocal or in-and-out motion. A hacksaw blade is also used in this machine. Such a machine is shown in use in Fig. 22.

Cutting with either machine is a simple matter and one which will not require much practice to learn. If you are starting a cut in the edge of a panel, simply bring the moving blade against the panel and move it forward along the cutting line only as fast as the metal is cleanly cut. Too much pressure against the blade, or forcing it along at too great a cutting rate, will result either in short life for the blade or breakage.

When it is desirable to start your cut in the center of a panel or

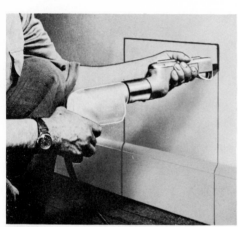

back from the edge, it may be necessary to drill starting holes which will accommodate the blade of the saw. This can most easily be accomplished by drilling three $\frac{3}{16}$ in. holes so that they overlap and form a slot long enough so that you can insert the blade of the saw through the panel. Then turn on the saw and start your cut. If a saw of the type shown in Fig. 22 is used, however, no starting holes are necessary. The saw blade is merely held almost parallel to the surface to be cut with the tool resting on the curved portion below the blade. After the saw is started, the tool is slowly tipped to a perpendicular position.

Fig. 22. Use of Power Saw Attachment for Electric Drill
(Courtesy Tri-Saw Corporation)

You will find that it is much easier to replace a piece of a body or fender panel if the edges to be welded are smooth. This makes it possible to cut the patch for the panel to exact dimensions.

IV. TYPICAL WELDING JOBS

Automotive bodies and frames generally are of welded construction. In most instances, both body sheet metal and the body inner construction are built up by spot welding.

Recently, portable spot welders have been used more frequently in body shops. A typical spot welder is shown in Fig. 23. Lap joints and flange joints (Fig. 24A and C) can be joined by spot welding. Recessed lap joints (Fig. 25) may also be spot welded.

Although instructions for using spot welders vary among the different brands available, they are relatively simple to follow. The repair man must use an electrode large enough to provide the intense

Fig. 23. Portable Spot Welder
(*Courtesy Ford Motor Company*)

heat necessary to fuse the metals being joined. Unlike other forms of welding, where a welding rod is introduced into the joint to form a fusing agent, spot welding is a direct fusing of two pieces of like material. Spot welding is fast and economical (no expensive welding rod is used). It produces a surface that can be quickly prepared for the refinisher.

Complete details on electrode sizes and heat ranges for various metal thicknesses are supplied with the welders when they are purchased. There are no rules of thumb for spot welding. Each piece of equipment must be used as directed by the manufacturer.

In collision work, however, most body welds are formed on flanges which permit seam welding, with either the gas torch or the arc welder, to serve the same purpose as the original spot weld. In replacing complete panels, the welding is generally confined to these flanges.

In the replacing of a portion of a panel, the usual practice is to form flanges on the two pieces and to perform the welding on the flanges rather than the outer surface. This holds the amount of metal finishing required to a minimum. In body repairing, tears in the metal, particularly on fenders and shields, are frequently encountered. These also are welded with either the gas torch or the arc welder.

This section is concerned with showing you when different welds are made, where they are made, and why. The different types of weld joints with which you will be concerned in body work are shown and a description of where each should be used is given.

a. **Types of Welds for Light Sheets.** Several different types of joints can be used in welding sheet metal. The more common of these are shown in Fig. 24.

Fig. 24. Different Types of Welds

(1) *LAP JOINT.* The lap weld shown at (*A*) in Fig. 24 is an easily made weld. This type of weld, of course, leaves a step in the surface which makes it impossible to perfectly match the original contour. Lap welds of this type, however, can sometimes be used where the joint is covered by molding or trim or is otherwise concealed.

(2) *RECESSED LAP JOINT.* A variation of the simple lap weld is the recessed lap weld shown in Fig. 25. With this type of weld it is necessary to sink the edge of the panel being patched so that the patch can be laid into the panel with the outer surfaces flush. This type of weld requires a considerable amount of time to prepare, but good welds can be made in this manner. The depth of the recess, of course, should be exactly equal to the thickness of the panel in order to make certain that the two surfaces will be flush after the weld is completed.

(3) *FLANGE JOINT.* The type of weld which produces what is probably the most reliable joint, and which also produces the joint most easily finished by the metal finisher, is called a flange weld. This is illustrated in (*C*), Fig. 24. With this type of weld, it is necessary to take a little more time with the preparations. The edges of the pieces to be joined must be flanged inward from the outside finished surface. The flange may be formed by using a hammer and a suitable right-angle edge of a dolly. In some cases where a weld is to be made in a

prominent place in a panel, a strip of ¼ x 1 in. steel can be formed to
match the contour of the inside of the panel at the point where the

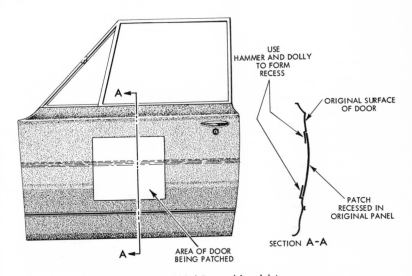

USE
HAMMER AND DOLLY
TO FORM
RECESS

ORIGINAL SURFACE
OF DOOR

A

PATCH
RECESSED IN
ORIGINAL PANEL

SECTION A-A

AREA OF DOOR
BEING PATCHED

A

Fig. 25. Welded Recessed Lap Joint

joint is to be made. This strip should extend for the full length of
the joint. With small screws and nuts, fasten the strip ½ to ¾ in. from
the point where the panel has been or is to be cut. (The holes drilled
in the panel can easily be filled while you are making the weld.)

Form the flange over this steel strip rather than over a dolly. The
strip will prevent any change in the panel contour as the flange is
formed. Once the flange is formed it will hold the contour. The strip
is then removed and fastened to the new piece of panel, and the flange
is formed on it in the same way. Once this flange is formed, it too will
hold the contour.

(4) *BUTT JOINT*. The butt weld shown at (*B*), Fig. 24, is quickly
and easily prepared. This is the main reason why it is so extensively
used. Particularly where the weld can be made from the inside, the
butt weld saves a lot of work for both the welder and the metal finisher.
However, most cases of buckled panels occur as a result of welding a
butt type joint.

(5) *USE OF SCREWS TO HOLD THE JOINT*. With flange or

lap joints, the two parts can be fastened together with a number of self-tapping screws. This permits you to move the parts up or down and in or out until the contour of the new and the old panel matches before you actually start to weld. With recessed lap joints, the threads of these screws may be tacked in place as you are welding. The heads of the screws are ground off as the surface is metal finished. With a flange joint, the screws can be tacked in place and left right in the flange.

Any of the welds described in the preceding can be used whenever you are replacing a portion of a damaged panel. One of the factors governing the type of weld to use is the location of the weld. In some instances, it will be impossible to perform a certain operation in the preparation of the weld because of interference with some other panel. In other instances, the weld itself might interfere with the other panels or mechanisms after it is made. You will have to decide which type of weld most effectively and efficiently will do each job.

b. Types of Welding for Frames. Frame welding is much the same as welding sheet metal. The major difference is in the thickness or

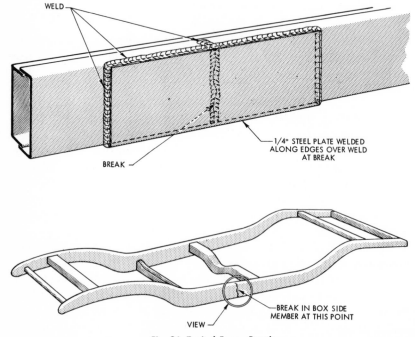

Fig. 26. Typical Frame Repair

gauge of the metal with which you are working. It is mandatory that the frame be just as strong after the repair as it was before it was broken. The frame is the part of the car or truck which holds everything together. It is essential for the body to be sound and strong enough to withstand certain types of blows which it may receive from the outside. But the body derives most of its rigidity from the fact that it is bolted to the frame in several places. Moreover, the suspension will not perform properly on a frame which is damaged or not properly aligned.

Whenever a frame is broken, the seam of the break is welded together, then a reinforcement plate is welded over the whole thing. As most of the frame members are of channel stock, this reinforcement plate is often made of channel material. Whether or not the reinforcement plate should be placed around the outside of the damaged member or on the inside depends on whether there would be any interference with body or chassis parts by its being installed on the outside. This can be decided only at the time the particular repair is made. Fig. 26 shows a typical frame repair.

V. PREPARATION OF THE METAL FOR THE METAL FINISHER

Whenever a weld is made, the surface left by the weld is not smooth. Since the intention of all body repairs is to restore the finish to a like-new condition or to its original smoothness, it is obvious that a good deal of finishing work is required after welding.

The welder is not concerned with metal finishing, which is a trade all in itself (a subsequent chapter of this volume is devoted to it). However, the welder is charged with the soundness of any weld he has made. It is in this respect that the welder is slightly concerned with metal finishing.

Even though flux is used during the welding process, a certain amount of scale or oxide is left on the weld when it is finished. This scale must be removed before the soundness of the weld can be attested to. Usually, it is ground off with a disk grinder. However, if a grinder is not available, it can be removed by hitting the weld with several sharp blows from a body mallet.

The amount of finishing necessary after welding is controlled by the type of weld used. All welding on outside surfaces of a body should be done from underneath or inside if possible. This will leave the weld metal stacked toward the inside of the body, and a minimum amount of filing or grinding will be required.

TRADE COMPETENCY TESTS

The following questions, while they represent only a small portion of the material in this chapter, may be used to determine the percentage of the information retained.

1. What process for fusing metal together is meant by the common name *torch welding?* (p. 123)

2. About how many pounds per square inch pressure is exerted on the acetylene cylinder when it is filled with acetylene? (p. 124)

3. How much pressure is exerted on the oxygen tank when it is filled with oxygen? (p. 124)

4. Is acetylene sold by weight or pressure? (p. 124)

5. Is oxygen sold by weight or pressure? (p. 124)

6. The flame at the tip of the welding torch is the result of what? (p. 124)

7. What are the necessary components of a gas welding outfit? (p. 125)

8. What six basic safety rules govern the operation of a gas welding outfit? (p. 125)

9. What color is generally used for the oxygen hose? (p. 125)

10. Generally, what color is an acetylene hose? (p. 126)

11. Why is it that on most welding equipment there is no danger of interchanging the oxygen and acetylene hose connections? (p. 126)

12. What is the name of the tool used most commonly for lighting a gas welding torch? (p. 128)

13. What is the purplish colored flame called which results from the use of too much oxygen? (p. 130)

14. In order to obtain the best weld, it is necessary to hold the torch at what angle to the plane of the work? (p. 131)

15. What type of motion should be imparted to the torch when you are welding light-gauge metal? (p. 132)

16. How much should the welding rod in gas welding be inclined to the plane of the work? (p. 132)

17. When should the welding rod be brought into contact with the work? (p. 133)

18. What will be the result if the welding rod is added to the edges to be joined before they are sufficiently heated to receive it? (p. 133)

19. How is the heat necessary to do arc welding derived? (p. 138)

20. Is it necessary to wear any kind of protective garments when you are arc welding? (p. 141)

21. What kind of current is most commonly used for arc welding in collision shops? (p. 141)

22. In electric or arc welding, what two things govern the quality of the weld? (p. 143)

23. What one control is usually provided on most small, portable, A.C. welding machines? (p. 144)

24. How is an arc struck on an arc welder when you are ready to weld? (p. 146)

25. What are four different kinds of weld joints that can be used in body sheet metal welding? (p. 152)

CHAPTER 4

SHRINKING, SOLDERING, AND METAL FINISHING

This chapter is designed to develop in you the knowledge of what is required and the skills involved in the preparation of automotive bodies and sheet metal for the painter. The trade of metal finishing employed in automotive factories involves bumping and filing, as presented in Chapter 2; welding, as presented in Chapter 3; and the use of power grinders and sandpaper for the purpose of preparing the surface for the painter, as presented in this chapter. This trade involves, as well, the shrinking of stretched metal, the sinking of welds and the building up of contours with solder, and the preparation of the metal for the painter.

Establishing the metal finisher's responsibility for the surface is important. When the metal finisher fails to properly prepare the surface for the painter, the painter is required to use other expedients, such as putty glazing, which often can result in an inferior paint job.

I. SHRINKING STRETCHED METAL

When body panels and fenders are formed in dies under high pressure, the sheet metal is stretched and drawn, then compressed. This displaces the molecules of metal. The high pressure of the press squeezing the metal locks the molecules in this new position, and they will resist any subsequent force which tries to change their arrangement.

The metal, of course, has some elasticity. That is, the metal can be bent or twisted without permanently disarranging the molecules. When the force thus applied is removed, the elasticity of the metal will cause it to resume the shape that it had when the molecules of the metal were locked together in the dies. It is the objective of the collision man to avoid destroying this natural tendency of the metal to return to its original shape. This, obviously, is not always possible in collisions where the normally smooth surface is badly creased. These creases represent a portion of the metal which has been distorted beyond its elastic limit and in which the molecules have been displaced. That is, they are no longer locked together in the same arrangement that was given to them in the forming die.

The exercises that were presented in Chapter 2 of this volume were intended primarily to relieve the strains created by such creases or folds in the metal so that the natural forces existing in the surrounding metal could return it to its original shape. Each hammer blow struck on a body or fender panel does, in a small measure, exactly the same thing that the original presses did. That is, it stretches, draws, or compresses the metal and has a tendency to lock the molecules in the new position. The body hammer, however, does not do this as well as the original forming dies because the hammer's area of influence is limited.

Every time you strike the surface of a panel in direct hammering, you are flattening out or stretching the metal slightly. This is why it is so important that in all dinging, you hold the number of separate blows down to just what is required, because every blow will to some degree stretch the metal. In most cases, the amount of hammering required is so slight that the stretching of the metal is negligible and cannot be detected. Nevertheless, on occasion you will encounter excessive stretching. This can be the result of correcting complex damage. Stretched metal is often found when you are reworking a fender or panel which has been excessively hammered by some amateur. When the metal has thus been stretched, it is not possible to make it conform to its original contour by using the hammer and dolly alone. In such cases, the metal will have to be shrunk.

In Chapter 2 of this volume, a method of cold shrinking by means of forming ribs in the stretched area was discussed. In that exercise, a shrinking dolly was used to sink a valley through the stretched area, thus effectively reducing the bulge. Such a method can be used if an oxyacetylene torch is not available to you for hot shrinking.

Hot shrinking is accomplished by heating a small portion (an area about the size of a nickel) of a panel red hot. This causes the metal to expand and rise slightly above the surrounding surface. If, while this metal is red hot, a dolly having no crown is placed under the heated portion and the heated portion is then struck several sharp blows with the hammer, the heated metal will be compressed. When that particular spot cools, it will have lost most, if not all, of its crown. By repeating this process on the stretched area of the panel, the stretched metal can thus be shrunk. The purpose of this section is to show you how to shrink metal that has been stretched, using this method.

Fig. 1. Using Torch To Heat Spot in Stretched Section of Hood Panel
(*Courtesy H. K. Porter*)

Hot shrinking is a simple process, but one which requires careful timing and the proper tools. The tools required are those which are used for many other operations in body work. You should have a welding torch equipped with the same size tip as used for welding the thickness of sheet with which you are working, a body hammer or mallet, a shrinking dolly, a medium-sized sponge, a water container, and water.

If you can find some portion of a discarded fender, door, or body panel that is stretched, use it for your first attempt at shrinking metal. If you are unable to locate a stretched area, merely assume that some area is stretched.

Arrange your tools so that they are within easy reach, as it is necessary to change quickly from one tool to another when performing a shrinking operation.

Locate the highest point in the stretched section of the panel with which you are working. Light the torch and heat a spot the size of a nickel in the center of the high spot to a cherry red (Fig. 1).

Use a circular motion when you are heating the spot. Be careful not to burn through the metal. As soon as the spot is cherry red, place the shrinking dolly under the spot and strike it several sharp blows with a hammer or mallet. The dolly block must be held loosely against the

Fig. 2. Hammering Down the High Spot on a Hood Panel
(Courtesy H. K. Porter)

underside of the panel exactly centered under the hot spot. The hammer blow must hit the hot spot accurately and with sufficient force to push the metal down while it is still red hot. Fig. 2 shows a high spot on a hood panel being hammered down.

After four or five hammer blows, the heated spot will turn black. Quench it immediately with the water-filled sponge. Fig. 3 shows the same spot on the hood being quenched with the water-filled sponge.

Repeat this operation, taking the next highest spot in the stretched section of the panel until the bulge is finally shrunk down below the level of the surrounding surface. It then can be brought up to its correct level by direct hammering.

Practice this operation a number of times. You will find that you can do an adequate job after just a few attempts. However, there are a few rules which you should observe at all times during a shrinking operation that will help you to do a much better job than would ordinarily result.

Never quench a red-hot spot. Wait until the metal has turned black.

Never heat an area greater than that where pressure can be applied with the hammer and dolly.

Never use anything but an acetylene torch for heating a stretched section.

Never attempt to shrink a panel until the panel has been roughed out.

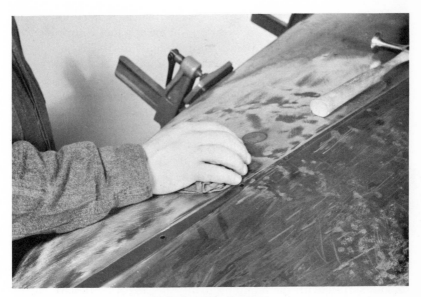

Fig. 3. Quenching Heat Spot
(*Courtesy H. K. Porter*)

Always hammer the stretched section outward before applying heat. If the stretched part of the surface is small, heat a smaller spot.

It is possible to shrink metal without quenching each spot with water. However, the shrinking operation is much faster when each spot is quenched with water. Less heat spots are required if the heat expansion is drawn out by quenching rather than by additional spots.

In some panels it is possible to use a spoon for the backing tool for the hammering operation. This is particularly true where it is necessary to shrink a section in a door panel or over inner construction of a body panel.

Whenever you are performing a shrinking operation, exercise care to avoid "overshrinking" the panel. This will cause the metal to warp and buckle both in and out of the stretched area. However, if this condition does arise, heat a small spot in the area where the panel is buckling, apply a dolly block or spoon with enough pressure to hold the buckling section up, then allow the metal to cool. Do not use the hammer or water in this instance. In extreme cases, it may be necessary to repeat this operation in several different places in the warped area.

II. SOLDERING

When adjoining panels do not exactly match, it is customary in automobile body factories to build up the lower panel with solder. In collision work, these same points must be built up the same way. In addition, any part of the body or fenders can also be built up with solder. Solder, of course, is expensive and heavy. In each instance, you must weigh the possibility of bringing the panel up to where it belongs by other means as against the time and cost of building it up with solder.

In many cases where you cannot get behind the damage to push it out without spending too much time in disassembly of trim panels, hardware, or inner construction, it will be practical to build up the low spot with solder.

Body soldering is performed with either an oxyacetylene torch or a blow torch and is referred to as torch soldering. A soldering iron is seldom used. This section deals only with torch soldering as practiced in automobile body shops.

In body repair work, it is often impossible to leave a completely smooth surface with the bumping tools. Also, irregularities are left in any surface that has been welded because the seams of the weld are sunk. It is necessary for all of these irregularities to be removed from the surface before the job can be completed. As it is not possible to sand or grind these small indentations out of a surface without removing too much metal, thus leaving the structure weak, some other means is necessary. Solder is the material used for filling the depressions, and soldering is the method of applying the solder. It is necessary to file or grind the solder smooth after it has been applied to a surface, but this presents no problem because solder is a lead compound which is easily worked, either in the molten or cold state.

The most commonly used method of soldering is with a torch, using a paddle to work the solder into the place where it is needed.

a. Preparation of the Surface. Before solder can be applied to a metal, it is essential that the surface be absolutely clean. This means that any paint remaining on a surface after it is dinged out must be removed. Paint can be removed either with a file or with a disk grinder.

In some instances, the surface needing solder build-up will be covered with rust. Rust can be removed in the same manner as paint, either with a file or with a disk grinder. Failure to completely remove rust or paint before soldering is attempted will result in a poor soldering job. The solder will not stick to the surface well, and it will break away when you attempt to blend the contour of the soldered and unsoldered areas together.

Another condition which you will encounter is a surface where welding was done. In most cases, the welder will have removed the oxide crust which is formed by welding. However, if he has not, it can be removed as described in Chapter 3 of this volume.

After the glaze or scale left by the welding process is removed, it is necessary to prepare the weld so that solder can be applied. A weld leaves a rough surface. In order to have a smooth surface after the finish operations are performed, it is necessary to force the welded area below the normal contour of the surface, then to build up the contour with solder. This process is called "sinking" the weld.

The sinking of welds is a hand operation. The best time to do it is after the weld has cooled so that the metal being formed is cold. The seam of a weld where a fender was torn is shown in Fig. 4. The metal finisher is using a hammer and dolly to sink the weld below the original surface.

The tools used for sinking welds are also used in some instances for shrinking stretched panels as described in Chapter 2 of this volume.

By not sinking the weld until it has cooled, any defects in the surface will immediately become apparent when a blow is struck with a hammer. The seam of the weld is usually sunk approximately $\frac{1}{8}$ in. below the normal contour of the surface. This valley or depression is then filled with solder, filed smooth, and an unbroken contour will result. A welded seam ready for soldering is shown in Fig. 5.

You should practice sinking welds until you can perform the operation with little or no difficulty. The easiest type of weld to sink for your first attempt is one where the weld runs into the edge of a fender. Simply start from the edge and work back along the seam.

After you have practiced and become proficient at hitting the dolly squarely with the hammer, sink a weld where it is necessary to start in the middle of a panel. Exercise care in this operation, as there is danger of deforming the surrounding area if you do not hit the dolly squarely.

b. Tinning. The process of tinning prepares a surface for receiving and holding solder. Tinning is actually the first operation of soldering.

Fig. 4. Hammering Seam below Original Surface
(*Courtesy H. K. Porter*)

Before any tinning is done, you should be certain that the surface is clean. In the case of a surface where welding was done, sanding and wire brushing may not remove all of the oxide scale. Sometimes a welded surface is rough and a wire brush or a grinder will not get into all of the small depressions. The scale can be removed in cases like this by applying muriatic acid to the rough spots with a small brush.

WARNING: *Never allow the acid to contact either your clothing or your body. If you should get some on your hands, rinse them immediately in clear, cold water.*

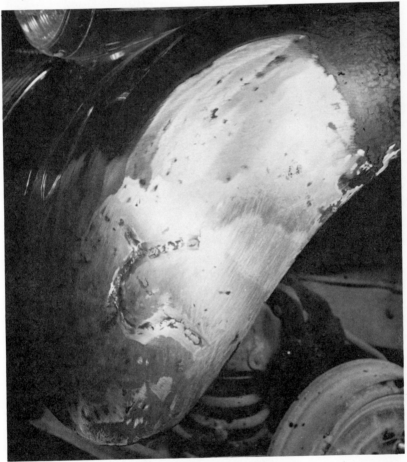

Fig. 5. Welded Seam Ready for Soldering
(Courtesy H. K. Porter)

When the surface to be soldered is absolutely clean and dry, light the torch and pass it back and forth, applying heat to the surface. This is called *preheating*.

Immediately after the surface is preheated, the flux should be applied, followed by the tinning coat of solder. Acid core solder is usually used because the flux is contained in the center of the solder. This solder comes in rolls of different sizes and is sold by the pound. The solder wire is about $\frac{1}{8}$ in. in diameter. Heat the entire area until it is hot enough to melt the solder. Then apply the solder and smear it over the surface with a rag until the entire area is covered. Always cover an area a few inches larger than that actually needing a solder build-up.

If acid core solder is not available, regular body solder and tinning acid may be used. Preheat the surface, apply the acid with a brush, heat the surface until solder will melt, then apply the solder, smearing it over the area with a rag.

c. Building Up. The actual application of solder is often called building up the contour. After the surface is tinned properly, the solder can be applied. If acid core solder is used, play the torch over the area just enough to keep the tinning coat sufficiently hot to hold the solder as it is applied. Heat a portion of the solder until it is ready to droop, then push it against the panel. If the area being worked on is allowed to become too hot, the solder will run. Keep applying solder in this fashion until a sufficient amount has been deposited to build the surface up to a higher contour than the original. How to handle the surface from this point on is explained later.

If regular bar solder is used, the torch is played over the tinned surface to keep it hot, then the torch is applied directly on the bar of solder. Heat the end of the bar until approximately one inch of it becomes soft and starts to sag, then quickly press it against the hot tinned surface. Continue applying solder in this manner until a sufficient amount has been deposited to build the surface up to the desired point.

Solder is applied in the same way on either a horizontal or vertical surface. On a vertical surface, however, you will find that it is necessary to keep the solder hot enough so that it can be worked, yet not so hot that it will run. Solder should be applied on a vertical surface in somewhat smaller amounts at each application than on a horizontal surface. The torch should be passed over the applied solder just often enough to keep it in a workable condition.

d. Paddling. As soon as enough solder has been applied, it is necessary to smooth it and work it into the general shape of the finished contour. This process is called paddling.

Before it is applied to the solder, the paddle should be covered with a light film of regular engine oil. This will prevent the solder from sticking to the paddle as it is worked.

Heat is applied over the entire area to the extent that a temperature is maintained which is just below that necessary for working the solder. Local areas are then heated to the workable state, and the solder smoothed to the desired contour with the paddle. Fig. 6 illustrates an acetylene torch and solder paddle being used to smooth solder over a fender. Notice that the torch is applied only as necessary to keep the solder in a workable state.

Fig. 6. Spreading Solder with Torch and Paddle
(Courtesy H. K. Porter)

Be sure to keep plenty of oil on the paddle at all times during the paddling operation. When one portion of the surface is smoothed to the desired contour, move along until the entire surface has been worked. Do not overheat the surface, for the solder will run off, and a second application will be necessary.

The area covered by solder should always be slightly greater (a few inches on every side) than that actually needed. This will make it easier to obtain the desired contour during the finishing operation. When solder is applied to a weld that has been sunk, the surface should be built up to a point beyond what it was originally. When you are using solder to fill a deep depression, be sure to keep the entire mass heated all the way to the bottom during the shaping process. If the bottom is allowed to cool, it may become impossible to work it further. Any attempt to reheat it will result in the surface melting and running off entirely.

e. Establishing the Contour. After the solder is paddled smooth, it is necessary to allow it to cool thoroughly before the finish contour is established. If any finishing is done while the solder is hot, the surface will peel or pit and additional work will be necessary to make it smooth.

Because solder is much softer than the surrounding steel body sections, it cuts away faster. Therefore, disk grinding is not advisable, because it may remove more solder than is desired, leaving a low spot in the body contour and, after painting and polishing, the low spot will show up as a "bull's eye." Always take care not to cut the solder down lower than the desired level.

Finish the edges of the soldered area first, and then finish the center of the area. Shape the area with a body file first; then with an open-cut solder float file. The float file cuts slowly and smooths out large file marks and small ridges.

Fig. 7. Fender with Soldered Surface Filed Smooth
(Courtesy H. K. Porter)

Fig. 7 shows a fender with a soldered surface filed smooth. It should be pointed out that this fender was photographed merely to show what can be done with solder. Ordinarily, if it is necessary to apply this amount of solder, it is more economical to replace the fender involved.

f. Exercises. Your first attempt at soldering should be to apply solder to a contour that is only slightly dented. Before you apply any solder, however, make two or three templates from a piece of cardboard so that you can check the final contour two or three ways. Then apply the solder as described here. Smooth it, and as soon as it is cooled, file or grind it to the desired contour.

As you develop the feel of applying the solder and working it as desired, you can move along to filling deeper depressions or larger areas.

As a final exercise, you should apply solder to a vertical panel, and then work it smooth. If you attempt only a small area until you learn to manipulate the tools quickly, you should have no difficulty.

Don't become discouraged if, on your first attempts at paddling, you lose the solder you so painstakingly applied. Just start over again. Everyone goes through this experience. Keep on trying until you can handle the solder expertly.

III. GRINDING AND SANDING

While the body file cannot be completely replaced, many of the jobs that can be done with a file can be done just as well and much faster with a grinder. A grinder can be used to remove rust or paint from the surface, to grind out minor irregularities in the metal, to locate low spots, and to develop the contour of areas built up with solder.

Two basic types of grinders are in common use. These are the flexible shaft grinders and the hand grinders. Except for the differences in portability, both types generally can be used for all of the jobs that have to be done.

With each type, by means of attachments, a variation in the method of holding and driving the abrasive is possible. These attachments convert the basic grinder to a disk grinder, a drum sander, and a cone sander.

A flexible shaft grinder is shown in Fig. 8. The principles of grinding are the same whether a flexible shaft grinder is used or whether a portable hand grinder is used.

A portable disk grinder is shown in use in Fig. 9. This is a heavy-duty 9 in. machine which turns from 4,200 to 5,000 rpm and is a good, general-purpose grinder.

The technique of grinding with a disk grinder is considerably different from grinding with a drum or cone grinder. Regardless of the type of grinding or sanding that you are doing, you should understand what abrasives are, how they are graded, and the forms in which they are made available to you. The story of abrasives is as follows:

a. **Abrasives.** Five different minerals are commonly used for manufacturing abrasives. Three of these—*garnet, flint,* and *emery*—are natural mineral abrasives. The other two are *aluminum oxide* and *silicon carbide,* which are manufactured at high temperatures in huge electric furnaces. Garnet, a semiprecious jewel, is by far the most important of the natural minerals. Emery and flint break down easily and are better suited for household use than for industry. Aluminum oxide is the

Fig. 8. Flexible Shaft Grinder
(*Courtesy Minnesota Mining & Mfg. Co.*)

more important of the two manufactured agents. It is the toughest, most durable abrasive available. The manufactured abrasives are best for use in the automotive field and, for that matter, in industry at large where the work is chiefly on metal.

The abrasive is put on a backing which is either of paper, cloth, or a combination of the two. For dry grinding or sanding, high-quality, hide glues are used for anchoring the abrasive grains to the backing. For wet sanding, resins are used as the binding agent.

Coated abrasives fall into two additional classifications based on how widely the minerals are spaced. If the minerals are close together, it is referred to as "close coat." If the minerals are widely spaced, it is referred to as "open coat."

In close-coated abrasives, the abrasive is applied in such quantity as to entirely cover the backing. In open-coat abrasives, the backing is from 50 to 70 per cent covered (Fig. 10, at left). This leaves wider spaces between the abrasive grains. The open coating provides increased pliability and good cutting speed under light pressures. Open-coated abrasives are used where the surface being ground is of such nature that closely spaced abrasive minerals would rapidly fill up, as shown

Fig. 9. Grinding a Door Surface
(*Courtesy H. K. Porter*)

by the disk in Fig. 10 at the right. This disk is now valueless since, through improper use, its grinding ability has been reduced to almost zero.

In the manufacture of coated abrasives, the abrasive minerals are applied to the backing either by the gravity method or by the use of an electrostatic field. The electrostatic field method is the more popular. In this method, a powerful electrostatic field compels the abrasive grains to

Fig. 10. Open-Coat and Close-Coat Abrasive
(*Courtesy Ford Motor Company*)

follow its lines of force and become anchored in the glue with their long axes at right angles to the backing (standing on end). Since the lines of force are evenly spaced, the abrasive grains are evenly spaced.

This upending of the abrasive crystals provides sharper, faster cutting power. Both close-coat and open-coat abrasives may be produced by either method.

(1) *GRIT SIZES AND MARKINGS.* The coarseness or fineness of abrasive particles is designated in three ways: by symbols, by mesh numbers, or by both.

SYMBOLS: *3/0, 2/0, 1/2, 1½, 2, etc.*
MESH NO: *400, 320, 280, 180, 100, 50, etc.*
BOTH: *9/0–320, 5/0–180, 2/0–100, 1½–40, 3–24, etc.*

All products are identified by one of these numbering systems. Flint and emery are graded to different standards than any other abrasive.

b. Disk Grinders. Most of the grinding you will be doing will be with a disk grinder. The grinder can be either the flexible shaft type (Fig. 8) or the portable grinder of the type shown in Fig. 9. The disk grinder can be used for removing paint, revealing low spots, shaping the contour of areas built up with solder, grinding down welds, and cutting away metal. The actual use of the disk grinder involves not only full knowledge of abrasives, but considerable skill as well.

(1) *BACKING PLATE.* In most disk grinding, the disk is placed directly on a slightly flexible backing plate usually made of molded rubber. The degree of flexibility is controlled by the thickness of the plate and the material of which it is made. Wood, hard rubber, and a phenolic plastic material all have been used as backing plate material.

When working on a convex surface, very little flexing of the grinding disk is required, and a backing plate the full size of the grinding disk can be used. When working on a concave surface, it is necessary to have the disk flex enough to permit it to follow the contour.

To permit grinding concave surfaces, many metal finishers use two 9 in. grinding disks with a 7 in. backing plate. The two grinding disks are placed back to back. By this method, the outer inch of the disk has only the support of the second disk and can flex enough to match most of the concave surfaces you will have to grind. With the outer one inch consisting of merely two grinding disks back to back, you will be able to grind right down into a sharp corner. If care is used, this double disk can be used to reach down into drip moldings to remove rust.

If you have a 9 in. grinder, you should have both a 9 and a 7 in. backing plate. The 7 in. backing plate will also permit you to cut down disks worn on the outer edge, thus almost doubling the disk life.

(2) *GRINDING DISKS.* The coated abrasive disk, of course, is what does the actual cutting. Selection of the right grit and coating for each job is important. Grinding disks represent a considerable portion of body shop expense. While they speed up the work considerably, it is important that you never lose sight of the fact that the disks are expensive. The cost of grinding disks, of course, varies with size, grit, and brand. Nevertheless, to enable you to appreciate the waste each time you see a torn disk or one loaded with paint, you can assume that each disk costs fifty cents. Thus, it becomes apparent that the skill that must be developed in their use must include not only doing the job in a satisfactory manner, but understanding and following practices which will permit full value received, as well.

Disks 9 in. in diameter have 82 per cent more abrasive area than 7 in. disks. The outer edge of

Fig. 11. Cutting Down Disk
(Courtesy Minnesota Mining & Mfg. Co.)

the larger disk runs 32 per cent faster. They can be cut down (Fig. 11). Cutting down sanding and grinding disks when they become worn or filled amounts to a considerable saving over a period of time.

Anything that will stick to the abrasive surface will quickly render it ineffective. For this reason, it is important to use only widely spaced abrasives when grinding anything that might have a tendency to clog the grit. This includes all kinds of paint, waxes, etc.

When grinding a fender or body panel, always use No. 16 grit open-coated disk or paper up to the time that the area being worked is completely free of paint. Then use a No. 24 close-coat abrasive to grind the metal to the point where the surface needs no further correction. The final finish is accomplished with a fine grit (between No. 50 and No. 80) to get the surface smooth enough for the painter.

In automobile factories, No. 80 grit is generally used for finishing the metal, for the metal finisher is working with bright, unpainted, new metal. In collision shops, you will be working with old metal that has previously been painted, and in some cases you will be working on metal that has rusted. Moreover, you will be working on surfaces that have been reworked with hammer and dolly, and in some cases with contours that have been built up with solder. In collision shops, even the finishing operation is generally performed with No. 50 grit.

Generally, only three different disks will be used. What they are and what they are used for are pointed out in the following paragraphs.

(a) 16B DISK. The 16B disk is coated with a coarse, open-coat abrasive. It must be used with reasonable caution to prevent making deep scratches in the surface. This disk is most generally used in rough grinding surfaces that have been painted. Grind until you notice a volume of sparks coming from beneath the disk, then stop. Any of the paint, rust, or solder left on the surface at this point will not tend to fill the disks subsequently used.

(b) CLOSE-COAT NO. 24 GRIT DISK. The No. 24 grit close-coat disk is used for several purposes in the body shop. It is most generally used for removing welds and for use in place of the file in showing up high and low spots in the bumping operation.

(c) CLOSE-COAT NO. 50 GRIT DISK. The only function of a No. 50 close-coat disk is for performing finish operations on metal surfaces, both steel and solder. This disk will remove the scratches left by the No. 24 grit disk.

(3) *DISK GRINDING.* Several general rules govern the use of the disk grinder. If you observe these rules, you will more easily and quickly be able to become proficient in the use of the grinder. These rules are considered good shop practice and are more for your own safety than anything else.

The first thing you should do when you are going to use an electrically operated device is to see that it is properly connected and grounded. Shop floors are usually of cement and are, therefore, relatively good conductors of electricity. If the grinder is not properly grounded, you may receive shocks when you are using it.

Always wear goggles to protect your eyes from flying particles of metal and from the small abrasive particles that come loose from the grinding disk. Always replace torn disks as soon as the tear is noticed. Torn disks may catch in the work and twist the grinder out of your hand.

Always maintain a balanced position when you are using the

grinder. This position not only permits you to have perfect control over the machine at all times, but it will also permit you to work for longer periods without tiring.

When you operate the grinder, hold it as flat as possible without permitting the center connecting bolt to come in contact with the surface being ground. Hold the grinder so that only 1½ to 2½ in. of the outer edge of the disk is in contact with the surface being ground. The grinder must never be tilted so that only the edge of the disk

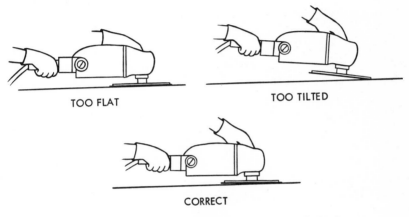

TOO FLAT TOO TILTED

CORRECT

Fig. 12. Correct and Incorrect Methods of Holding the Disk Grinder

contacts the surface. Failure to observe this will cause gouges or deep scratches in the metal which will be hard to remove. The correct and incorrect methods of holding the grinder against the metal are illustrated in Fig. 12.

Move the grinder from left to right, overlapping the previous stroke with each new stroke. Make the cutting lines as clean and straight as possible. Move the grinder in the same manner whether you are removing paint, rough grinding, or finish grinding. For most grinding operations, finish grind the long way on the repaired surface.

Fig. 9 illustrates a door panel which was damaged across the complete width along the trim molding. The body repairman pictured has had to adjust his position in order to reach the work so that he is not moving the grinder exactly from his left to his right. He is, however, moving the grinder approximately from left to right in a straight line. He is also grinding lengthwise to the area being repaired.

(a) GRINDING EXERCISE. Use an old fender, door, hood, or body panel for practicing with the disk grinder. Fasten the fender or panel in such a manner that you have a horizontal surface to work on and so it cannot move about as you move the grinder back and forth over the surface.

Place two 9 in. open-coat, No. 16 grit disks back to back, and fasten them to the grinder backing plate. Be sure the center hold-down bolt is securely tightened. It is well to disconnect the grinder from the source of power whenever you are changing or installing a disk. Doing so will eliminate any chance of accidentally touching the grinder switch, causing the grinder to run.

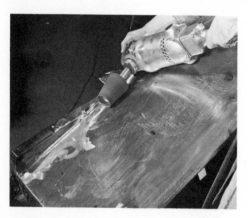

Fig. 13. Cone Mandrel in an Electric Grinder
(*Courtesy Minnesota Mining & Mfg. Co.*)

Hold the grinder with your right hand so that the grinder disk lies on the surface to be ground with the side of the disk farthest away from you touching, as shown in the lower picture in Fig. 12. Let the handle lie loosely in your hand. You will only be using the one hand in this exercise. Be sure the disk is contacting the surface correctly, then turn on the switch.

You will find that by turning your wrist slightly, the grinder will start to move in one direction. Allow it to travel about ten or twelve inches, then turn your wrist the other way and the grinder will move in the opposite direction. Continue with this exercise until you have made about twenty or twenty-five complete strokes of from eighteen to twenty-four inches long. At the completion of each stroke, move the grinder about ¾ in. farther away from you. Do not lean on the grinder or otherwise try to apply pressure. The weight of the grinder itself will provide sufficient pressure.

Stop the grinder and compare what you have done to the two surfaces shown in Fig. 8. What you are trying to do is to obtain a surface covered with innumerable scratches which cross each other, and to entirely eliminate parallel scratches. If you find you are making the wrong kind of grind marks, change the angle of the grinder or the way you are holding it until you are able to obtain the correct grinder mark pattern (Fig. 15).

When all of the paint has been removed from the practice surface, remove the No. 16 open-coat disk, install a No. 24 close-coat disk, and continue the exercise.

If, after all of the marks made by the open-coat disk have been removed with the close-coat disk, the grinder marks are still crossing each other as they should, change to a No. 50 close-coat disk. You are now finish grinding.

All of these exercises (on a horizontal surface) are performed with one hand. You will find that it is easier to obtain the correct grind pattern if you just allow the grinder to lie on the surface and let the machine do the work. When you are satisfied with the way you grind a horizontal surface, move the fender or panel so as to provide a vertical surface to grind in the next exercise.

In grinding a vertical surface, you will have to use both hands. However, remember that in the previous exercise it was apparent that very little pressure was required on the grinder. In this exercise, you will use the second hand merely to support the weight of the grinder and to assist in the guidance of the machine. Do not push the grinder against the surface; merely let it contact the surface.

Continue to practice on a vertical surface until you can grind this way as well as you can on a horizontal surface. Don't fail to change the grinder disk each time the disk has completed its particular function.

The disk grinder is a valuable tool which, when properly used, will save you a lot of manual labor. For example, you can use the grinder instead of a file to aid in the location of low spots. However, don't lose sight of the fact that the grinder removes metal fast. Unless you are careful in its use, you will grind the body panels or fenders too thin. When you use a grinder to locate low spots, just pass the grinder over the surface lightly.

Remove the low spots with the pick hammer, then lightly grind the surface again. Repeat the process until you have successfully removed the low spots from the entire damaged area.

c. Drum or Cone Grinders. In the automotive body factories, special drum type grinders are used almost exclusively for finish grinding. In collision shops, the disk grinder is used for most jobs. Mandrels, however, are available for most grinders, which will permit their use as a drum or cone grinder.

The abrasive for drum grinders is in the form of a replaceable sleeve which is fastened to the mandrel. Drum or cone grinders usually are used only for the finish grinding of hard-to-get-at places. They merely are time-saving devices to be used for special contours such as around headlights, fender joints, panels adjacent to rear decks, etc. Fig. 13 shows a cone mandrel in use. Cone mandrels are used with coated abrasive cloth cones. Cone mandrels and drum type grinders are operated in the same manner as a disk type grinder.

IV. PREPARATION OF THE METAL FOR THE PAINTER

Fig. 14. Remove Paint from Damaged Area
(*Courtesy Ford Motor Company*)

The preparation of the metal for the painter involves doing whatever is required to provide the painter with a surface to which the paint can adhere. The surface must be free of deep scratches, otherwise the paint will not be of uniform thickness or the deep scratches will show after the paint is dry.

A surface which is sufficiently smooth is established by the use of No. 50 close-coat abrasive. This may be accomplished with a cone, disk, or drum grinder, or any combination of them.

As a final operation, the metal finisher should remove any sharp edges left by the grinding operation. Lightly scuff the entire surface that has been ground or filed with No. 30 to No. 120 grit sandpaper or emery cloth held in the hand.

In all grinding or sanding, remember that the painter must taper the edge of the paint in all direc-

Fig. 15. Correct and Incorrect Patterns Left by Grinding
(*Courtesy Ford Motor Company*)

tions from the damaged area. This enables him to have a smooth paint job with no ridge where the new paint overlaps the old. Leave the paint intact where you are not working so he will have something to work with. Anything you do toward tapering the edge of the paint around the damaged area while you are grinding will save the painter some hand work.

a. Complete Repaint Jobs. On jobs that are going to be completely repainted, the metal finisher usually removes all rust from the body whether it happens to be in the collision damage area or not. Places in which rust is liable to form are along fender seams, along body panel seams, around door locks and windows, and any place where the paint has been chipped.

Fig. 16. Finish Grinding Chalked Surface
(Courtesy Ford Motor Company)

At the same time you are using the open-coat disk grinder to remove the paint from damaged sections on complete repaint jobs, inspect the rest of the job for rust and remove any you find. If, in grinding away rust to get bright metal, you find the panel has rusted through, repair it either by welding or soldering, whichever is required.

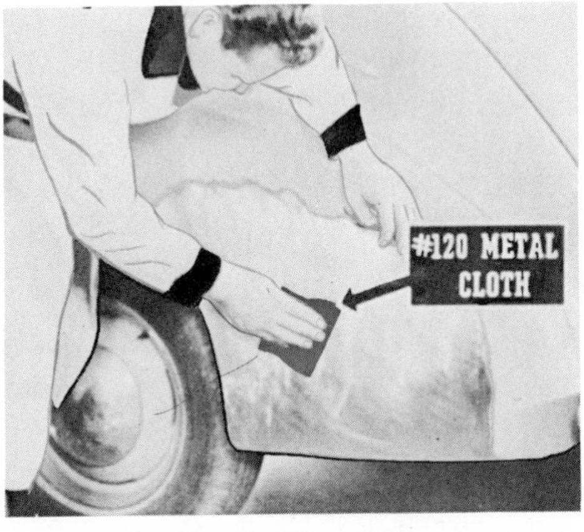

Fig. 17. Remove Burrs
(Courtesy Ford Motor Company)

b. A Typical Job. In Chapter 2, a typical fender job was discussed and illustrated. At that point the surface was brought back to its normal contour.

On such a job, after the fender is straightened and made as smooth as possible with a hammer and dolly, the grinder comes into play. First, remove all the paint from the damaged area (Fig. 14). Use a No. 16 grit, open-coat disk, otherwise the disk will load up with paint. (An open-coat No. 24 grit disk may be used for synthetic enamel finishes if preferred.)

Be sure to use the grinder so that the scratches run crisscross instead of parallel to each other. Correct and incorrect patterns left by grinding are shown in Fig. 15. This will save considerable work and time later on. Pick up the low spots with a pick hammer or dolly as soon as they are revealed. Don't try to grind them out. Again use the hammer and dolly and grinder or file as required to smooth out the metal. In the early stages, use chalk on the surface to check the smoothness of the metal instead of frequent grinding.

Once all of the low spots are removed, regrind the surface with a No. 50 grit, close-coat abrasive until it is entirely smooth. Some shops use as high as a No. 80 close-coat disk for the final finish grinding operation. A metal finisher is shown grinding the surface in Fig. 16.

At this point the job is ready for the paint shop with the exception of the final operation of going over the entire damaged area by hand with fine sandpaper or emery cloth. This operation (Fig. 17) will remove any burrs or sharp edges left by the finish grinding operation.

The grinder is a tool which can save much manual labor, but it must be handled with care. When using the grinder, do not allow your clothing to come in contact with the rotating disc. Body grinders are very powerful, and the disc may snag your clothing, draw itself close to your body, and cause injury. Always wear goggles for eye protection as shown in Fig. 16 when you are grinding. Always maintain a balanced position to make your work easier and to avoid the possibility of an accident. Never apply excess pressure. Let the grinder do most of the work.

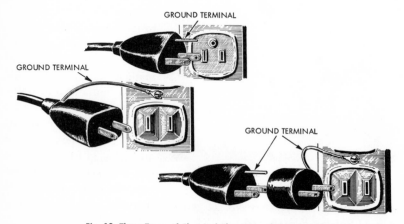

Fig. 18. Three Types of Electrical Plug Grounding Terminals

Remember to hold the grinder fairly flat as shown in Fig. 12 so that you avoid creating gouges or low spots.

Grinders, as well as other heavy-duty shop tools, are provided with electrical grounding terminals at their plugs (Fig. 18). Make sure the terminals are in operating condition so that you will not receive an electrical shock. The plugs and receptacles should be checked by a qualified electrician at least once a year.

TRADE COMPETENCY TESTS

The following questions, while they represent only a small portion of the material in this chapter, may be used to determine the percentage of the information retained.

1. When hot shrinking, how large should each heat spot be? (p. 158)
2. What are the tools used for a hot shrinking operation? (p. 159)
3. What type of motion should be imparted to the torch when a heat spot is made? (p. 160)
4. What color should the heat spot be when it is quenched with water? (p. 160)
5. Should the entire stretch area be heated at one time? (p. 161)
6. Can other than an oxyacetylene torch be used for hot shrinking? (p. 161)
7. Is it possible to shrink stretch areas without quenching each heat spot with water? (p. 161)
8. Are more or less heat spots required when water is used? (p. 161)
9. Is it possible to apply solder to a surface if rust or paint is still on the surface? (p. 163)
10. What material is used for building up contours or filling depressions in a finished surface? (p. 166)
11. What is the name of the method used for applying this material to the depressions? (p. 166)
12. When a wire brush or a grinder will not suitably clean a welded surface for soldering, what other method of cleaning can be used? (p. 165)
13. What is the process called for preparing the surface to receive solder? (p. 164)
14. Name the two materials, either of which may be used for tinning the surface. (p. 166)
15. Why should the soldering paddle be dipped in oil before it is used to spread solder? (p. 166)
16. If any grinding or filing is done to establish a contour while solder is hot, what will the result be? (p. 168)
17. Name three natural minerals which are abrasive in nature. (p. 170)
18. Which of the natural mineral abrasives is the most important? (p. 170)
19. What are the two types of coating in which abrasives are applied to backing? (p. 170)
20. Name two methods which are used for applying the abrasive to the backing. Which is the more popular? (p. 171)

21. What are the three ways in which the coarseness or fineness of abrasives is designated? (p. 172)

22. What grit grinding disk is usually used in collision work for rough grinding? (p. 174)

23. What grit grinding disk is usually used in collision work for removing welds and showing up high and low spots (p. 174)

24. What is the function of a No. 50 close-coat disk in collision work? (p. 174)

25. When grinding on a body panel with a disk grinder, how much of the grinding disk should actually come in contact with the work? (p. 175)

26. What undesirable condition will be created if only the edge of the disk is allowed to contact the work? (p. 175)

POWER TOOLS

In the preceding chapters, the use of the various hand tools for restoring the body and sheet metal to its original contour were presented. However, in actual collision work, a large percentage of the jobs you will encounter require the use of power tools to push or pull large areas or sections back to, or somewhere near, their original position.

Power is supplied by hydraulic jacks which can be extended to the desired length and for which a number of attachments are available for pushing or pulling.

As explained in Chapter I of this volume, the outer skin of the body is fairly light-gauge metal, placed over a framework of heavier, stiffer metal which is reinforced with various types of supports and braces, In addition to the damage (as the result of a collision) to the outer skin of the body that is apparent, this inner construction also becomes damaged. Since the inner construction is attached to the outer skin, the outer skin is prevented from being restored to its original contour. This means that the inner construction must be restored to its original shape and position, either before or at the same time that the outer metal is corrected. In some instances, you will find that once the inner construction has been restored to normal position, the outer panel will have been corrected at the same time.

The inner construction of automobile bodies is of much heavier metal than the outer panels and cannot be restored to normal by the same process. Once the interior trim panels have been removed where the side of the automobile body has been pushed in, you will find that the inner construction has been bent and permanently deformed. Quite often this occurs at a point where the inner construction is attached to the body sills. Since the body sills are rigidly fastened to the vehicle frame, they represent the strongest part of the body. When the force of the impact is received above the sills, the inner construction usually bends at or near the body sill. Before any correction can be made of such damage, it is necessary to restore this inner construction. This is generally accomplished by applying pressure to the damaged member or members. In damage of this kind, the piece that is attached to the body sill will be bent or kinked. Where a sharp kink or crease has been formed at any point in the inner construction, use heat while the pressure is being applied. This permits the metal to go back to its original shape with little danger of cracking. If you attempt to straighten sharp kinks cold, you may crack the metal. Body metal is of low-carbon steel, and little or no loss of strength occurs due to such heating.

In using power tools, it is important that you understand that power is being applied at both ends of the jack. That is to say, power is being applied to whatever the jack is resting against and to whatever it is pushing against at the other end. This makes it necessary to block the base of the jack, usually with a piece of 2 x 4 or several 2 x 4's, at the point you are pushing from, so as to spread the force over a large area. Use a special adapter of some kind at the end with which you are pushing. In general, these adapters localize the pressure, whereas the 2 x 4 or block at the other end spreads the pressure over a larger area, thus does not result in the deformation of any parts.

In addition to being required for straightening body inner construction, power tools are useful in providing support or pressure at otherwise inaccessible portions of the outer panels, as well as applying controlled pressure, in a higher degree than is possible with hand tools, on panels and fenders themselves. In addition, the use of power tools in many instances will permit backing up your work with a dolly at places where it would be impossible to hold a dolly and still manipulate a hammer. In progressive body shops, it is not uncommon to see as many as four power jacks being used at one time on a single job. The use of more than one jack on a rather involved damage saves considerable time in resetting of the power tools.

Power dollies are used in essentially the same way as hand dollies are used in either direct or indirect hammering. The power dolly can be used to apply pressure to the low part of the damage, and the crease around the damaged area is relieved by indirect hammering, or by spring hammering through a spoon. Generally, however, power dollies are used for direct hammering rather than for indirect or spring hammering. Rubber heads on the jack will apply pressure to the low areas for indirect hammering. Being compressible, they will follow the work, thereby reducing the number of separate jack adjustments required.

As mentioned in Chapter 2, the bulk of the collision jobs is done with hand tools alone. Although the use of power tools will speed up and make easier a great many jobs, you will find that practically every job will have to be finished with hand tools.

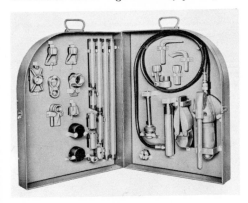

Fig. 1. Small Power Tool Set
(Courtesy H. K. Porter)

The amount of power tools that are available to you will, in a large measure, control the speed with which you can do collision work. In some cases, lack of sufficient power tools or adapters will limit you to certain types of jobs. An economical way of getting started would be by the purchase of a small power set similar to the one

shown in Fig. 1. This set will handle a fairly large percentage of the jobs you encounter. As your business increases and you purchase heavier equipment, this assortment of power tools will be of value as a second set which in many instances can save considerable time. This lighter set will permit you to learn all of the principles involved in the use of power tools and at the same time will avoid a large expenditure of money at the start.

I. JACKS

The basic part of power tool equipment, the jack, is the part of the equipment that actually supplies the power. A body jack consists of three basic units as shown in Fig. 2.

The jacks most widely used are hydraulically operated and are similar in principle to the kind of hydraulic jack used in tire repair work. The jacks used in body work are, of course, much more powerful than common car jacks. "Pneudraulic" jacks (jacks in which air pressure is used to exert force on a liquid [oil] column which in turn actuates the ram) are also used to some extent in body shops. Regardless of how the power is developed inside the jack, however, the principles involved for their correct application are the same.

a. Types. Only the different types of hydraulic jacks which are generally available are discussed here. However, you may consider the information set forth as applicable to pneudraulically operated equip-

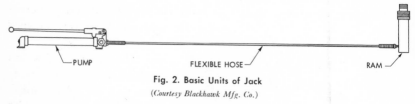

Fig. 2. Basic Units of Jack

(Courtesy Blackhawk Mfg. Co.)

ment, because the different types described are also available in pneudraulically operated jacks.

The types of jacks in general use in body shops are (1) direct-acting and (2) remote-controlled. A jack which exerts power in either direction is called a push-pull jack. These jacks may be either direct-acting

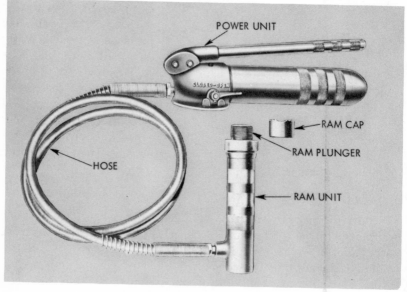

Fig. 3. Remote-Controlled Jack

(Courtesy H. K. Porter)

or remotely controlled. Any job may be done with any one of these types. The main difference in jacks is in the manner in which the setup for the repair at hand is made. Probably the most commonly used jack is a remote-controlled type similar to the one shown in Fig. 3.

A direct-acting jack is one in which the power unit or hydraulic pump is integral with the ram. With this type of jack, the action may be in only one direction or it may work in either direction (push or pull).

In a remote-controlled jack (Fig. 3), the hydraulic power supply unit is separate from the ram unit of the jack. The two units are connected by a reinforced rubber hose. This hose is of sufficient length to permit you to work freely about the vehicle.

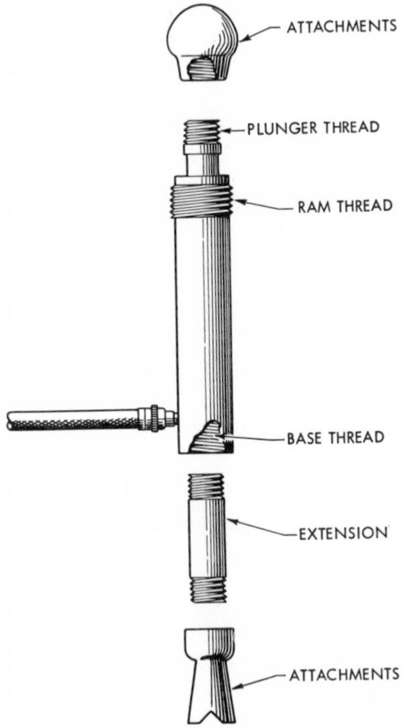

A push-pull jack is one in which the plunger in the ram unit can be moved under power in either direction at the discretion of the operator.

Jacks in which the ram unit can be moved under power only in one direction are used to pull through attachments in the form of chains and pull plates. These attachments convert the outward action of the plunger to a full, powerful pull action.

The ram unit of all jacks is basically the same. All the threads on the ram and the ram plunger are standard pipe threads. The threads on all of the tools and attachments match perfectly the threading on the ram and plunger (Fig. 4). The tools and attachments from one manufacturer usually will fit on the ram and plunger of the jacks of any other manufacturer.

Fig. 4. Arrangements of Ram Unit of Jack
(*Courtesy Blackhawk Mfg. Co.*)

b. Care and Maintenance of Power Tools. It will be necessary for you to do your own maintenance work on any power equipment which you may purchase, as well as on the power equipment at your disposal in any body shop where you may work. Moreover, there are several things which you should remember when you are using power equipment that will lengthen the life of the equipment appreciably.

(1) *CARE OF THE HOSE.* On the remote-controlled jacks where

the hydraulic pressure is supplied to the ram through a hose, it is well to exercise care so that the hose does not become damaged. The hose is made from oilproof rubber reinforced by woven steel wire which is covered on the outside by a fabric and rubber combination. Do not permit heavy objects to drop or fall on the hose. A sharp, hard impact may kink the wire strands in the hose. Because of the rubber covering, the kink may not be noticeable. Subsequent applications of pressure will subject the kinked wires to a bending and unbending process which will eventually cause them to break. With the wires broken, the fabric by itself will not be strong enough to withstand pressure, and the hose will leak or break altogether.

In making setups with the jacks, always be careful to anchor the ram unit so that its pushing force will not tend to bend or break the hose fitting.

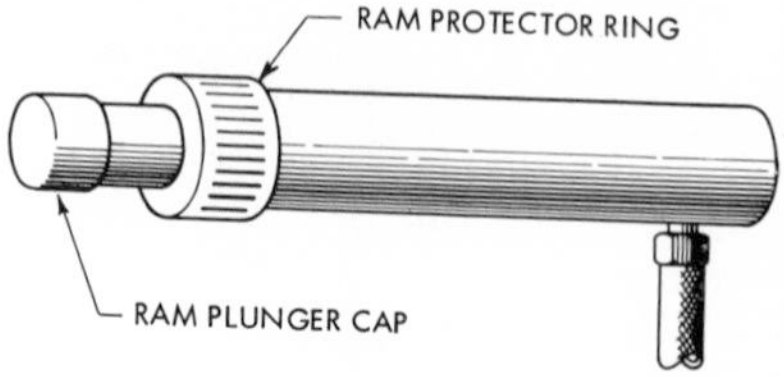

Fig. 5. Plunger Cap and Ram Protector Ring in Place
(*Courtesy Blackhawk Mfg. Co.*)

Do not subject the hose to high pressure if it is twisted or kinked. Frequent use under such conditions will cause hose failure.

(2) *CARE OF THREADS ON RAM AND ATTACHMENTS.* Whenever the ram is not in use, the attachments provided for protection of the plunger threads and the ram body threads should be in place (Fig. 5).

Use all of the threads when you make connections, and always turn the attachments until they are tight. This will assure long thread life. Always keep the threads in both the ram and the attachments clean and free from grease. Threads that are gummed up prevent proper connection, and damage may result when pressure is applied. Whenever threads become marred or bent, they should be straightened or filed so that the proper fit can be obtained when connections are made.

(3) *ADDING OIL TO PUMP UNIT.* The only part of the jack needing attention is the pump or hydraulic unit. It is necessary to replenish the supply of hydraulic oil in the pump periodically.

Add oil according to the manufacturer's recommendations for the particular jack with which you are working. Do not add an excessive amount of oil or the pump will not operate properly. In an emergency, SAE 10w engine oil can be used for filling the hydraulic unit. However, most jack manufacturers specify a fluid of their own. You should never use hydraulic brake fluid, shock absorber fluid, alcohol, glycerine, or castor oil. These fluids will corrode the valve seat and cylinder wall surfaces, and will dissolve the sizing which seals the pores in the pump leathers.

(4) *CARE OF CHAINS*. The following precautions will prolong the life of the chains:

Do not twist the chain excessively for a setup.

When you are working on a frame, see to it that the chain is wrapped around the frame or frame member several times, so that the load is distributed over as many links as possible.

Protect the chain links whenever they rest on sharp corners. This may be done with wood blocks, pieces of old tire casing, etc. Unless protection is given, the links will break when they are subjected to pressure.

Always fasten the chain hook securely to a chain link. If the hook does not grasp the link adequately, the entire setup can slip, causing, perhaps, further damage.

II. TOOLS AND ATTACHMENTS

Tools and attachments harness and direct the powerful force of the hydraulic power units. These tools and attachments, when coupled to the ram and the ram plunger, make possible hundreds of working combinations. All of the tools and attachments are described and illustrated in use in this section, and are presented here so as to familiarize you with the equipment with which you will be working. Later in this chapter, the principles of power tool application are presented.

As each of these pieces of equipment has several uses, only the main application is described and illustrated here. After you understand what the tools are and become familiar with their working principles, you will be able to apply this knowledge to making up special combinations to suit any job you may encounter.

Some of the tools can be attached directly to the ram or ram plunger. However, the majority of the setups you encounter will require either that you use several different tools in sequence or that you apply power over a wide space so that the ram, even with the plunger extended, will not reach. Tubing is available for spanning distance, and an adapter is supplied with each set of tools for quick setups.

With any of the power tools, it is always necessary to anchor the jack firmly against something before power is applied. Different attachments, called jack bases, are available for this purpose.

Certain of the tools described in this section are used for a variety of pushing operations. The tool is usually named for the main operation for which it is designed, although it may be used for other operations. What is considered as an ordinary set of pushing tools is shown in Fig. 6.

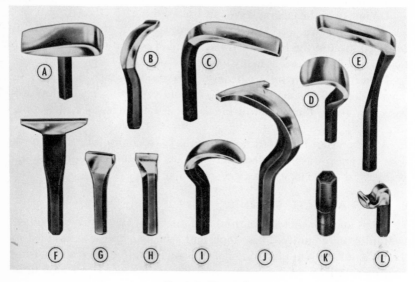

Fig. 6. Pushing Tools

(A) Power Dolly
(B) Drip Molding Spoon
(C) Cowl and Lower Quarter Panel Spoon
(D) Corner and Header Panel Spoon
(E) Quarter Panel Pusher Spoon
(F) Quarter Panel Molding Spoon
(G) Calking Iron
(H) Offset Pushing Tool
(I) Upper Rear Quarter Panel Spoon
(J) Top Rail Spoon
(K) Hex Adapter
(L) Fender Hook

(Courtesy H. K. Porter)

It is often necessary to perform an operation where two panels can be pushed back to normal by pushing directly from one to another. This is referred to as a spreading operation. The tools used for this type of work are described in this section, as well as push-pull attachments and chain attachments commonly used with one-way jacks.

a. Tubing. A typical tubing set is illustrated in Fig. 7. Tubing is usually made from seamless steel. The tubing couples to the ram or the ram plunger. It is fully threaded and chamfered for speedy coupling. The connector nipples have holes along the side so that a screwdriver can be inserted for tightening. A quick coupling tubing set is shown in Fig. 8. With this set, the tubes slip together and are fastened in place

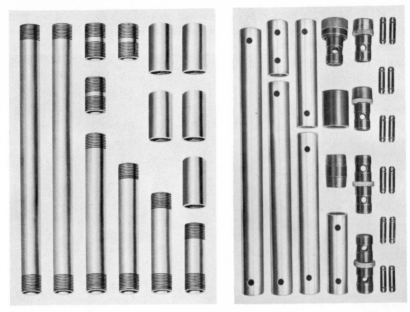

Fig. 7. Tubing Set   Fig. 8. Quick Coupling Tubing Set

(*Courtesy H. K. Porter*)

with a snap pin. Fig. 9 shows a typical setup where several lengths of tubing are used to span a distance.

b. The Adapter. The hex adapter (Fig. 10) couples directly to the ram plunger. Most of the spoons and pushing dollies have hex shanks which slip into the hex well in the outward end of the adapter.

The hex arrangement allows you to position the tool six different ways without disturbing the jack setup. You can also slip the tool in and out of the adapter quickly.

c. Standard Jack Base. The standard jack base (Fig. 11) is used in all operations where a special base or other attachment is not required.

d. Rubber Bases. Rubber bases usually come in a variety of shapes and sizes (Fig. 12). They are particularly valuable, since they conform to almost any shape under pressure and distribute the pressure over a fairly large area. They likewise permit you to straighten damage or apply pressure in some instances without damaging the paint. Fig. 13 shows three rubber bases being used in a setup for applying pressure to a window opening.

e. Right-Angle Base. The right-angle jack base is very versatile and can be used in a large number of setups. It is particularly useful on frame work. The sharp point (Fig. 14) is especially useful for pushing into alignment those parts of a frame where two members come together to form a sharp, right-angle corner.

f. Heavy-Duty V Notch Base. The heavy-duty, **V** notch base (Fig. 15) is used mostly for holding the jack when pushing either frame side or cross members into alignment. The notch in the end of this attachment permits you to anchor the jack against any edge of the frame which is strong enough to withstand the pressure of the application.

g. Ram Cap. The ram cap (Fig. 16) connects di-

Fig. 9. Setup Involving the Use of Tubing
(Courtesy H. K. Porter)

rectly to the end of the ram. It is used where a straight push is required in straightening when the space available for working is limited.

Fig. 10. Hex Adapter
(Crurtesy H. K. Porter)

h. Offset Pushing Tool. The application of this tool in conjunction with the hydraulic jack for working around an obstructed area (thus eliminating the necessity for removal of inner reinforcements) is illustrated in Fig. 17. The offset design of this tool makes it suitable for pushing operations on radiator shells, grilles, fenders, and body brackets. It can be used to push directly into reveal panels without disturbing the surrounding panel sections.

i. Cowl and Lower Quarter Panel Spoon. One of these tools is shown in Fig. 18 being used to push out a left-hand cowl panel. This spoon is designed to fit most quarter panel and cowl contours by reaching behind inner construction.

j. Drip Molding Spoon. Fig. 19 shows a drip molding spoon being used to jack out kinks and dents in the drip molding section of a top panel. The lip on this spoon enables you to hook it under the drip

Fig. 11. Standard Jack Base

Fig. 12. Rubber Bases

(Courtesy H. K. Porter)

molding without danger of its slipping. You will find this tool useful when it is necessary to push an upper quarter panel out as well as up.

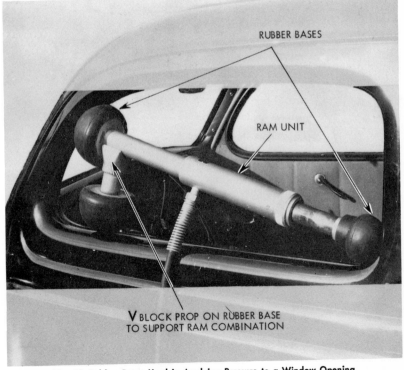

RUBBER BASES

RAM UNIT

V BLOCK PROP ON RUBBER BASE
TO SUPPORT RAM COMBINATION

Fig. 13. Rubber Bases Used in Applying Pressure to a Window Opening
(Courtesy Blackhawk Mfg. Co.)

Fig. 14. V Block Base   Fig. 15. Heavy-Duty V   Fig. 16. Ram Cap
                              Notch Base
                         (*Courtesy H. K. Porter*)

k. Power Dolly. A power dolly, shown in Fig. 20, applying pressure to a damaged rear hinge pillar, is usually used where a straight push is needed. You will find a straight push is often an essential operation when you are working on pillars, metal floor panels, upper dash panels, or in trunk compartments.

l. Fender Hook. This tool is used for relieving backward strain in fenders prior to roughing them out. A typical setup off the car is shown in Fig. 21.

m. Calking Iron. The calking iron is a heavy-duty tool used mainly in quarter panel work. Fig. 22 shows a calking iron being used

Fig. 17. Offset Pushing Tool in Use
(*Courtesy H. K. Porter*)

to push a rear quarter panel molding into alignment. The calking iron may also be used for pushing and aligning frames, dash panels, and curved inner construction.

Fig. 18. Cowl and Lower Quarter   Fig. 19. Drip Molding Spoon in Use
        Panel Spoon

(*Courtesy H. K. Porter*)

n. Upper Rear Quarter Panel Spoon. On most cars, the high-crown radius of this tool is necessary for working around the upper back sec-

tions. This type of panel spoon is shown in Fig. 23 being used to push out an upper rear quarter panel.

o. Quarter Panel Molding Spoon. Fig. 24 illustrates a quarter panel molding spoon being used for pushing out the rear quarter panel moldings.

p. Corner and Header Panel Spoon. The corner and header panel spoon is used to

Fig. 20. Power Dolly in Use

(Courtesy H. K. Porter)

get in behind header panel inner construction to push up crushed panels. Such an operation is illustrated in Fig. 25. This tool can also be used as a high-crown dolly for hand dinging.

Fig. 21. Fender Hook in Use

Fig. 22. Calking Iron in Use

(Courtesy H. K. Porter)

Fig. 23. Upper Rear Quarter Panel
Spoon in Use

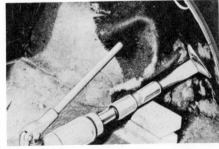

Fig. 24. Rear Quarter Panel Molding
Spoon in Use

(Courtesy H. K. Porter)

q. Quarter Panel Pusher Spoon. Because of the long working end, the quarter panel pusher spoon is used for getting behind inner con-

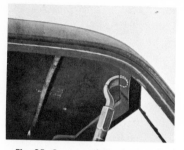

Fig. 25. Corner and Header Panel
Spoon in Use

Fig. 26. Quarter Panel Pusher Spoon

(Courtesy H. K. Porter)

struction around the quarter panel area. It is particularly useful for getting behind drain gutter inner construction without removing the drain gutter, as shown in Fig. 26.

r. Top Rail Spoon. The top rail spoon is used in the same manner as the quarter panel pusher spoon. It is designed for use in straightening roof rail outer panels without removing the roof rail inner construction.

This spoon has a deep throat and a curved surface anvil which will match the contour along the side of metal roofs. The top rail spoon is shown in use in Fig. 27.

s. Rocker Action Spoon. A rocker action spoon is shown in use in Fig. 28. It has a universal hinge arrangement which permits

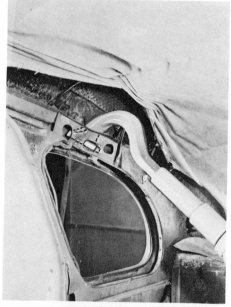

Fig. 27. Top Rail Spoon in Use
(Courtesy H. K. Porter)

the anvil face of the spoon to adjust itself in four different directions. This enables you to make applications easily, especially behind inner construction.

The rocker-action spoon, in conjunction with hammers, can be used for both roughing operations and finish work on all surfaces and in all areas except those having special shapes or contours.

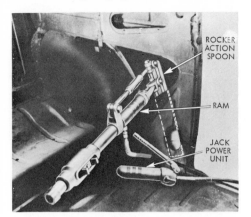

Fig. 28. Rocker Action Spoon in Use
(Courtesy H. K. Porter)

t. Hinge Pin Pusher. Hinge pins are usually difficult to get at for removal. Usually, the hinges are built as close to the body as possible to provide a smoother, more streamlined appearance. Without a suitable tool for removing hinge pins, the operation is sometimes a long and laborious procedure. With a hinge pin pusher (Fig. 29), the job is relatively a simple one which requires only a minimum amount of time.

Hinge pin pushers consist of the pusher itself and pusher pins of various lengths and diameters. The pusher is the part of the tool which is connected to the jack. Different lengths and diameters of pins enable you to work on a large variety of cars and with situations in which the damage has caused the hinge area to be deformed.

Fig. 30 shows the hinge pin pusher in position for the first operation in removing a hinge pin. Hinge pins can be installed as well as removed with this tool.

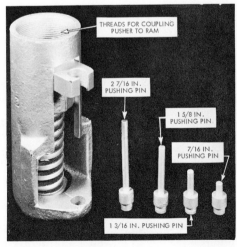

Fig. 29. Hinge Pin Pusher and Pin Assortment
(Courtesy Blackhawk Mfg. Co.)

It is not always necessary to use a pusher pin to push in a hinge pin because the hinge may be so narrow that the broad head of the pusher pin would not fit the hole. When this is the case, you can install the hinge by simply removing the pusher pin from the hinge pin pusher and using the bottom lug of the pusher to push the hinge pin in until it is flush with the surface of the hinge.

u. V Type Toggle Action Spreader. The **V** type toggle action spreader is for use where it is not necessary to reach too far between the units being spread. It is particularly useful around the front end sections for spreading the grille of bars, fender panels, and hoods.

The **V** type toggle action spreader attaches directly to the ram unit of the jack. When power is applied, the ram plunger comes forward and actuates the jaws of the spreader through a cam action which forces the jaws apart. When pressure is released, the plunger returns and the jaws of the spreader, being spring loaded, immediately close. In Fig. 31 a **V** type toggle action spreader is being used to force two grille bars apart.

Fig. 30. Hinge Pin Pusher in Position
(*Courtesy Blackhawk Mfg. Co.*)

You can see from the illustration that this tool is easily adaptable for working in small spaces because it does not require much operating space when it is attached to the ram.

v. Hydro-Method Spreader. The Hydro-Method spreader also employs a toggle action. This spreader, shown in use in Fig. 32, has a maximum spread of 16 in. and a minimum closed width of $1\frac{1}{2}$ in. A hinged dolly effect is incorporated in the end of each jaw which allows it to follow contours and permits the body repairman to do direct hammering while the dolly acts as the backing tool.

w. Small Wedge Spreader. A small, wedge-type spreader which will lie in the palm of your hand is available. This spreader (Fig. 33) has several attachments which screw into the bottom side of the lower jaw. These attachments, shown in Fig. 33, allow a variety of action in a confined working space. This tool is especially useful for removing small dents, low spots, or kinks from panels where it is difficult to reach with other tools.

Fig. 31. V Type Toggle Action Spreader on Front Grille Section
(Courtesy H. K. Porter)

The attachment shown at (*A*), Fig. 33, has a rocking action which allows the spreader to be used at an angle. The attachment shown at (*B*) is called a mushroom pick. It is used for removing larger dents or creases. The extended edge can be used to reach behind beads or lips. The attachment shown at (*C*) is used for bringing out pinpoint type dents and other small dents. The blunt-nosed attachment shown at (*D*), Fig. 33, is also used for removing very small dents and low spots.

x. Push-Pull Attachments. The push-pull tools are used with either direct-action or controlled, push-pull jacks. (Chain setups for pulling are described under chain attachments.) A group of push-pull tools which are typical are illustrated in Fig. 34.

Fig. 32. Hydro-Method Spreader in Use
(Courtesy H. K. Porter)

These tools are made to withstand extreme pressures and for use in extremely close quarters. They are extremely versatile and find many uses in both body and framework. Because most frame straightening is done with the body in place on the frame, it is often necessary to

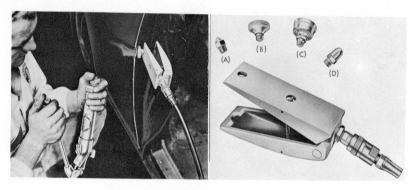

Fig. 33. Small Wedge Spreader
(Courtesy Blackhawk Mfg. Co.)

work in close proximity to the under portions of the body when straightening a frame. In these instances, you will find these tools particularly helpful.

y. Chain Attachments. Chain attachments are used primarily on one-way, remote-controlled jacks. However, certain setups, particularly in frame straightening, require the use of chains regardless of the type of jack used. Chain attachments are also used extensively for straightening axles and other suspension units which become damaged due to accident.

Different attachments are necessary for attaching the chain to the jack. These attachments are shown in typical arrangements on the jack in Figs. 35, 36, and 37.

In Fig. 35, the large chain at-

Fig. 34. Push-Pull Tools
(Courtesy H. K. Porter)

tachment is threaded onto the ram body. A ram cap is placed over the end of the ram plunger. When pressure is applied so that the ram moves outward, a pulling effect can be achieved when the chain is hooked as shown. Any of the jack bases can be used instead of the ram cap, depending on the surface being worked against.

All of the attachments pictured in Fig. 33 are illustrated in use on an actual job in Fig. 38. This is a combination setup in which the adjustable body spoon is hooked behind the rear door post while the chain is anchored to the frame. The arrow indicates the direction of pull.

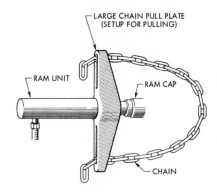

Fig. 35. Large Chain Attachment and Chain Attached to Ram
(Courtesy Blackhawk Mfg. Co.)

The setup of chain and chain attachments shown in Fig. 37 is shown in actual application in Fig. 39. This combination of attachments gives a two-way pulling effect. It consists of the two chain plates which attach to the ram and plunger and the two chains which hook around the frame members, as shown. The direction in which the frame will move when pressure is applied is indicated by the arrow.

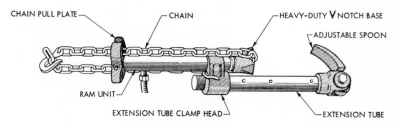

Fig. 36. Chain Pull Plate, Extension Tube Clamp Head, Adjustable Spoon, and Chain Attached to Ram
(Courtesy Blackhawk Mfg. Co.)

III. APPLICATION OF POWER TOOLS

The previous sections of this chapter have served merely to introduce to you the power tools. No attempt has been made to explain how they are used.

This section deals with the "how" of using power tools. Because of the tremendous power developed by the jacks, it is necessary for you to harness it in the proper fashion or more damage will be created to add to the damage which you are attempting to straighten.

The application of power tools to specific types of jobs is presented in this section under self-explanatory headings. Under these headings, the methods most commonly used are discussed and illus-

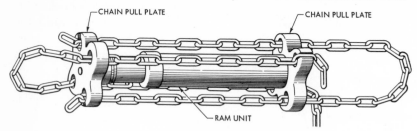

...

RAM UNIT

Fig. 37. Two-Way Pulling Combination
(Courtesy Blackhawk Mfg. Co.)

trated. These methods embody the principles of power application which you should remember when you are devising setups on your own.

a. Using Body Hammers with Power Tools. Where deep damage is encountered, much time can be saved and a satisfactory job can be accomplished by using either indirect or direct hammering with power equipment. Power equipment is indispensable where you cannot reach the underside of the damage with a hand dolly.

In this application, the power tool plays the same role as your one arm and the dolly block or backing tool in hand hammering. The difference is that instead of the return effect imparted from the dolly to the panel when the dolly bounces up after each blow, the power tool exerts a continuous force. As the panel is straightened, the tool is forced right along

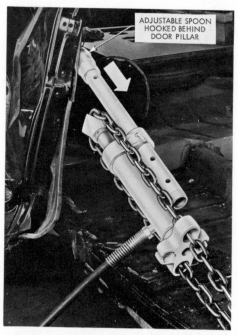

ADJUSTABLE SPOON
HOOKED BEHIND
DOOR PILLAR

Fig. 38. Chain Attachments Used in Pulling Rear Panel Section
(Courtesy Blackhawk Mfg. Co.)

behind it by additional applications of power from the jack. By this method, the panel will be quickly returned to its normal contour.

When you intend to do direct hammering, apply the power tool directly underneath the point where you intend the hammer blows to strike.

When you intend to do indirect hammering, apply the power tool on the deepest portion of the ding, and hammer around the outside, following the upward movement of the panel with the power tool until the damage is corrected.

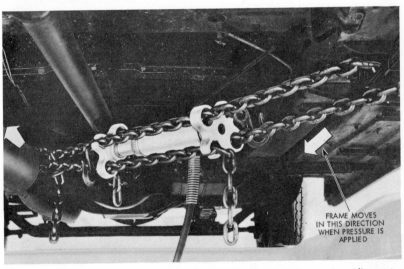

FRAME MOVES IN THIS DIRECTION WHEN PRESSURE IS APPLIED

Fig. 39. Chain and Attachments Being Used To Pull Diamond-Shaped Frame into Alignment
(*Courtesy Blackhawk Mfg. Co.*)

Whether you are using power tools or hand tools, always remember the one basic rule of all collision work: The corrective force should be applied as near as possible in a direction directly opposite to the force which caused the damage.

b. Pushing Out Body Panels. Instances will sometimes occur where, for one reason or another, it will be necessary for you to bring a damaged body panel to a near normal contour by use of power tools alone. When this is the case, apply the power for pushing out a body panel in a manner similar to that shown in Fig. 40.

In this instance, you do not push at the deepest portion of the dent. Instead, work around the outer edges of the damaged area in an ever-decreasing circle. The dent will be "walked" right up out of the surface, and you will have a contour ready for the finishing operations. If power is applied directly at the lowest portion of the ding without relieving the strain as the pressure is applied, the metal may become kinked or stretched.

c. Spreading Force over an Area. It is sometimes necessary to anchor the jack against a panel which will not bear the force which the jack will exert when pressure is applied. However, if the force were distributed over a large area of the panel, no damage would be caused.

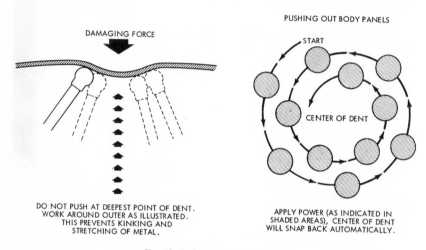

DAMAGING FORCE

PUSHING OUT BODY PANELS

START

CENTER OF DENT

DO NOT PUSH AT DEEPEST POINT OF DENT.
WORK AROUND OUTER AS ILLUSTRATED.
THIS PREVENTS KINKING AND
STRETCHING OF METAL.

APPLY POWER (AS INDICATED IN
SHADED AREAS), CENTER OF DENT
WILL SNAP BACK AUTOMATICALLY.

Fig. 40. Pushing Out Body Panel
(*Courtesy Blackhawk Mfg. Co.*)

Fig. 41 illustrates a setup where a piece of 2 x 4 is used to distribute the force of the jack base. In this case, the roof needs straightening. To exert the proper force, it is necessary to base the jack against the floor which would not withstand the pressure concentrated in a small area without becoming damaged. By using the board, the force is spread over the floor, and the roof can be straightened easily.

In Fig. 42, another instance of using a board to spread force over an area is illustrated. The jack in this setup is based against a piece of 2 x 4 which is laid in the curve of the quarter panel inner construction. Without the 2 x 4 the quarter panel would not be able to withstand the pressure.

d. Application of Diverse Lines of Corrective Force. With certain types of complex damage, it is expedient to use more than one jack to exert pressure against several points of the damage area alternately to

Fig. 41. Board Used To Distribute Force
of Jack Base
(Courtesy Blackhawk Mfg. Co.)

Fig. 42. Jack Anchored on Board against
Quarter Panel
(Courtesy H. K. Porter)

Fig. 43. (Below) Straightening Center Pillar. "Power-Pull," shown above, has a number of features including vertical lift, a pull range of 10,000 to 40,000 pounds and anti-backlash protection.

(Courtesy Guy-Chart Tools, Ltd., Scarborough, Ontario)

Fig. 43. (Above) Pushing Out Rear Quarter Panel.
(Courtesy Blackhawk Mfg. Co.)

restore the panel to its original shape. A setup involving the use of three different jacks to push out a rear quarter panel is shown in Fig. 43.

You can see from this illustration that boards are used freely to distribute the power exerted by the jacks against the undamaged area from which the pushing is to be done.

Two of the jacks are equipped with rubber flex heads and the necessary extensions so that the heads can be properly applied. The other jack is used with a quarter panel pusher spoon. The combination of two jacks with flex heads, positioned near the roof, prevents distortion to other parts of the body while the quarter panel is straightened by pressure on the lower setup.

Pressure is applied to each of the jacks alternately and in small amounts so that the movement of the panel is not great enough

Fig. 44. Three-Jack Setup for Rear Section of Rear Quarter Panel
(*Courtesy H. K. Porter*)

at one time to dislodge the other units which are being employed in the setup.

Another three-jack setup is illustrated in Fig. 44. In this setup, one ram is placed crosswise to the body across the front of the rear quarter panel to prevent distortion of this section of the body when pressure is applied to the rear section. One of the remaining jacks is equipped with a rubber flex head and the other with a toggle action spreader. When power is applied alternately to the two jacks in the rear section, the section will be quickly straightened. The jack across the body need have pressure applied only enough to keep it snug against the panel on either side of the body.

When you encounter complex damage, the need for more than one jack will immediately become apparent as you study the damage to determine the line or lines of destructive force.

Always remember to spread the pressure as much as possible on the base end of the jack on a dual setup to prevent distortion of the panel from which the pushing is done.

IV. MISCELLANEOUS POWER TOOLS

Certain tools used in the automobile repair shop for general repair work are also used on body repair and collision work. Some of these pieces of equipment are hydraulically operated and some are operated by air (pneumatically).

Most of the tools explained and illustrated in this chapter have been of the type that derive their power from the application of hydraulic pressure. However, there are tools on the market which use air pressure instead of hydraulic pressure. The most commonly used tools, of course, are of the hydraulic variety.

Air equipment is equally as fast and easy to operate as the hydraulic equipment already explained, and the principles of application are the same.

a. Pneudraulic Pump. The pneudraulic pump, which is manufactured by the Chicago Pneumatic Tool Company, embodies both the principles of pneumatics and hydraulics. This type of jack is operated by an air-over-hydraulic system which is similar to that used in many large trucks and busses for their braking system. Air is applied to the oil reservoir in the ram. Release of this jack is either automatic or manual. This means that any amount of pressure you apply to the work will be held until you turn the release valve to the release position. Fig. 45 shows a pneudraulic pump being used to straighten the rear section of a car which has been damaged. The pump in the illustration is being used in conjunction with a portable body and frame straightener which you will become familiar with during your study of frame and unitized body straightening and repair in Chapters 7 and 8.

Fig. 45. Using Pneudraulic Pump To Straighten Windshield Pillar

(Courtesy Chicago Pneumatic Tool Company)

This tool can also be used to operate stationary presses similar to the one shown in Fig. 46. When the pump is used in this fashion, the addition of an extra reservoir is necessary to boost the amount of pressure which is built up by the pump.

b. Pneumatic Fender Iron. Calling this tool (Fig. 47) a fender iron is somewhat of a misnomer because it can be used for repairs other than on fenders.

The fender iron consists of a yoke with an air hammer attachment. The end of the yoke opposite the hammer face is so designed that several different dollies or dies, as they are sometimes called, can be attached, depending on the contour of the surface being worked. Fig. 48 shows the different dollies in the rack which is provided for them. The upper die or dolly hammers on the outside of the surface while the lower dolly backs up the surface being hammered.

In addition to having several dollies provided which can be interchanged on the yoke, several different yokes are also available

Fig. 46. Pneudraulic Pump Operating Forty-Ton Hydraulic Press
(*Courtesy Chicago Pneumatic Tool Company*)

Fig. 47. Pneumatic Fender Iron
(*Courtesy Chicago Pneumatic Tool Company*)

(Fig. 49). These yokes are different so that the tool will be useful in a greater variety of places. Some yokes are short and some are deep for reaching up under a fender or out into the middle of an all-metal top. Any of the dollies provided will fit any of the yokes, which means that this tool can be used for almost any contour where you can reach the damage.

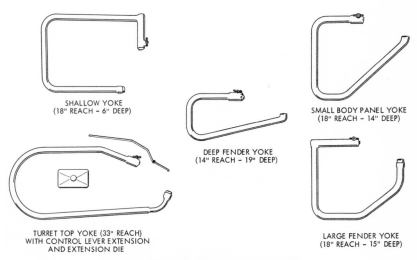

Fig. 48. Dollies Used with Pneumatic Fender Iron

(Courtesy Chicago Pneumatic Tool Company)

A regulator valve (Fig. 47) controls the air pressure at the discretion of the operator. If care is not used in the operation of the fender iron, it is possible to stretch the metal when you are hammering.

A high-speed cylinder head and a high-speed piston are available for use with the fender iron. They will double the number of blows per minute which the fender iron will strike on the surface. The high-speed cylinder head should never be used without using the high-speed piston, however, or else the tool may be damaged.

SHALLOW YOKE
(18" REACH – 6" DEEP)

DEEP FENDER YOKE
(14" REACH – 19" DEEP)

SMALL BODY PANEL YOKE
(18" REACH – 14" DEEP)

TURRET TOP YOKE (33" REACH)
WITH CONTROL LEVER EXTENSION
AND EXTENSION DIE

LARGE FENDER YOKE
(18" REACH – 15" DEEP)

Fig. 49. Yokes Used with Pneumatic Fender Iron

(Courtesy Chicago Pneumatic Tool Company)

It is always necessary to metal finish the job after the damaged surface has been hammered back to a near normal surface.

c. Shop or Arbor Press. In the course of repairing damage to an automobile, it is sometimes necessary to straighten the bumpers or other easily removable parts. Because of the thickness of the bumper material, it is not possible to straighten a bumper unless it is rigidly held and has a great deal of pressure applied to it.

Fig. 50. Arbor Press with Bumper in Place
(*Courtesy H. K. Porter*)

An arbor press is usually used for this purpose. Fig. 50 shows a hydraulically operated arbor press which is mounted on a rigid base, but is portable. In this

Fig. 51. Leverage Dolly in Place
(*Courtesy H. K. Porter*)

press, the bumper is merely laid on the supporting members which leaves the center of the bumper unsupported. Pressure can be applied to the unsupported section of bumper through the hydraulic pump and ram, and the damage can be straightened.

Arbor presses vary in size from the small one pictured in Fig. 50 to sizes which are able to develop many tons of pressure. An arbor press is usually standard equipment in any shop which is doing automobile repairing, whether the shop has a body repair shop or not.

Some inexpensive arbor presses rely on the leverage and gear principle to derive their power. A long handle is geared to a spindle coming down to an anvil. By rotating the handle, the spindle is raised or lowered to contact the work. After the spindle contacts the work, the operator can apply the necessary pressure at the handle to move the spindle and make whatever displacement is desired.

d. Leverage Dolly. The leverage dolly is not a power-operated tool, but it is considered a power tool because it provides power through leverage. It is used mainly on metal tops to aid direct or spring hammering. A rubber base keeps it from slipping or damaging the floor. The long arm enables the operator to readily control its location under the work. Fig. 51 illustrates the leverage dolly being used for spring hammering.

The leverage dolly can be purchased complete with attachments for length adjustment and with different bases and dollies with different contours. It is very useful when doing finish-hammering tops after roughing out with hydraulic equipment.

e. Mechanical Push-Pull Jack. The mechanical push-pull jack, like the leverage dolly, provides mechanical power through leverage (Fig. 52). The jack may be adjusted for pulling or pushing by sliding the body off the shaft and replacing it in reversed position. The jack is compact, light in weight, and requires no hoses or hydraulic fluid. Various accessories can be purchased.

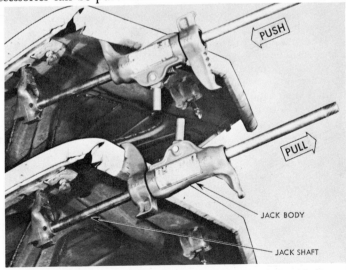

Fig. 52. Straightening a Hood with a Mechanical Push-Pull Jack (Practi-Jack)
(Courtesy Guy-Chart Tools, Ltd., Scarborough, Ontario)

TRADE COMPETENCY TESTS

The following questions, while they represent only a small portion of the material in this chapter, may be used to determine the percentage of the information retained.

1. What is probably the most commonly used hydraulic jack? (p. 188)

2. How is a one-way acting jack adapted to a pulling operation? (p. 187)

3. How many different types of hydraulic jacks are in general use in collision shops? (p. 186)

4. What attachments can protect threads on a ram cap and body? (p. 188)

5. In an emergency, what kind of oil can be used to fill the hydraulic unit in a jack? (p. 188)

6. What is provided with most jacks to add distance? (p. 189)

7. With a quick coupling tubing set, how do the tubes fasten together? (p. 190)

8. What arrangement that connects directly to the ram is provided for quickly adapting power tools to a dolly? (p. 191)

9. For what two reasons is a rubber jack base of great value? (p. 191)

10. **V** block type jack bases are used almost exclusively on what type of collision work? (p. 192)

11. What is the major value of an offset pushing tool? (p. 192)

12. When is a power dolly generally used? (p. 194)

13. In what respect is a rocker action spoon different from all other body spoons? (p. 196)

14. In how many different directions can a rocker action spoon be adjusted? (p. 196)

15. What tool is available for removing hinge pins? (p. 197)

16. What feature of a toggle action spreader causes the jaws to close immediately if the pressure is released? (p. 198)

17. What effect is incorporated in each jaw of a hydro-method spreader that allows the spreader to follow contours? (p. 198)

18. Chain attachments are used primarily with what type of jack? (p. 200)

19. When power tools are used with either direct or indirect hammering, they replace what hand tool in a hand hammering operation? (p. 202)

20. What can be used to spread jack force over a large area? (p. 204)

21. When it is necessary to remove damage by using power tools only, how is pressure applied to the damaged area through the jack and attachment used? (p. 204)

22. Can more than one jack be used at one time to remove damage? (p. 204)

23. What power arrangement is necessary for straightening bumpers which have been bent? (p. 210)

24. Is a leverage dolly a power-operated tool? (p. 211)

25. How is power applied with a leverage dolly? (p. 211)

26. What are some of the advantages of the mechanical push-pull jack (p. 211)

CHAPTER 6

DOORS, HOODS, AND DECK LIDS

The straightening of doors, hoods, and deck lids and their fitting into or alignment with the openings provided for them is not only an important part of collision work, but is a service that almost every auto mechanic is, on occasion, called upon to perform. At least a portion of the material presented here can be used by other than accomplished collision men. Door fitting actually is considered a trade within itself in the automobile factories. In some instances, the trade includes not only car body and truck cab doors, but deck lids and hoods as well. The material presented in this chapter will not only equip you to master this trade, but will provide you with the necessary knowledge to make repairs as may be required.

Aside from the serious damage to doors, hoods, and deck lids that will be encountered as a result of collisions, these parts can become distorted or sagged as a result of misuse and, in some instances, as a result of normal use. The readjustment of hinges, striker plates, and locking mechanisms to provide a uniform clearance around the door is considered as a part of alignment.

Doors, hoods, or deck lids that have become damaged in a collision fall into the classification of collision work. However, these parts must be aligned to match the body after they are straightened or repaired.

As indicated by the list of section titles at the beginning of this chapter, alignment of doors, hoods, and deck lids is presented immediately following the instructions for straightening the particular unit. In addition to the straightening and aligning presented in these sections, information on replacement is also given. Replacement panels for many popular cars are generally available.

I. DOOR PANEL REPLACEMENT

Outer door panels are usually damaged in any collision which involves the side of an automobile. As a general rule, the door can be satisfactorily restored with a minimum of straightening, bumping, and metal finishing. When the damage is severe (involving rips or tears in the metal), when part of the panel metal is missing, or where bends or kinks exist beyond the point where the panel can be straightened economically, either the panel or the complete door should be replaced.

a. Rusted Panels. As cars grow older, the bottom of the panel often rusts through. In these cases, it is generally economically practical to replace the panel only. All doors are provided with drain holes at the bottom so that water which runs down the outside of the glass between the door panels can run out. Most of the rusting through that you will encounter will be the result of failure to keep these drain holes open.

Where a door panel has rusted through, you can reasonably expect some damage to the inner construction as well. In some cases, you will have to weld in reinforcements to strengthen rusted inner construction. Look particularly at the inside of the lower corners.

b. Complete vs. Part Panel Replacement. When a door is made, the door panel covers the entire door. That is, in addition to the lower portion of the door, the same piece of metal extends on around the window opening. Replacement panels, however, end just below the window opening. Such a panel is considered a complete door panel.

In repairing doors, whether you install the complete panel or whether you install only a portion of it is determined by a number of separate considerations. Of course, if the entire door panel is damaged to the extent where it cannot be repaired, the entire door panel must be replaced. When a complete panel is replaced, openings must be provided for door locks, hinges, decorative strips, etc. If the door panel below the lock is replaced, then these extra steps are avoided. In some instances where the bottom of a door is rusted through, and only the lower portion of the panel is to be replaced, you may even find it possible to make the repair without removing body hardware, such as window regulators, door glass, etc.

Replacing a portion of a panel in such a way that the joint is at some point not concealed by a decorative strip or an abrupt change of contour, requires careful matching of the two contours. Moreover, a joint of this kind should not be welded by any process which might cause undue expansion of the metal, since it is virtually impossible to shrink the metal if a flange type welded joint has been made in the center of the contour.

The decision as to which kind of panel is going to be installed (whether it will be a complete panel, a panel cut under a molding, or whether the panel joint is to appear at some point below this) must be made before you actually start to work on the door.

c. Body Patch Panels. Just as many car and truck manufacturers and a number of independent manufacturers provide or make available replacement door panels, so also are a number of body panels available both in the form of complete panels and patch panels. When a particular make or model of automobile for some reason starts to rust through at a given panel, the replacement parts manufacturers in some cases have a replacement patch panel on the market before the car manufacturer does. Needless to say, in the case of body repairs, these patch panels permit a satisfactory repair of panels at a fraction of the cost of the entire panel. The following instructions on the replacement of door panels in general apply equally to the installation of such patch panels on other parts of the body. Body patch panels, consequently, are not covered elsewhere in this volume.

d. Panel Replacement Procedure. With the wide variation in design among the many makes and models of cars and trucks, it is obviously impossible to give detailed instructions and illustrations here on each. However, the panel in general is replaced in the same manner regardless of the make or model of the vehicle. A discussion of the considerations involved, and detailed instructions on how to effect panel replacement are given here in the following paragraphs.

(1) *REPLACEMENT CONSIDERATIONS.* Several things should be considered and evaluated before an actual panel replacement is made. It is necessary to decide how much of the panel needs replacement, then to determine just how much of the panel it is economically feasible to replace. Several factors must enter into and govern any decision reached concerning panel replacement. All of these factors are reviewed here so that when you encounter badly damaged panels in actual practice, you will be able quickly to reach a decision as to what is

needed. For example, a door may be so badly distorted or otherwise damaged that it will be necessary to replace the entire door. This is determined by the time and material required for the repair as compared to the cost of the new door. Don't fail to take into account the considerable amount of work involved in transferring the hardware, glass, and trim to the new door.

(a) DOOR LOCKS. Whether or not it will be necessary to remove the door lock depends on how much of the panel is replaced. If the entire panel is replaced, cut off the old panel either at the belt line or the belt molding. In either case, the removal and relocation of the door lock is required. Some replacement panels come with all of the necessary holes already in them. Generally, however, this is not the case, and when the entire panel is replaced, a hole must be cut in the new panel to accommodate the lock. While this is a fairly easy operation, it does consume some time. Whenever possible, therefore, you may want to cut off the old panel below the door handle.

If it is necessary for you to relocate a door lock hole in the new panel, use a hole saw of the correct size. It is generally easier to locate and cut the hole after the replacement panel has been fastened in place.

(b) DOOR GLASS. If only the lower portion of a panel is replaced, it may not be necessary to remove the door glass for the operation. An exception to this would be if the door is sprung so that the entire door needs straightening. The window might crack during the straightening operation. If the inner panel is distorted so that hammering is necessary, it is best to remove the glass. This, of course, depends on how much hammering will be required.

When the glass is left in the door, it should be kept in the fully raised position during the time the replacement is taking place. This will keep the regulator mechanism up out of the way.

(c) INTERIOR TRIM. The interior trim of the door consists of the trim pad, window garnish molding, door lock handles, and the door and window regulator handles. Any time all or any portion of the door panel is replaced, the interior trim pad must be removed. Openings are provided in the inner panel through which you can work. These openings, of course, are normally covered by the trim pad. Completely remove the trim pad. If you merely loosen it at the bottom, the trim may be torn or otherwise damaged while you are working on the door. The trim should be removed carefully so that it can be used again after the panel replacement is completed.

(d) MOLDINGS. If the belt moldings are to be removed, the operation should be done after the interior trim pad is removed. Once this pad is removed, you can see which type of fastening is used to hold the molding in place. Working from the inside, you can remove the molding without damaging either the molding or the fasteners.

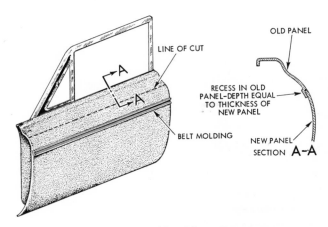

Fig. 1. Recessed Lap Joint on Door

(e) DOOR REMOVAL. Whenever a panel or a portion of a panel is replaced, the door should be removed. You will find that the ease of working on the door after it is removed more than offsets the little extra time involved in removing and reinstalling the door

(f) TYPES OF JOINTS. How much of the panel is replaced governs the type of joint used to fasten the remaining portion of the old panel and the new panel together.

(1) RECESSED LAP JOINT. A recessed lap joint is used only when the entire panel is replaced and the old panel is cut off either at the belt line or above the molding. An illustration of this is shown in Fig. 1. A considerable amount of both time and skill are involved in preparing a recessed lap joint. However, a fine finish job can be done with this type of welded joint if the one panel is recessed to a depth which is exactly equal to the thickness of the other panel.

(2) FLANGE JOINT. A flange joint is usually used when only the lower portion of a door panel is replaced. An example of this is shown in Fig. 2. This type of joint cannot be used where there is any chance that it will interfere with the inner workings of the window mechanism or the door lock mechanism. A very nice finish job can be attained with this type of joint, provided the flanges are accurately formed and care is used in matching the contour of the two panels exactly. This type of joint can be used on any body panel where the joint is to be made at any unconcealed portion of the panel.

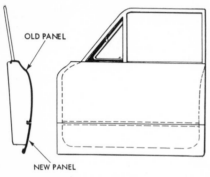

Fig. 2. Flange   Joint on Door

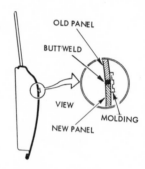

Fig. 3. Butt Weld Joint on Door

(3) BUTT WELD JOINT. A butt joint can be used wherever it is possible to conceal the joint. This usually means that it can be used at any point where the joint comes under a molding. An example of this is shown in Fig. 3. A butt weld is quickly made. However, it generally is not considered as strong as a lap or flange joint. For this reason, it is not generally used where the strength of the weld is a factor.

(2) *REMOVING OLD PANEL.* The way in which the old panel is removed depends on how much of it is removed. The old panel is cut off at one of three locations: at the belt line, at the belt molding, or somewhere below the molding. These three different possible locations for a cut are shown in Fig. 4, which shows a door ready for the cutting operation. Once the cut is made, some additional work is necessary to remove the old panel. This also is described.

(a) CUT OFF AT BELT LINE. When the entire panel is to be replaced, the old panel is cut off at the belt line. As previously mentioned, it is necessary to remove the hardware and trim from the door before a complete panel is removed. A door ready to have the complete panel removed is shown in Fig. 4.

The belt line acts as a natural line to follow. The actual cut is made with either a power saw or a special cutter. The method of cutting is determined by the type of joint you intend to make. Generally, the power saw or cutter is preferable for all kinds of joints. Cuts with welding equipment leave rough edges which require a lot of work, and are not practical except for flanged joints. Even with flanged joints, considerable extra work is involved in preparing the flanges if the edges of the metal are too rough.

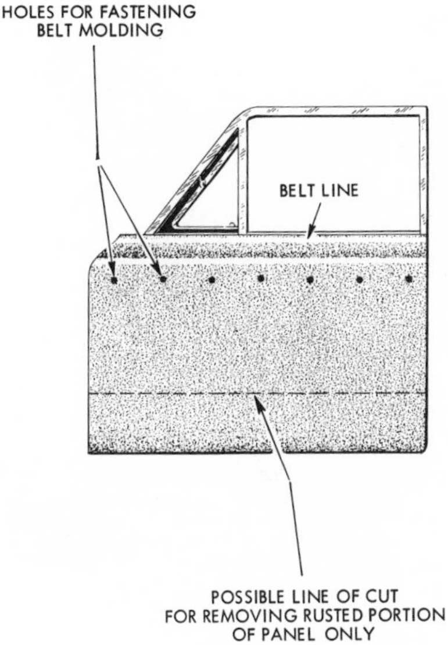

Fig. 5 shows the door panel being cut with a special cutter. The panel is cut all the way across in this manner. If a lap joint is desired, the extra panel material for the lap may be left either on the old panel or allowance made for it on the new one. The other panel is cut straight across. Where a recessed lap joint is made at the belt line, the extra material generally is left on the old panel. This extra metal is then recessed or sunk the exact thickness of the new panel. The new panel lies on top of this recessed portion with the visible joint straight across the door at the belt line.

HOLES FOR FASTENING
BELT MOLDING

BELT LINE

POSSIBLE LINE OF CUT
FOR REMOVING RUSTED PORTION
OF PANEL ONLY

Fig. 4. Door Ready for Cutting Operation

An instance of where the recess is formed in the new panel rather than the old is shown in Fig. 6.

If you are forming the recess in the old panel, make the cut ¾ in. below the belt line. Start the cut at the inside of the inner construction on one side of the door and cut straight across to the inside edge of the inner construction on the other side of the door. Working from this cut, make a vertical cut up to the belt line (¾ in. up). Then, using a hacksaw, make a cut on the belt line through the outer panel where it is folded over the inner construction. Fig. 7 is a sketch showing the exact line of the cut. The new panel and the old panel will butt one another at the step portion of the joint and will lap in the center.

(b) Cut Off at Belt Molding. One advantage of cutting the panel at the belt molding is that the joint is later concealed by the molding. This permits the use of the easily made and easily finished butt joint. In fact, a flange or lap joint might interfere with the installation of the molding.

The hardware and trim must be removed. The belt molding is removed and the cut is made directly under the molding. The cut should

Fig. 5. Cutting Door with Special Cutter　　　　Fig. 6. Recessed Lap Joint

(Courtesy Anzich Manufacturing Company)

exactly intersect all of the holes used for fastening the molding in place. Scribe a line to intersect the molding holes and make the cut along this line. Finish the cut over the inner construction with a hacksaw (Fig. 8).

(c) Cut Off Lower Portion Only. Where only the lower portion of the panel is to be replaced, much of the hardware and decorative trim can be left on the door. In some cases, you may not have to remove either the glass or the window regulator. The glass, of course, should be run all the way up during the entire procedure.

The most satisfactory joint is the flange joint. To form the flange, a step must be cut at both ends of both the old and the new panels.

Scribe a line straight across the panel at the point where the final joint is to be made. If you want a ½ in. flange, scribe a second line ½ in. below the first. If you want a ¾ in. flange, use a ¾ in. measurement. The long cut is made along this second line between the inner surfaces of the door inner construction straight across the panel. Two

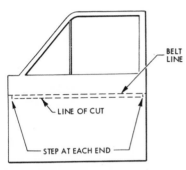

vertical cuts ½ in. (or ¾ in.) long are then made toward the top of the door up to the upper line. The length of this vertical cut establishes the width of the flange you will be forming (Fig. 8). The two horizontal cuts (one on each end) are made with a hacksaw. Saw through the outer skin only and continue the cut around the edge of the door flange.

Fig. 7. Line of Cut for Lap Joint at Belt Line

(d) REMOVAL OF FLANGE. After the cut is made across the panel, it is necessary to loosen the old panel around the edge to remove it. (The outer panel is folded around the inner panel at its outer edge.)

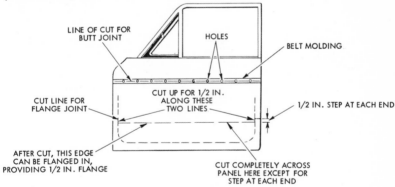

Fig. 8. Cut Lines for Butt and Flange Joints

Grind through the fold as shown in Fig. 9, and the old panel can be lifted off. Be careful during this operation not to grind too deeply or you will grind away a portion of the outer edge of the inner panel. A grinder in position for cutting the edge of the outer panel is shown in Fig. 9.

The final operation in removing the old panel is to remove the flanging strip of outer panel, which is left on the inside of the edge of the inner panel after the grinding operation. When the door is manu-

factured, the door outer panel is folded around the edge of the inner
panel and is spot welded. It is these spot welds which hold the flanging
strip in place. With a hammer and chisel, break the spot welds and
remove the flanging strip.

(3) *INSPECTION AND REPAIR OF DOOR.* During the process
of removing the old panel, some damage may be inflicted on the outer
edge flange of the inner panel. If this flange is bent or otherwise distorted, it must be straight-
ened. Straighten, also, any
damage to the inner panel.
Weld any cracks, breaks, or
tears. Give the entire door a
close visual inspection and
correct any damage found.

If you have to straight-
en the door, it is a good
plan to check the door in
place in the door opening
to see that it matches both
the contour of the body
and fits the door opening
before putting the new
panel in place. If it does
not fit, it can be straightened by one of the methods
presented in Section II or
III of this chapter.

**Fig. 9. Grinder in Position for Cutting Off Edge of
Door Panel**

(Courtesy Anzich Manufacturing Company)

(4) *PREPARING THE
NEW PANEL.* Several
things have to be done to the new panel before it can be installed. The
preparation necessary depends on the type of joint used to secure the
old and new panels together. The steps necessary in preparing a new
panel for the three commonly used types of joints are covered here in
the following paragraphs.

(a) BUTT JOINT. When a butt welded joint is used, little preparation
is required. Be sure the edges to be joined are straight and meet each
other perfectly. Be sure enough material is allowed around the outside
of the door for forming a flange around the entire edge of the door.
The panel can then be fastened in place.

(b) RECESSED LAP JOINT. As previously mentioned, either the old or the new panel can be recessed to make a recessed lap joint. In general, it is easier to sink the recess in the old panel since it is held rigidly in the door and will not tend to flop around while you are sinking the recess.

If the recess is formed in the old panel, the new panel is merely cut straight across.

In some instances where an abrupt change of contour occurs, it is possible to eliminate the recessing operation and just lay the new panel on top of the old, as shown in Fig. 10.

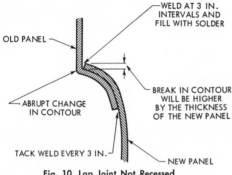

OLD PANEL

WELD AT 3 IN. INTERVALS AND FILL WITH SOLDER

BREAK IN CONTOUR WILL BE HIGHER BY THE THICKNESS OF THE NEW PANEL

ABRUPT CHANGE IN CONTOUR

TACK WELD EVERY 3 IN.

NEW PANEL

Fig. 10. Lap Joint Not Recessed

(1) FORMING THE RF-CESS. The ideal way to form a recess would be to have a dolly with a $\frac{1}{16}$ in. step running its full length. Scribe a line on the underside of the panel at the point where the step is to occur. This will be $\frac{1}{16}$ in. farther from the edge of the panel than the point where the outer surface of the two panels will meet. Using two **C** clamps, clamp the dolly at one end of the panel with the step on the scribed line. Use a square-headed hammer as shown in Fig. 3 in Chapter 2.

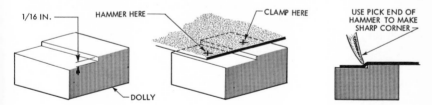

1/16 IN.

HAMMER HERE

CLAMP HERE

USE PICK END OF HAMMER TO MAKE SHARP CORNER

DOLLY

Fig. 11. Forming Recess for Lap Joint

Form the edge of the panel down into the step in the dolly. Use the other side of the same hammer to hammer the corner into the corner of the recess in the dolly. Fig. 11 illustrates several of the points involved in the formation of the recess.

Complete the recess for the full length of the dolly, then move the dolly about $1\frac{1}{2}$ in. and form the recess this additional distance. Complete the recess each time before moving the dolly, and continue across the panel. Each time the dolly is moved, make sure the step of the dolly is on the scribed line.

A less accurate, but generally satisfactory, recessed lap can be made without the recessed dolly just described. However, a dolly having a square edge is required.

Bend the panel to a 45° angle as shown at (A), Fig. 12. Then make a second bend as shown at (B). It may make the job easier if you make hacksaw cuts in the edge of the panel at about 3 in. intervals. These cuts should be about ⅔ the width of the lap.

Lay the new panel on the door to make certain it is the right size and that enough material is available all around the edge for turning at least a half-inch flange around the inner panel.

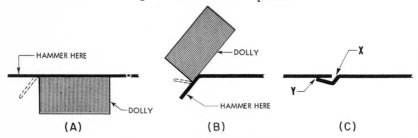

Fig. 12. Alternate Method of Recessing Joint

(c) FLANGE JOINT. Once a flange is formed on a curved panel, it will hold the curvature of the panel. However, in the forming of the flange, there is always a possibility of changing the panel curvature slightly. This, of course, could cause some difficulty in making the two contours match for the entire length of the joint. Generally, the flange is formed with a square-edged dolly and a hammer. However, if you are doing a lot of work on one particular model, you might find it advisable to make a form for making flanges. Fig. 14 shows several views of a flanged joint.

The flange, of course, is formed on both the old and the new panels. This means that it is necessary to allow either an extra ½ or ¾ in. for forming a flange across the top of the new panel. A step is cut at each end of the new panel at the edge to be flanged. This will prevent having a double thickness where the new panel forms over the edge of the door inner panel. Be sure to form the flange straight so that it will fit perfectly against the flanged edge of the old panel.

(5) *SECURING THE NEW PANEL IN PLACE.* It is necessary to hold the panel securely so that it cannot move out of position during

the welding operation. Regardless of the type of joint to be made, fasten the new panel to the door at the bottom and two sides by means of **C** clamps so that the new panel is in exactly the position you want it. The joint, of course, also must be held. This is accomplished in different ways, depending upon the kind of joint to be made.

(a) BUTT JOINT. A butt joint can be held at one point with a **C** clamp until a tack weld can be made to hold the joint. Arrange the **C** clamp so that it grips both the old and new panels equally, then tack weld the two panels together at both sides of the **C** clamp. Make the welds as close to the clamp as possible. Move the clamp several inches and repeat the operation.

If good tacks are made every few inches, it may not be necessary to do further welding. The remainder of the joint can be filled with solder. Generally, however, a better job is obtained if a continuous weld is made. If possible, weld the joint from the inside as well.

If the weld is made from the inside, it will not be necessary to sink the weld. If you cannot weld from the inside, weld from the outside. Sink the weld about ⅛ in. and fill the valley thus formed with solder as a part of the metal finishing operation.

When welding a continuous seam in a butt type joint with an arc welder, you may find the welding job will be speeded up and the danger of burning through the panel reduced if you lay a piece of soft wire in the joint. As you weld, the wire and the two edges of the panel are fused together.

(b) LAP JOINT. Either a straight lap joint (Fig. 10) or an accurately recessed lap joint of the type shown in Fig. 11 can be fastened with self-tapping screws spaced about 4 in. apart. Drill a ⅛ in. diameter hole through both panels at 4 in. intervals, then enlarge the holes in one panel to provide clearance for the screw. Tighten the screws in place.

Weld the joint on both sides. Either remove the screws or tack the threads of the screws to the panel. If you remove the screws, weld up the holes. If you tack the screws in place, you will grind off the heads during the metal finishing operation and will fill in around the screw with solder.

If the recessed lap joint is of the type shown in Fig. 12, the depth of the recess may not be exactly the thickness of the panel, and a different procedure is required.

With the panel in place in the recess, as shown in (C), Fig. 12, lay a straightedge across the joint. See X in (C) of Fig. 12. If the two panels are not flush, raise or lower the panel at point Y by bending the edge of the lower panel with a pair of pliers.

Tack weld the two panels together at point X, (C) of Fig. 12. Make a weld every two inches. Tack weld every two inches on the underside of the panel at point Y, (C) of Fig. 12.

The recessed lap joint at the belt molding shown in Fig. 6 (in which the recess was formed in the new panel rather than the old) was completed without welding. The new panel was lapped under the old one approximately one-half inch. The two were fastened together by six or eight self-tapping, sheet-metal screws. Simply drill six to eight one-eighth inch holes through the panels, countersink the holes in the outer panel, and install the screws. Provide sufficient holes to accommodate whatever device is used to retain the molding in place. If desired, the exposed edge of the overlapped panel can be soldered, although it is not absolutely necessary. Then install the molding and the whole joint will be concealed.

Another method of joining panels with a lap joint is by using "pop" rivets. Several types of pop rivet tools are available. An inexpensive tool is shown in Fig. 13. Notice the rivet lying alongside the tool. Insert the rivet in the tool. Then insert the rivet into the hole and press the rivet flange against the surface and squeeze the handles.

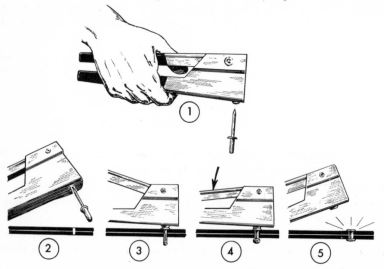

Fig. 13. Blind or "Pop" Rivet Tool in Action
(*Courtesy United Shoe Machinery Corporation*)

The rivet will be pulled into itself and an "upset" will be produced. The panels are drawn tightly together and the excess length of rivet is cut off, leaving the rivet smooth on both sides.

Commercial rivet tools are available for heavier duty requirements. Rivets can be obtained in standard sizes and lengths. The rivet tool is especially suitable for joining panels or light inner construction where the rivets do not show.

(c) FLANGE JOINT. The flange type joint, where the flanges are accurately made, permits a perfect match of the two contours. Using a C clamp, hold the two flanges together at the center of the joint. Make sure the two surfaces of the panel are the same height, then drill the flanges at a point near the clamp, as shown at (A), Fig. 14. Install a self-tapping screw and run it up snug but not tight. Use a straightedge. If one panel is higher than the other, tap it down until they are flush, then tighten the screw.

Move the C clamp about four inches and repeat the foregoing procedure at four-inch intervals to one end of the joint. Starting four inches from the first screw, install a screw every four inches from the center out to the opposite end of the joint. Always start at the center of the joint and work out toward the edges. Details of fastening the flanged panel in place are shown in Fig. 14.

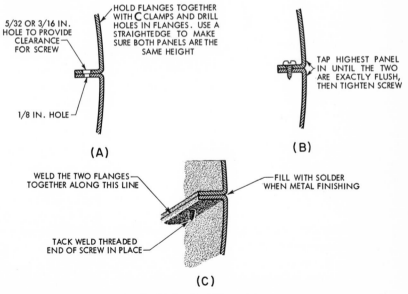

Fig. 14. Details of Flange Joint

(6) *TRIMMING*. After the new panel has been fastened in place, it is necessary to trim off the excess material around the edge of the door. The trimming operation is done in the same manner, regardless of the type of joint that was made on the door or where the joint was made.

Turn the door over on the bench, or other type of rest on which you have been working, so that the inner panel side is up. Mark around the edge of the new panel, allowing approximately one-half inch for forming a flange around the inner panel. How to trim the new panel is shown in Fig. 15.

The actual cutting off of the excess material can be accomplished with a pair of ordinary tin snips. This will leave a smooth edge which can be turned over the edge of the inner panel to form a flange.

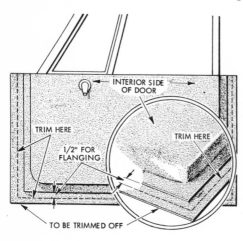

Fig. 15. Trimming New Panel

(7) *NOTCHING*. Special consideration must be given to the corners of the new panel before it can be flanged around the inner panel. The corners will either be rounded or square. Each case must be handled in a slightly different manner.

If the corner with which you are dealing is rounded, it should be notched as shown in Fig. 16A. This notching will permit the metal to be flanged around the corner without causing wrinkles or cracks which would spoil the entire job. Notice that the notches are only cut to approximately $\frac{3}{16}$ in. from the inner panel. If the notches are cut too deeply, the opening formed by the notch will show on the outside edge of the door after the flange is formed. You will have no difficulty in forming this small amount of metal into shape.

If the corner with which you are working is square, the notching should be done as shown in Fig. 16B. In this instance, an actual cut is taken out of the metal which takes the whole corner out of the new panel. When the flanging is done, however, the two edges will form

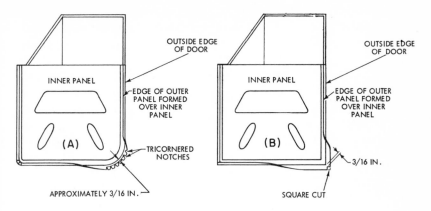

Fig. 16. (A) Notching for Round Corners; (B) Notching for Square Corners

one solid flange at this point. The dimensions for such a cut are given in Fig. 16. These dimensions can be followed, no matter what type or size door you encounter. As when notching for round corners, you should not notch too deeply or else the cutout made by the notch will show when the new panel has been flanged over the inner panel. The deepest portion of the notch should be approximately $\frac{3}{16}$ in. away from the inner panel. The notch can be made easily with tin snips or a hacksaw.

(8) *FLANGING.* After the new panel is fastened in place and the necessary notching has been done at the corners, the edges of the panel can be flanged. This completes the job of fastening the new panel into place on the door. Start at the top of the replacement panel on either edge of the door and form the flange with a hammer and dolly. Forming the flange is simply a matter of turning the new panel around the outer edge of the inner panel all around the edge of the door. Fig. 17 shows a body man in the process of forming a flange around the edge of a door.

Notice that the panel is first turned down by the body man at a 90° angle to the plane of the panel for a distance. The body man then goes back and finishes turning the edge under to complete the flange. This will prevent splitting the edge of the metal as might result if the flange were turned under in one operation.

After the flange is completed, tack weld the flange to the door inner panel at intervals of about three inches. It is usually a good plan to

Fig. 17. Flanging Outer Panel around Inner Panel
(Courtesy Anzich Manufacturing Company)

weld up the relief cuts that were made in the panel on the corners (Figs. 16A and 16B.)

(9) *METAL FINISHING.* If any screw holes are left in the outer panel, they should be filled with solder, then filed and sanded smooth. All welds which show from the outside should be ground down, covered with solder, then filed smooth. If, when soldering along a joint made at the belt line, you accidentally fill the holes for the belt molding with solder, redrill them. The door should be all ready for the refinisher when the panel replacement is complete.

(10) *INSTALLING HARDWARE AND TRIM.* The door should be mounted on the car before the hardware and trim are installed. Holes for the door handle and lock are sometimes provided in replacement panels. If not, they must be drilled at this time. Even when holes are already provided, it may be necessary to do a certain amount of filing to get them to line up properly.

Be sure the belt molding and other trim moldings (if any) are firmly in place. If they are part of a continuous molding, be sure they mate perfectly with adjoining body moldings.

Install the interior trim last. Be sure the handles for the door lock and window regulator are in the same relative position as the handles on the opposite door of the vehicle. Try all the door mechanisms to make certain they are operating properly before installing the interior door trim panel.

In some instances, considerable work might be saved for the painter if you wait until the door is painted before you install the door hardware and trim. This is particularly true if you have made a panel joint under the belt molding. The joint should be painted to protect it from rusting. This, of course, is not possible if the molding is in place.

All of the various holes such as are used for door lock, handles, or moldings, should be made before the door is painted.

II. DOOR STRAIGHTENING

This section deals with the correction of damage to car doors which can be considered major or serious, and which involves the removal of the door from the car.

The different aspects of straightening typical door damage are presented in the following paragraphs. Typical damage to a door is pictured during the various stages of straightening. However, you will encounter doors where some of the operations discussed here will not be necessary.

Since the instruction given in previous chapters of this volume covers the removing of minor dings from panels, little mention of straightening such damage is made here. Minor distortion in which it is not necessary to remove the door from the vehicle

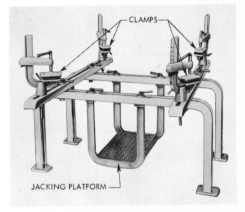

Fig. 18. Holding Unit
(Courtesy H. K. Porter)

is considered as a part of door alignment and is not covered in this section. Door alignment is presented in Section III of this chapter.

a. Roughing Out. The best method of straightening a damaged door is by using a holding unit such as shown in Fig. 18. This unit consists of a clamping device mounted above a jacking platform. Fig. 19 shows a damaged front door clamped in position on a holding unit in preparation for roughing out the damaged area with power tools. A rigid device for holding the door is necessary, otherwise the door might be sprung during the straightening operation. As discussed in Chapter 5, a rocker action spoon can be used with a jack to perform the first operation. The rocker action spoon, because of its ability to reach under inner construction and its general versatility, is ideally suited for this job. Fig. 20 shows the door after both a fourteen- and an eighteen-inch rocker action spoon have been used to rough out the panel. Fig. 21 shows one of the different setups which are necessary to produce the result shown in Fig. 20.

By using both a fourteen- and an eighteen-inch spoon, only two setups were necessary on this job. Otherwise, it would have been necessary

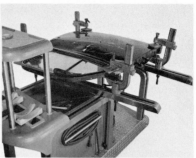

Fig. 19. Door in Position on Holding Unit

Fig. 20. Door with Damage Partially
Removed

(Courtesy H. K. Porter)

Fig. 21. Fourteen-Inch Rocker Action Spoon
Positioned for Straightening Upper
Half of Door

Fig. 22. Cutaway Panel Showing Face of
Rocker Action Spoon

(Courtesy H. K. Porter)

to move one single spoon several times. You can note also that these
spoons have a low-crown contour which nearly matches that of the
door panel being straightened.

Whenever you are using a rocker action spoon for door straightening, be sure to position it to match the contour of the surface being
worked. Fig. 22 shows a portion of a door panel cut away so you can see
how the face of the spoon should fit the contour.

At the same time the rocker action spoons are used, a hammer and
low-crown surfacing spoon are used from the outside to relieve the
strain by spring hammering (Fig. 23).

b. Checking Door Fit. Once the panel is restored to its approximate
normal contour (Fig. 20), remove the door from the holding fixture

and try it in the door opening of the body. This will permit you to determine if the inner construction has been distorted. If the inner

Fig. 23. Hammer and Low-Crown Surfacing
Spoon Being Used

Fig. 24. Door Panel Hammered Smooth,
Ready for Grinding

(Courtesy H. K. Porter)

construction has been distorted so that the door contour does not match the body, or if too much or too little clearance exists around the door, the inner construction should be straightened at this time before the panel is finished. The holding fixture and power tools are also used to straighten the door inner construction.

c. Hand Bumping. After the roughing out and the correction of any misalignment or distortion of the inner construction, continue with the rocker-action spoon in much the same manner as with a hand dolly. It absorbs the blows of the hammer for either direct or indirect hammering, or the blows of the hammer through the surfacing spoon in spring hammering. Fig. 24 shows the door panel ready for metal finishing.

d. Welding. After the door is bumped out and ready for the metal finishing operations, any necessary welding should be done. Cracks or tears cannot be welded until after the bumping is done, as a buckled metal condition may result. If a panel has a tear in the center and is severely dinged over the entire area, the edges of the tear will be quite far apart. As the surface is straightened, the edges of the tear will be brought closer together until, when the bumping is done, they may almost touch. If the welding is done before the panel is bumped smooth, it will be necessary to fill the tear with weld. Then, when further bumping is done, you will find that you have too much metal in the panel and it will buckle.

e. Shrinking. If a door panel is found to be stretched after the bumping operations, it will be necessary to shrink the stretched portions before the metal finishing can be done.

Fig. 25. Panel in Position for Grinding   Fig. 26. Use Pick Tool To Remove Low Spots
(*Courtesy H. K. Porter*)

All bumping and any welding necessary should be done before stretched areas are removed. If an attempt is made to remove a stretched portion of a panel before the bumping is complete, it might be necessary to repeat the operation after further bumping.

f. Metal Finishing. After all the necessary roughing, bumping, welding, and shrinking operations are done, metal finish the door to prepare it for the painter. The door pictured in the sequences here is the same door pictured in the sequences in roughing out and hand bumping. In Fig. 25, the position of the door has been changed slightly in the holding unit to provide a better working position for grinding. Grind the damaged area, using a No. 16 open-coat disk. As the paint is removed, the low spots are revealed, and pick tools can then be used for raising them (Fig. 26).

The intelligent collision man will remember that any grinding operation, such as the one explained above and shown in Fig. 25, requires eye protection. In the illustration, the repairman is shown wearing cup goggles for the protection of his eyes. Care must also be exercised when prying. (Shown in Fig. 26.) The proper tool is the safe tool. The pry bar should be used for prying operation rather than the screw driver which may be at hand.

In checking your progress with the pick tools, use the body file (Fig. 27) rather than the grinder. You will find the job will be speeded up and, at the same time, less physical effort will be required. The file is given a slight convex adjustment to eliminate the possibility for the surface to become wavy. With the blade slightly convex, you can file exactly where you want. Whether you file a large or a small area is

determined by where you start and end each stroke. If low spots exist that cannot be raised, fill them with solder.

After all the low spots have been eliminated, disk sand the panel with a No. 50 closed coat disk to make it perfectly smooth and ready for the painter.

If it is possible, obtain an old door and practice a door straightening job. If a holding fixture is not available to you, one can be

Fig. 27. Body File Being Used
(Courtesy H. K. Porter)

improvised. Create some damage in the practice door, then follow the operations in the sequence given. You will find that the damage will be quickly and easily removed.

III. DOOR ALIGNMENT

Door alignment actually is a separate trade in many of the automotive factories. Door alignment is also a necessary part of collision work. Much of door alignment has nothing whatsoever to do with the car having been involved in a collision. Rather, it is the result of what might be considered normal usage.

A large percentage of the misaligned doors you will encounter can be corrected whether or not you have mastered the techniques involved in the other aspects of collision work. The purpose of this section is to show you how to align doors regardless of the kind of misalignment encountered. The following paragraphs will show you what misalignment consists of, the kinds of misalignment you will encounter, and how you will check for them. Each of the various units which are factors of misalignment and any condition of the door itself which results in misalignment are discussed, and just what you can do and how to do it are presented under each heading.

An additional aspect of door alignment has to do with the dimensions of the door—how the door fits into the opening of the body, and how the opening in the door fits the glass. How to check and correct the window openings, how to make a comparative check of the door in question as compared to a door known to be correct, and how to check the door opening in the body by **X** checking are also presented in this section. In each of these instances, the method of checking and the means of making the corrections are presented.

a. What Misalignment Is. The doors of an automobile body or the doors of a truck cab are misaligned when they do not fit the contour of the body or when they are not centered in the door opening. Doors, of course, must provide a good seal against dust, water, and air. In order to do this, they must match the contour of the body at all points. When closed, doors must be centered in the opening provided for them. This is necessary for two reasons. If the door is not properly centered, it will not close properly. If the door is not properly centered, the gap around the door will not be uniform.

Centering the door in the opening involves moving the door up or down and forward or backward. In addition, it may involve moving either the top or the bottom of the door forward or backward and leaving the other end of the door in its original position. It may even be necessary to move the top and bottom of the door in opposite directions.

Doors will be encountered which fail to match the contour of the body in several different ways. The door can be bulged out too far at the center, or it may not be bulged out enough with the result that the top and bottom of the door do not fit into the body opening as they should. In the aforementioned example, it is assumed that the degree of bulge is the same at both the front and the rear of the door. However, in addition to these cases, you will also encounter doors which are bulged too much or too little at one side of the door, while at the same time the opposite side of the door matches the contour perfectly.

Sometimes you will encounter jobs where the trouble appears to be misalignment of the door, when actually the door itself is not the cause of the fault. In cases where the door does not match the contour of the body, it might be well to **X** check that portion of the body at the front of the door and at the back of the door to determine whether the reason of the failure to match body contour is due to distortion of the body or distortion of the door itself.

In some cases, a lack of uniform clearance at the front of the door might be due to a mispositioning of the front fender. Most present-day cars are so designed that the fender can be moved up or down and forward or backward. This possibility should be considered before any great amount of work is performed on the door itself.

b. How To Check Door Alignment. Door alignment is checked by making a close visual inspection of the door and its relation to the surrounding body panels. First open and then close the door, observing the up-and-down movement of the edge of the door at the lock pillar. If, as the door latches, you get up-or-down movement, the door is out of alignment. Actually, the alignment is being corrected by the dovetail

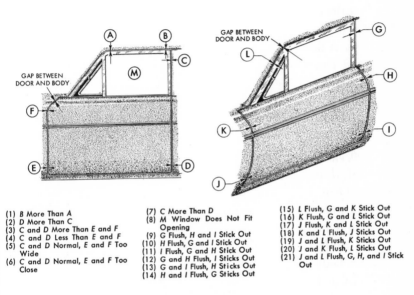

(1) *B* More Than *A*	(7) *C* More Than *D*	(15) *L* Flush, *G* and *K* Stick Out
(2) *D* More Than *C*	(8) *M* Window Does Not Fit	(16) *K* Flush, *G* and *L* Stick Out
(3) *C* and *D* More Than *E* and *F*	Opening	(17) *J* Flush, *K* and *L* Stick Out
(4) *C* and *D* Less Than *E* and *F*	(9) *G* Flush, *H* and *I* Stick Out	(18) *K* and *L* Flush, *J* Sticks Out
(5) *C* and *D* Normal, *E* and *F* Too	(10) *H* Flush, *G* and *I* Stick Out	(19) *J* and *L* Flush, *K* Sticks Out
Wide	(11) *I* Flush, *G* and *H* Stick Out	(20) *J* and *K* Flush, *L* Sticks Out
(6) *C* and *D* Normal, *E* and *F* Too	(12) *G* and *H* Flush, *I* Sticks Out	(21) *J* and *L* Flush, *G*, *H*, and *I* Stick
Close	(13) *G* and *I* Flush, *H* Sticks Out	Out
	(14) *H* and *I* Flush, *G* Sticks Out	

Fig. 28. Kinds of Door Misalignment

as the door closes. Look also for signs of rubbing or scraping by the door on the scuff plate or sill. If scrub marks are found, a condition known as door sag exists.

With the door closed and properly latched, notice the outer surface contour of the door in relation to the surface contour of the adjacent panels. The contour should match perfectly.

With the door closed and latched, look for uniform spacing at the front, top, and rear of the door. The door should center exactly in the opening provided.

c. Kinds of Misalignment. All of the different possibilities of door misalignment are listed and illustrated in (1) through (21), Fig. 28. The conditions listed in (1) through (8) are discussed here under those headings. The cause and correction of each type of misalignment is given in each case. The conditions listed in (9) through (21), Fig. 28, are cases where the door does not match the contour of the body. All these cases are corrected as described under the sidehead, *Contour Correction.*

(1) *B MORE THAN A.* When the gap between the door and the body is more at *B* than at *A* (Fig. 28), the gap at *D* will be more than the gap at *C*. This condition is commonly called door sag. It is possible for *B* to be more than *A* without having door sag if the opening in the body happens to be distorted at this point. A correction for this condition is given under the sidehead, *Door Opening in Body.*

When the condition is sag, the fault is either in the upper hinge or the dovetail. In general, the dovetail is more apt to be at fault than the hinges. A dovetail adjustment, as described under sidehead, *Striker Plates and Dovetails,* will correct the misalignment in most cases. If the hinge is at fault, a hinge adjustment to close the upper hinge, as described under *Hinges,* will correct the condition. It may be necessary to spread the lower hinge slightly to get perfect alignment.

(2) *D MORE THAN C.* When *D* is more than *C* (Fig. 28), the condition again is usually known as door sag. In this case, *B* will be more than *A* and the correction will be made as just described under *B More Than A.* When the door opening is distorted at this point, causing a wider gap between the door and body at *D* than at *C,* the correction is made as described under sidehead, *Door Opening in Body.*

(3) *C AND D MORE THAN E AND F.* When the opening between the body and door is more at *C* and *D* than between the door and fender at *E* and *F* (Fig. 28), either the hinge leaves are too close, or the front fender is out of alignment. If the hinges are at fault, it will be necessary to spread the hinge leaves as described under the sidehead, *Hinges.* If the front fender is too far to the rear, it will be necessary to move the fender forward by the adjustments provided.

(4) *C AND D LESS THAN E AND F.* When a condition where the gap between the door and body is less at *C* and *D* than the gap between the door and fender at *E* and *F* (Fig. 28), either the hinge leaves are too far apart or the front fender is out of alignment. It is also possible for the opening in the body to be distorted at *C* and *D.* This would require correction as discussed under the sidehead, *Door Opening in Body.*

If a door is forced open beyond the limit of the hinge, the hinge leaves will be spread apart. The correction in this case will be to close the hinge leaves as described under *Hinges.*

If the front fender is too far forward, it will be necessary to move the fender to the rear by making one of the possible fender adjustments.

(5) *C AND D NORMAL, E AND F TOO WIDE.* When the opening between the door and body is normal at *C* and *D*, but the opening between the fender and door at *E* and *F* is too wide (Fig. 28), the fault is usually in the fender and not the door. In rare instances, the opening

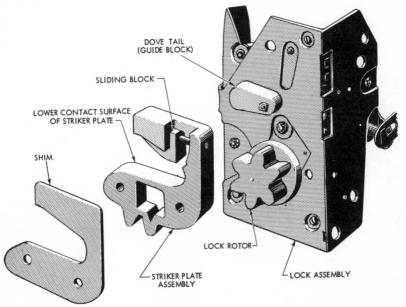

Fig. 29. Separate Striker Plate and Dovetail

(*Courtesy Ford Motor Company*)

in the body might be distorted to cause this condition. The correction usually lies in moving the fender to the rear a suitable amount to close the gap at *E* and *F* to normal.

(6) *C AND D NORMAL, E AND F TOO CLOSE.* When the gap between the door and body is normal at *C* and *D*, but is too wide between the door and fender at *E* and *F* (Fig. 28), the front fender is usually at fault. The fender has been moved to the rear, and a fender adjustment is needed.

(7) *C MORE THAN D.* If the gap between the door and body is more at *C* than it is at *D* (Fig. 28), the trouble usually lies in the hinges.

Of course it is possible that the door opening is out of alignment, but this possibility should be explored last. Door openings are discussed under the sidehead, *Door Opening in Body*.

If the hinges are at fault, it will be necessary to spread the upper hinge or close the leaves of the lower hinge, or both. Spreading and closing hinges are covered under *Hinges*.

(8) *WINDOW DOES NOT FIT OPENING*. In cases where the window glass (M), Fig. 28, does not fit the opening, the trouble lies either in the way the glass is mounted or in the door itself. This can be checked by merely raising the glass and determining whether or not

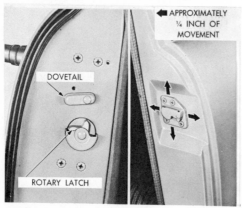

it makes proper contact across the top in the fully raised position. An adjustment of the window glass in the regulator may correct this condition. If it does not, the fault is in the door itself, and it will be necessary to correct the opening with power tools.

Fig. 30. Door Lock Striker Plate and Dovetail
(Courtesy Dodge Div.—Chrysler Corp.)

d. Striker Plates and Dovetails. The function of a striker plate is to hold the door in the closed position. The function of a dovetail is to limit the up-and-down movement of the door when it is in the closed position.

Several types of striker plate and dovetail arrangements are now in common use on the different makes of cars. In Fig. 29, an arrangement is shown where a rotary latch is used and where the striker plate and dovetail are separate. In this case, the dovetail is mounted on the door and slides into the recess provided in the striker plate assembly when the door is closed.

Fig. 30 shows another arrangement where the striker plate and dovetail are separate. A rotary latch is used in this case, and the way the striker plate and dovetail mesh is merely a variation.

In Fig. 31, no dovetail is used. The striker plate is also the guide for the door. The housing over the door latch rotor performs the function of the dovetail or quide block.

(1) *STRIKER PLATE ADJUSTMENT*. In all cases when a striker

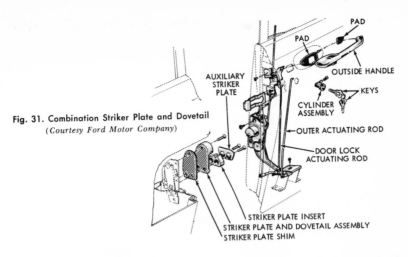

Fig. 31. Combination Striker Plate and Dovetail
(*Courtesy Ford Motor Company*)

PAD

PAD

OUTSIDE HANDLE

AUXILIARY
STRIKER
PLATE

KEYS

CYLINDER
ASSEMBLY

OUTER ACTUATING ROD

DOOR LOCK
ACTUATING ROD

STRIKER PLATE INSERT
STRIKER PLATE AND DOVETAIL ASSEMBLY
STRIKER PLATE SHIM

plate needs adjustment, check to see if it is worn to the extent that it needs replacing. The striker plate needs adjustment when the door fits too loosely, or sometimes when the door will not close. It is possible to have a striker plate loosen and move in when the door is shut. If it moves in far enough, the latch will not close over it and the door will not fasten shut. In cases like this, the striker plate should be loosened sufficiently and moved outward, then retightened.

In cases where the door is not closing tight enough, note the distance the door sticks out beyond the body. The striker plate must be moved inward slightly more than this distance before the door will close and latch properly. Loosen the screws holding the striker plate in place until it is possible to move the striker plate by tapping it lightly with a mallet. Tap the striker plate inward the desired distance, then tighten it securely in place. Open and close the door to check the door fit. It may be necessary to readjust slightly to get the exact fit desired.

(2) *DOVETAIL ADJUSTMENT*. On cars so equipped, a dovetail adjustment is necessary only when you wish to move the lock side of the door up or down slightly. A dovetail adjustment will not correct an excessive sag condition, but it will align the door if the door is only slightly out of alignment. Always check the dovetail to see whether or not it is worn to the extent that it should be replaced.

As when adjusting the striker plate, you should check the door in the closed position to see how much movement is required. Then loosen the screws holding the dovetail until it can be moved by tapping it lightly with a mallet. Tap it in the direction desired. When it has been moved into the proper location, tighten the screws securely. Close the door and open it a few times to be sure the dovetail is seating properly, then check the alignment. It may be necessary to readjust slightly to get the exact alignment desired.

e. Hinges. A typical hinge arrangement as used in many cars is shown in Fig. 32A. A device called a *door check* is used with most hinge arrangements to prevent the door from opening beyond the limit of the hinge travel.

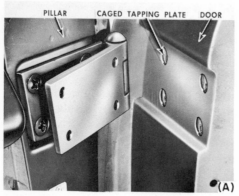

Fig. 32. (A) Typical Non-Adjustable Hinge Arrangement; (B) Fiber Block in Position for Spreading Lower Hinge

(*Courtesy Ford Motor Company*)

Door hinges figure in the correction of door alignment quite frequently. It is not uncommon for an individual to catch the door of his car on some immovable objects and to spring the hinges. Hinges can be adjusted in several different ways: by spreading and by closing and, in more recent models, by moving the hinges with adjustments which are provided.

(1) HINGE SPREADING. When a condition of door sag is encountered, on cars without adjustable hinges, it is usually necessary to spread the leaves of the lower hinge. This moves the bottom of the door toward the lock pillar. You will undoubtedly encounter situations where it will not be possible to entirely correct by spreading the lower hinge. In these cases, it will be necessary to close the upper hinge leaves.

If it is determined that the lower hinge needs spreading, it can be done easily and quickly. With the door closed, determine how much the hinge needs spreading. This can be done by measuring the clearance between the door and the lock pillar at the lower corner of the door. Check this dimension against what the clearance should be. The amount to spread the hinge is the difference between what the clearance should be and what it actually is.

Open the door and place a fiber block, slightly thicker than the distance which you wish to move the door, between the hinge halves as shown in Fig. 32B. Fasten the fiber block in place with glue or some other sticky substance. Close the door with the block in place. Be sure the door is closed tightly. It may be necessary to open and close the door several times to obtain the desired spread. It may also be necessary to use another block of a different thickness to get exactly the alignment desired. Be careful not to overspread the hinge. It is better to spread a little at a time until the desired spread has been accomplished than to spread too much.

(2) *CLOSING HINGES.* When it is found desirable to close a hinge to attain perfect door alignment, it is necessary to remove the hinge from the door and the body. With the hinge removed, the distortion will be evident.

Place the hinge in a vise, then tighten the vise until the hinge leaves are close enough to one another and parallel when they are in the closed position. It is usually necessary to close the upper hinge more often than the lower one. However, the closing is accomplished in the same manner in either case.

Before reinstalling the hinge, make certain that the hinge mounting surface on both the lock pillar and the door is straight. If it requires straightening, a good job usually can be done easily and quickly with a hammer and a low-crown surfacing spoon. Place the spoon against the pillar or door surface and hammer against the back face of it until the surface is straight. It may be necessary to move the spoon about slightly as the hammering is done in order to get the entire mounting surface straight.

After the hinge mounting surfaces are straight, install the hinge. Replace the weatherstrip if it was removed, cementing it firmly in place. Try the door a few times to make sure it is in perfect alignment.

(3) HINGE ADJUSTMENT. When you are correcting door alignment on a car that has adjustable hinges, remove the door lock striker plate to allow the door to hang free on the hinges. When properly adjusted, the door should be centered in the door opening. If the door does not require a correction of the contour, it can be aligned by the adjustment provided at the hinges. The front doors can be adjusted, fore or aft, up or down, or in and out. The adjustment point may vary between

models as to whether the adjustment is made at the door end, or the pillar end of the hinge. Figs. 33A and 33B show two possible hinge arrangements and the adjustments possible with them.

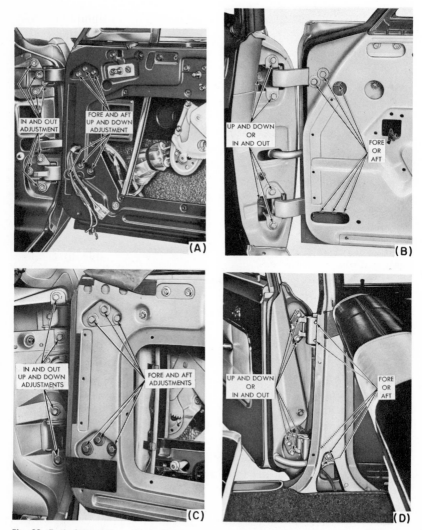

Fig. 33. Typical Front Door Hinge Adjustments (A and B) and Rear Door Hinge Adjustments (C and D)

(Courtesy Lincoln-Mercury Division, Ford Motor Company)

You will notice immediately that the major difference is whether the adjustment is made at the door end or the pillar end of the hinge. In all cases, the cap screws are threaded into floating type tapping plates. For this reason the cap screws should not be loosened too much. Also, if the adjustment required can be accomplished at the pillar end of the hinge, it will not be necessary to remove the door trim panel.

Figs. 33C and 33D show rear door hinge adjustment points. The major difference in these two arrangements is that it is not necessary to remove the door trim pad to accomplish the adjustments on the door hinges shown in Fig. 33D.

f. Contour Correction. All of the conditions of door contour misalignment described in (9) through (21), Fig. 28, can be corrected by one or more of the methods described here.

The type of equipment most commonly used for correcting door contour is a door-bar unit. Two types of door-bar units are available—a single door-bar unit (Fig. 34) and a double door-bar unit (Fig. 35). Single door-bar units are used on doors which are of light construction with simple contours. Double door-bar units are used on doors of heavy construction with complex contours.

All contour misalignment problems are corrected by either increasing or decreasing contour. It may be necessary to do both on one door, increasing the contour at one point and decreasing it at another. How to use both a single door-bar unit and a double door-bar unit to correct door contour is described here in the following paragraphs.

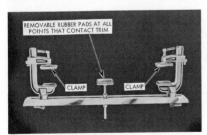

Fig. 34. Single Door-Bar Unit   **Fig. 35. Double Door-Bar Unit**
(Courtesy H. K. Porter)

(1) *INCREASING CONTOUR*. The contour of a door can be increased with either a single door-bar unit or a double door-bar unit, depending on how heavy the construction of the door happens to be.

(a) SINGLE DOOR-BAR UNIT. To increase the contour of a door with the single door-bar unit, place the two vertical clamps in position as shown in Fig. 36. The vertical bar, the two clamp handles, and the

Fig. 36. Vertical Clamps of Door-Bar
Unit in Position

Fig. 37. Setup Showing Method
of Applying Pressure

(*Courtesy H. K. Porter*)

Fig. 38. Clamp Assembly in Place on Belt Molding

(*Courtesy H. K. Porter*)

center support are then added to complete the setup. Pressure is applied by turning the nut on the center support against the inside of the vertical bar (Fig. 37). The amount of adjustment can be judged by screwing the outer nut on the center support outward for the desired amount. It is sometimes necessary to allow for spring back in the door reveal section (the section above the belt molding) before it takes a permanent set.

(b) DOUBLE DOOR-BAR UNIT. The alignment of doors which are of an irregular shape is possible with a double door-bar unit. The setup pictured in the following illustrations is made on a door having irregular and heavy construction. The problem in this case is that the door does not fit into the door opening properly along the outside rear edge of the door in the area from the bulge to a point above the division bar between the large window and the ventilator or flipper window (Fig. 38).

To bring the door into proper alignment, it is necessary to increase the contour of the door along this side. To do this, first place a clamp assembly on the hinge pillar section of the door at the belt molding line (Fig. 38).

Place a second clamp assembly in a vertical position above the division bar between the vent window and large window (Fig. 39).

Fig. 39. Clamp Assembly in Vertical Position above Division Bar

Fig. 40. Third Clamp Assembly in Vertical Position on Bottom of Door

(*Courtesy H. K. Porter*)

Place the third clamp in a vertical position, as far back along the bottom of the door as possible without touching the bulge part of the panel (Fig. 40). Fasten the vertical bar securely on the two outer clamps (Fig. 41).

VERTICAL BAR

Fig. 41. Vertical Bar of Door-Bar Unit
in Place

Fig. 42. Center Support Assembled to
the Horizontal Bar

(Courtesy H. K. Porter)

Loosely assemble the center support to the outer end of the horizontal bar (Fig. 42). This will enable you to position the center support correctly when the horizontal bar is assembled to the vertical bar.

The complete setup is shown in Fig. 43. The horizontal bar has been placed in position, and the repairman is adjusting the door by turning the inner nut on the center support against the inside of the horizontal bar. The amount of adjustment can be gauged by backing

Fig. 43. Complete Setup of Double
Door-Bar Unit

Fig. 44. Outside Anchorage Position
of Clamps

(Courtesy H. K. Porter)

off the outer nut on the center support, then screwing the inner nut outward against the inside of the horizontal bar.

The contour of the door can be increased at any point by simply positioning the clamps differently around the edge of the door. A few experiments you can make yourself will soon show you this.

Fig. 44 shows the outside anchorage position of the three clamps used in the setup illustrated in Fig. 43. You can also see that pads are provided under each clamp so that the door finish will not be marked. From this illustration, you can see that it is possible to move the clamps into several different positions.

(2) *DECREASING CONTOUR.* Decreasing the contour of a door is much the same as increasing it. Instead of forcing the door one way, it is merely forced in the opposite direction. How to decrease door contour with the two types of equipment used for this purpose is discussed in the following paragraphs.

(a) SINGLE DOOR-BAR UNITS. The setup for decreasing the contour of a door with a single door-bar unit is shown in Fig. 45. Anchor the top clamp to the outer edge of the door. Fasten the vertical bar in place on the top clamp. Next, place the center support at the position on the door which will give you the adjustment you desire. Place the lower clamp in position. On the door illustrated in Fig. 45 it was necessary to open the clamp until it would catch over the inner construction. Power can then be applied by screwing the adjusting nut against the inside of the vertical bar. In this particular instance, the center of the door stuck out too far. Investigation revealed that the lower portion of the door had too much contour and was actually holding the center portion out of alignment. The setup just explained decreased the contour until the door was in perfect alignment.

Fig. 45. Setup for Decreasing the Door Contour

(*Courtesy H. K. Porter*)

(b) DOUBLE DOOR-BAR UNIT. Decreasing the contour of a door with a double door-bar unit is done in a manner similar to that for decreasing the contour with a single door-bar unit. The problem shown in Fig. 38 where the door had too much contour at the top was corrected by increasing the contour at the middle of the door. This might well have been a case where the door fitted perfectly at the top but had too much contour at the middle. In this situation, the setup for decreasing the contour would be like that in Fig. 43 for increasing the contour, except that the equipment would be mounted on the outside of the door instead of the inside as shown.

g. Door Dimensions. In cases where a door is severely damaged and a good deal of straightening is necessary, it is a good policy to check the door before any attempt is made to reinstall and align the door with the body.

Make measurements on the damaged door, working from points that can be easily established on an undamaged door. Then make a measurement on the undamaged door, using the same points to measure from as you used on the damaged door. Compare the readings obtained to determine whether or not the damaged door requires further attention. Always be sure to take the measurements from the same points on both doors.

h. Window Openings. When the window does not fit the opening, and it is found that the difficulty is in the door itself and not in the way in which the window glass is mounted, the correction is necessarily one involving collision techniques. A typical example of a setup with power tools for straightening the window opening in a door is shown in Fig. 9, Chapter 5. Any collision involving the windshield pillar will, in all likelihood, damage the door. The setup in Fig. 9, Chapter 5, is for correcting this type of misalignment.

The window opening

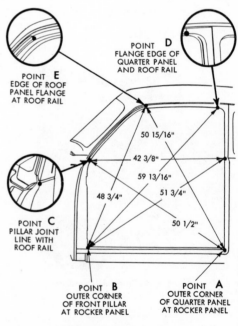

Fig. 46. Front Door Opening Dimensions
(Courtesy Ford Motor Company)

can be checked by trying the glass to see how it fits in the closed position, or by taking comparative measurements with the opening in a door known to be in alignment.

Always exercise care not to push the door out too far in correcting window openings, since a good, snug fit with the edge of the glass is desired all around the door.

i. Door Opening in Body. When a door is known to be in alignment, but does not fit the opening in the body, the opening in the body needs correcting. In many instances, a misalignment condition in the door opening will be discovered only when the door is placed in the opening. A quick check of the gap around the door between the door and the body will quickly show where the opening is off. The two most commonly used methods of determining whether or not the opening is in alignment are checking the known dimensions and **X** Checking.

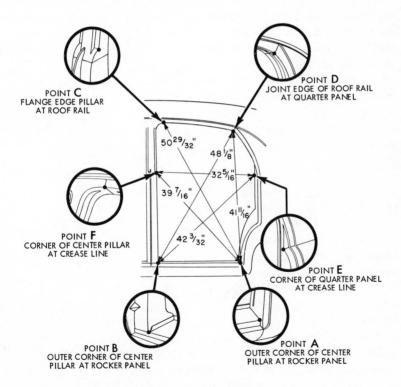

POINT **C**
FLANGE EDGE PILLAR
AT ROOF RAIL

POINT **D**
JOINT EDGE OF ROOF RAIL
AT QUARTER PANEL

$50\frac{29}{32}''$

$48\frac{1}{8}''$

$32\frac{5}{16}''$

$39\frac{7}{16}''$

$41\frac{11}{16}''$

$42\frac{3}{32}''$

POINT **F**
CORNER OF CENTER PILLAR
AT CREASE LINE

POINT **E**
CORNER OF QUARTER PANEL
AT CREASE LINE

POINT **B**
OUTER CORNER OF CENTER
PILLAR AT ROCKER PANEL

POINT **A**
OUTER CORNER OF CENTER
PILLAR AT ROCKER PANEL

Fig. 47. Rear Door Opening Dimensions
(*Courtesy Ford Motor Company*)

(1) *CHECKING KNOWN DIMENSIONS.* It is sometimes possible to obtain the dimensions for door openings from car manufacturers. When this can be done, it is a simple matter to check the dimensions of the door opening against what the dimensions should be. Any discrepancy immediately shows where the opening needs realigning. An example of how known dimensions are taken on a front door is shown in Fig. 46. An example of how known dimensions are taken in a rear door is shown in Fig. 47. In each case, enough cross dimensions are made so that a misalignment condition can be isolated to a small area. After the condition is found and the extent of misalignment of the opening determined, the corrective measures can be applied.

Correction of the door opening involves the use of power tools and collision techniques. Some good examples of the techniques involved were given in Chapter 5.

(2) **X** *CHECKING.* If the door opening is suspected of being out of alignment, and the dimensions of the door opening are not known, the opening can be compared to another opening on either the other side of the car or on another body of the same make and model. The basic principles of **X** checking, as discussed in Chapter 1, are merely applied to comparing the one door opening with the other.

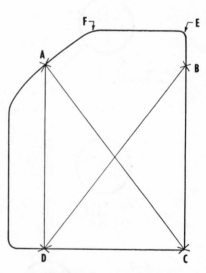

Fig. 48. Door Opening Comparison Reference Points for **X** Checking

To check for misalignment of the door opening, a quick comparison of the over-all dimensions is made first. If this check shows the opening to be correct, no further check is needed. How to compare a door opening with one known to be correct by the **X** checking method is shown in Fig. 48.

First, arbitrarily establish point *A* on the sloped portion of the door opening. A plan that will work on most cars is to establish points *A* and *B* seven inches below point *E*. Set your body trammel so that when one end is placed at *C*, the other end of the tram is seven inches below *E*. Draw a reference mark at the end of the tram. This is point *B*.

Move the tram to the slope of the door and let it hang from the point where it just touches the bottom of the opening. Mark point *A* at the upper end of the tram and point *D* at the lower end. Mark points *A*, *B*, and *D* in the opening to which you wish to compare the first opening in the same way.

Dimensions *A* to *C* and *B* to *D* should be the same on both openings. Compare dimensions *A* to *B* and *D* to *C*. This comparison, plus the comparison of the two diagonal dimensions, will quickly show how much the opening is distorted and will provide a clue as to the needed correction.

IV. HOOD STRAIGHTENING

The hood of an automobile or truck is substantially anchored when it is closed. Many models have spring-loaded hinges so that the tension of the springs hold the hood firmly in place at the hinged side. At the front or other point of locking, a sturdy latch holds that end or side of the hood down under spring tension. Completely around the hood —front, back, and around the two sides—a number of rubber pads are provided, on which the hood rests. When the hood is open, however, it is virtually unsupported. It is held in place by the hood hinges alone. This means that for any hood straightening operation involving the use of power tools, the hood will have to be removed and held in some manner to permit the application of power tools.

Fig. 49. Damaged Hood Clamped in Holding Unit

Fig. 50. Damage Partly Removed

(Courtesy H. K. Porter)

Generally, when damage occurs to the hood, you will find that the hood flange will crack. Usually, as a first step of any hood repair, the flanges should be rewelded as early in the operation as possible so as to prevent the crack from extending during the time the hood is under pressure from the power tools.

Minor damage, local in area, of course, can usually be corrected by using a hand dolly and hammer. In cases where the damaged area is quite extensive, much time can be saved by using power tools. Nevertheless, if you do not have power tools available or if you do not have a suitable means of holding the hood to permit the use of power tools, a surprising amount of the damage can be readily worked out by use of the hand tools alone.

The hood of an automobile is constantly under the eye of the driver and passengers. Any defects in workmanship, such as ripples or low spots, can be easily seen from the driver's seat. Any bulges or stretched portions of the panel are also apparent. When straightening hoods, you must exercise the utmost care to see that the surface is perfectly smooth when you complete the job. Work on the hood is exacting.

In this section, a fairly common type of hood damage which is difficult to straighten is explained and illustrated. All of the operations necessary to restore this hood to a like-new condition are presented. The instructions given here can be applied to almost any hood damage you will encounter.

a. Roughing Out. Fig. 49 shows a damaged hood clamped securely in a holding unit. The damage is toward the front of the hood, adjacent to the high-crown area of this particular hood. This means that it is in the section of the hood most easily seen by the driver.

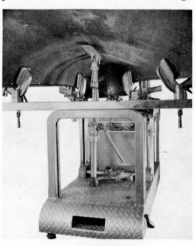

Fig. 51. Rocker Action Spoon and Jack Positioned for Removing Damage
(*Courtesy H. K. Porter*)

Notice that the hood has been clamped in the holding unit with the damaged area directly over the jacking platform. Fig. 50 shows the damaged section partially straightened. An eighteen-inch rocker action spoon was used, along with the necessary tubing, a small rubber base, and a direct-acting jack. The power was applied from the underside with the jack based on the jacking platform (Fig. 51). Note that the rocker action spoon is positioned directly under the center of the hood.

Fig. 52. Hammering Surface Smooth,
Using Dolly

Fig. 53. Hood Roughed Out

(*Courtesy H. K. Porter*)

This minimizes the chance of stretching the metal beyond the point where it can be quickly restored to normal.

b. Hand Bumping. After the surface has been roughed out with the power tools, it can then be further straightened with a hammer and dolly (Fig. 52).

Fig. 54. Removing Stretched Portion of Hood
with Heat Spots

Fig. 55. Hammering Heat Spots
in Stretched Area

(*Courtesy H. K. Porter*)

The possibility of stretching the metal is ever present when you are hammering on a hood. Use a wooden mallet, if possible, so as to hold metal stretching to a minimum. Fig. 53 shows the hood bumped out in preparation for the removal of the paint. A grinder with a No. 24 open-coat disk is used for removing the paint. The low spots are brought up with a pick hammer. It may be necessary to alternately file with a body file and work with the pick hammer to remove all of the low spots.

Fig. 56. Quenching Heat Spots with Cold Water

Fig. 57. Filing Hood

(*Courtesy H. K. Porter*)

c. **Shrinking.** During the final hand bumping operation of removing low spots, any stretched portions of the damage area will become visible. These stretched areas should be shrunk back to normal at this time. It will generally be necessary to pick up additional low spots created by the shrinking operation. Fig. 54 shows a stretched section being shrunk by the method explained in Chapter 4. Figs. 55 and 56 show the subsequent hammering and quenching operations required to complete the shrinking of the stretched section.

Fig. 58. Surface Ready for the Painter
(*Courtesy H. K. Porter*)

The heat spots should be about the size of a nickel and they must be hammered down while they are still cherry red. The heat spots should not be quenched until after the metal has turned black.

d. **Metal Finishing.** After all the roughing, hand bumping, shrinking, soldering, and welding that may be necessary are done, grind or file (Fig. 57) the entire damage area. Use a No. 50 close-coat disk to finish the whole area. This removes all of the minute scratches left by the file and leaves the surface ready for the painter (Fig. 58).

V. HOOD ALIGNMENT

Any time an automotive vehicle is involved in a collision where the grille, front fenders, or hood is damaged, an alignment problem usually arises. Even though each damaged panel is bumped out and straightened, they usually do not fit together as they did originally.

In some instances, you will find that misalignment is due to a condition that exists in the hood itself. At some previous time, perhaps, the hood may have been damaged in a collision, and whoever straightened the job may not have restored it to its original shape or dimensions. In this case, of course, the misalignment can be repaired by making a correction of the hood. However, you will often find that you can make up for a discrepancy in one part by an adjustment in some other part. The purpose of this section, therefore, is, first of all, to define what is meant by proper hood alignment. How to check hood alignment and the various things that can be done to correct the particular aspects of hood alignment are also discussed.

With the large variation in body design and the large number of makes and models of cars and trucks on the road, it obviously would be impossible in a volume of this kind to give a step-by-step procedure for the alignment of each type of hood. This section, then, rather than to present a procedure for alignment for a specific make or model, is designed to acquaint you with principles of alignment and to point out to you the methods whereby the desired results can be achieved.

a. Proper Hood Alignment. Automobile hoods, when latched in position, are generally held in place at the rear with spring-loaded hinges and at the front with a spring-loaded latch, both of which pull the hood downward under tension. The hood itself rests on small blocks of hard rubber or on a lubricant impregnated fabric sometimes known as "antisqueak."

In most automobiles, the front grille work, the two front fenders, and the hood are intended to form a smooth-flowing silhouette. If any of the parts stick forward or are to the rear of their normal position, a step appears in the contour. Hood alignment, or at least one aspect of hood alignment, involves the maintenance of a smooth-flowing contour for these separate parts at the front end.

At the rear of the hood, the cowl is recessed so that when the back of the hood is in this recess, the outer surface of the hood flows in a continuous line which matches the surface of the cowl immediately adjacent to this recess. If the hood is too high or too low, a step occurs in the silhouette.

If the hood is too far forward, a large gap exists between the rear of the hood and the raised portion of the cowl. On the other hand, if the hood is too far rearward so that less than a normal gap exists between the back of the hood and the cowl, there is a possibility that, when the hood is raised, it will strike the cowl panel and chip the paint on either or both the cowl panel and the hood.

The contour of the hood must match the contour of the cowl exactly, that is, the two surfaces should be exactly flush with each other at all points.

On the sides of the hood, a uniform gap should exist for the full length of the hood on each side. As has been explained in previous sections of this chapter, a number of rubber blocks are provided for the hood to rest on. Since the hood is under tension, the gap at the point where the rubber block should be might be less than normal if one of these blocks is missing. On the other hand, if the hood, when held down under tension by the hinge springs or the latch spring, fails to touch the rubber blocks, then not only will the gap at that particular point be wide, but vibration and possible noise might result.

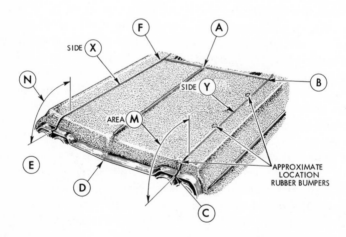

(1) A Too High, B and F Normal
(2) A Normal, B or F Too High
(3) A, B, and F Too High
(4) A, B, and F Too Close to Cowl
(5) A, B, and F Too Wide
(6) C Sticks Out, D and E Normal
(7) E Sticks Out, C and D Normal
(8) E and C Normal, D Does Not Match Contour
(9) C, D, and E Too Far Forward
(10) Side X Too Wide, Side Y Normal
(11) Side X Too Close, Side Y Normal
(12) Side Y Too Close, Side X Normal
(13) Side Y Too Wide, Side X Normal
(14) Sides X and Y Too Wide
(15) Sides X and Y Too Close
(16) Side X Too Wide at Area N, Normal at E and F
(17) Side X Too Close at Area N, Normal at E and F
(18) Side Y Too Close at Area M, Normal at B and C
(19) Side Y Too Wide at Area M, Normal at B and C

Fig. 59. Hood Misalignment

All of the various kinds of hood misalignment that might occur are shown in Fig. 59. In the list accompanying the illustration, each condition of misalignment is given. Each condition is numbered. This number agrees with the number of one of the following paragraphs where the condition is fully discussed, and the correction needed is given.

(1) *A TOO HIGH, B AND F NORMAL.* When the center of the hood sticks up and both rear corners are down, a hinge adjustment (to be described subsequently) will usually correct the condition. It may be possible in some instances to draw the hood down by tightening the screws which hold the hood to the stiffener which runs crosswise near the rear of the hood. If a hinge or a stiffener adjustment does not remove the condition, a contour correction (described subsequently) is needed.

(2) *A NORMAL, B OR F TOO HIGH.* When the center of the hood is down at the rear, but one or both of the corners at the rear stick out, a hinge adjustment is necessary. On occasion, a contour correction will be necessary.

(3) *A, B, AND F TOO HIGH.* Where the hood sets too high all across the rear, a hinge adjustment is necessary. However, you should make a quick check to be sure that nothing is holding the hood out of alignment before a hinge adjustment is made.

(4) *A, B, AND F TOO CLOSE TO COWL.* Even though the rear of the hood is supposed to rest on the cowl in the recess provided, a gap between the edge of the hood and the shoulder of the recess is necessary. If this gap is too narrow, the hood may catch on the cowl when it is opened, causing the paint to chip on both the hood and the cowl. In this case, it is necessary to move the hood forward. This is accomplished by a hinge adjustment.

(5) *A, B, AND F TOO WIDE.* Aside from the fact that a wide gap between the hood and the cowl looks unsightly, the hood may stick out in the front at the grille and the latch may not work properly. In this case, a hinge adjustment is needed.

(6) *C STICKS OUT, D AND E NORMAL.* When a corner of the hood sticks out at the front, the hood may be cocked in the hood opening, and another condition of misalignment may exist at some other portion of the hood. In most instances, however, the contour of the hood is out of alignment and needs attention.

(7) *E STICKS OUT, C AND D NORMAL.* Again, this is a condition where one corner of the hood does not fit properly at the front. The same correction applies here as it does for the previous condition.

(8) *E AND C NORMAL, D DOES NOT MATCH CONTOUR.* Usually, the center of the hood at the front is made to match the contour of the grille or to line up with a molding or ornament. When the fit is poor at this point, one of several things may be wrong.

If the hood fits well at all other points, the grille and the front-end sheet metal may need adjusting. Since the hood latches into the hood strainer it is possible that the strainer is too low or too far forward. The correction of all of these possibilities is discussed subsequently. If the opening is not at fault, the contour of the hood is out and needs attention.

(9) *C AND D TOO FAR FORWARD.* When the front of the hood is too far forward, it is a good idea to make a quick check to determine whether or not the gap at *F A B* is too wide. If it is, an adjustment is necessary to move the hood to the rear. Another possibility to explore is whether or not the fenders and front-end sheet metal are too far to the rear. An adjustment (described subsequently) will correct any undesirable condition found. If the contour of the hood is not correct, this same condition can exist, and a correction of the hood contour will be necessary.

(10) *SIDE X TOO WIDE, SIDE Y NORMAL.* When the gap between the hood and the fender is too wide at one side but is normal at the other, the hood opening is too large. An adjustment of the fender will correct this condition. If the hood itself has been badly damaged, it may have too much contour to one side of the center line, and a contour correction is needed.

(11) *SIDE X TOO CLOSE, SIDE Y NORMAL.* When the gap between the hood and fender is too close at one side but normal at the other, the reverse of the instructions given for the previous condition applies. It will be necessary to correct either the hood opening or the hood contour.

(12) *SIDE Y TOO CLOSE, SIDE X NORMAL.* This condition is the complement of that described just previously. The correction is the same as described when side *X* is too wide, and side *Y* is normal.

(13) *SIDE Y TOO WIDE, SIDE X NORMAL.* Again, the condition described here is a problem involving the gap between the hood and fender. The correction is the reverse of that given in "*(10) Side X Too Wide, Side Y Normal.*" Instead of closing the gap, it is widened.

(14) *SIDES X AND Y TOO WIDE.* When the gap between the hood and fenders is too wide at both sides, one or the other of two conditions exists. Either the opening for the hood is too large and the

fender needs to be adjusted closer to the hood or the contour of the hood needs correcting.

(15) *SIDES X AND Y TOO CLOSE.* When the gap between the hood and fenders is too close at both sides, the opening or the hood contour is at fault, and the correction necessary is the same as that just given.

(16) *SIDE X TOO WIDE AT AREA N, NORMAL AT E AND F.* A hood generally has a contour which sweeps downward at the front. The hood opening usually becomes narrower at the front. Both of these factors contribute to a type of hood misalignment commonly encountered. Where the hood sweeps downward, it is apt to fit too closely, or not well at all. The correction needed is dependent to some extent on the type of damage which has been inflicted on the hood. The correction in this case can require either attention to the hood opening or a correction of the hood itself.

(17) *SIDE X TOO CLOSE AT N, NORMAL AT E AND F.* The condition described here is another possibility of misalignment between the hood and the fenders. The correction needed is called for under the previous heading.

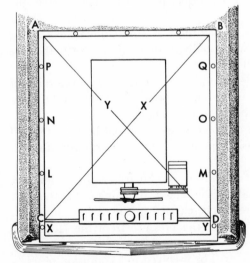

Fig. 60. **X** Checking Hood Alignment

(18) *SIDE Y TOO CLOSE AT M, NORMAL AT B AND C.* When the hood does not fit at the portion described here, the correction needed is explained under the heading "*(16) Side X Too Wide at Area N, Normal at E and F.*"

(19) *SIDE Y TOO WIDE AT M, NORMAL AT B AND C.* The correction needed when the hood and fender contour does not match is given under the heading "*(16) Side X Too Wide at Area N, Normal at E and F.*"

b. Checking Hood Alignment. Hood alignment is easily and quickly checked in most instances by a visual examination. With the hood in the closed position, check the gap all around between the hood and the adjacent panels. The gap should be uniform. If it is not, one of the conditions of misalignment shown in Fig. 59 exists. Each manufacturer has specifications for what this gap should be. Whenever possible, you should work to the manufacturer's specifications. However, in the absence of specifications, a good general rule to follow is to see that the gap is not greater than $\frac{1}{4}$ in. nor less than $\frac{1}{8}$ in. If the clearance at the joint is not within specifications, it will be necessary to shift the hood or make some other adjustment to correct the misalignment.

In some instances, it will be necessary to examine the hood opening and the hood separately to see which one is at fault. When this is necessary, it is done by a method of **X** checking. The hood opening is measured as shown in Fig. 60. Any misalignment in the over-all opening will be obvious as soon as the dimensions for X and Y are compared. The measurements, of course, should be the same.

To more closely isolate a condition of misalignment, **X** measurements can be taken from points A and B to any of the corresponding opposite points along either side of the opening. The points shown in Fig. 60 are the holes in which the rubber pads or bumpers which support the hood are secured.

c. Hood Opening. When a condition of misalignment exists that affects the hood opening, it will usually be necessary to shift either the fenders or the front end sheet metal.

(1) *FENDERS.* In some cases, only one fender will be the cause of misalignment. The reason for this may be that the fender is too high, too low, too far forward, or too far toward the rear.

A high or low condition can be quickly corrected by loosening all of the fender attaching bolts. Using a 2 x 4 for a lever, either force it up or down.

If either fender is too far forward or too far back, a hydraulic jack can be used. Simply loosen all of the fender attaching bolts, then anchor the jack so that pressure can be exerted in the desired direction. Tighten the attaching bolts before the pressure from the jack is relaxed.

In some cases, both fenders will be involved in a condition of misalignment. When this is the case, it will be necessary to loosen the attaching bolts of both fenders. The fenders can then be moved as necessary to effect the alignment desired.

(2) *FRONT-END SHEET METAL.* Occasionally the hood, when

properly aligned at the rear, will be misaligned at the front. The hood should lie evenly between the fenders at the grille. If the opening is too narrow, the bolts which attach the fender to the radiator support bracket and the grille should be removed. A hydraulic jack should then be placed between the fenders as far forward as possible. The fenders should be forced apart until the proper distance exists between them. This distance can be determined by measuring across the front of the hood, then adding the desired clearance on each side to the measurement taken.

Before the pressure is relieved on the fenders, additional shims or flat washers should be placed between the fender brackets and the radiator supports. These shims will hold the fender in the position to which it was forced.

As soon as the shims are installed and the bolts tightened, remove the jack and bring the hood into the closed position. If too much clearance exists, it will be necessary to repeat the operation and remove shims until the desired clearance or fit is obtained.

It may also be necessary to move the front-end sheet metal up or down. All of the attaching bolts holding the hood strainer in place should be loosened. The hood strainer can then be raised or lowered and secured in place by the use of shims or washers. It may be necessary to straighten some of the support brackets in order to effect the desired alignment of the front-end sheet metal.

d. Hinges. The hood hinges on most cars are constructed so that they can be adjusted to move the hood forward, rearward, or to move either rear corner in or out or up or down. (Fig. 61A).

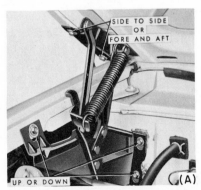

Fig. 61. (A) Hood Hinge and Adjustments; (B) Hood Latch and Adjustments
(*Courtesy Lincoln-Mercury Division, Ford Motor Company*)

(1) *MOVE HOOD FORWARD.* To move the hood forward, loosen the bolts fastening each hinge to the cowl. Shift the hood forward as much as desired, then carefully raise and lower the hood to see whether or not the desired alignment has been achieved. If it has, tighten the bolts holding both hinges to the cowl.

(2) *MOVE HOOD REARWARD.* To move the hood to the rear, loosen the hinge attaching bolts at both hood hinges. Move the hood to the rear as desired, then work the hood to see whether or not it is in proper alignment. If it is, tighten the bolts fastening the hinges to the cowl.

Whenever the hood is adjusted rearward, be sure that the safety catch (if one is used) holds properly when the hood is in the unlatched position.

(3) *HOOD REAR CORNERS.* After all of the adjustments are made, you may find that the bottom rear corner of the hood is either too close to the fender or too far from it when the hood is closed. When this condition exists, it can be corrected quickly and easily by bending the hood hinge plate on the cowl. If the plate is bent toward the cowl, the corner of the hood will be forced away from the fender. If the corner is too far from the fender, bend the plate away from the cowl and the hood will be brought closer to the fender.

A large pry bar or a monkey wrench with a piece of pipe on the handle can be used as a tool for the bending operation.

e. Contour Correction. Whenever any condition of misalignment exists where it is necessary to correct the contour of the hood, it will be necessary to remove the hood. After the hood has been removed, it can be corrected by the usual collision methods. It is necessary, however, to fasten the hood in a rigid device to effect any contour corrections. Detailed instructions on contour correction were described previously in this chapter.

f. Hood Latches. A typical hood latch is shown in Fig. 61B. The hood can be adjusted up and down to match the top contour of the front fenders by moving the hood latch lock dowel up or down.

VI. DECK LID STRAIGHTENING

As is true of doors and hoods, the deck lid on an automobile is securely held in place when closed. A lock or latch keeps the lower edge under tension. In many designs, the hinges are spring loaded so the upper edge also is under tension. With the deck lid opened, as would be required to correct any collision damage that may have occurred to it, the deck lid is supported only by the hinges. This means that in any instance where the use of power tools is required, it will be necessary to remove the deck lid and hold it in a suitable holding fixture. Even if you do not have a holding fixture, the deck lid should be removed. All of the pressure that you must apply to the deck lid will be transferred to the hinges. There is a possibility, therefore, that during the correction of the deck lid damage you may cause some damage to occur to the body through the hinges.

The principles involved in straightening the deck lid are much the same as those involved in straightening any door.

One disadvantage you will encounter in working on deck lids lies in the fact that in some areas, the deck lid inner construction does not provide enough space between the inner construction and the outer skin or panel. This means that some of the long, thin spoons and the long picks are almost a necessity. Even with these tools, you will often find that it is necessary to remove a portion of the inner construction during the bumping operation, then, after the outer skin is corrected, to weld it back in place. In other instances, you will find that time can be saved by drilling small holes through the inner construction which will permit the use of a punch or drift as a pick. In all operations of this kind, you always have the additional possibility of filling in with solder where it is too difficult to bring the surface up to the required smoothness.

Many kinds of damage occur to the deck lid, since it is subject to rear collisions and is also often damaged when the vehicle is struck at the quarter panel. It would, of course, be impossible in a volume of this kind to present all of the possible varieties of damage that can occur to a deck lid on even one make or model of car. When one considers the large number of makes and models that are on the road, the problem is even more apparent. The principles, however, are pretty much the same, and for the purpose of illustrating the techniques involved in deck lid straightening, the example shown in Fig. 62A might be considered as typical.

This particular deck lid was restored to normal, and various stages of its correction were photographed to illustrate this section. This section, then, traces the steps involved in correcting this particular deck lid. In general, it is felt that these steps will apply to almost any kind of damage that you will encounter.

Of course, when you encounter a seriously damaged deck lid, the advisability of replacing rather than repairing it should be considered. Estimate the amount of time that you will have to spend to correct the deck lid, then compare this cost to that for a new part. This is

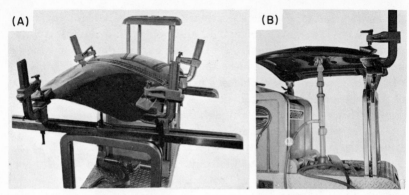

Fig. 62. (A) Deck Lid Mounted in Holding Unit; (B) Eighteen-Inch Rocker Action Spoon in Position
(*Courtesy H. K. Porter*)

particularly true if the top and quarter panels of the car have been damaged. By using a new deck lid, you will be providing yourself with one part, the condition of which you know, and the deck lid can be used as a template or gauge in restoring these other panels to normal.

a. Roughing Out. When a deck lid is to be straightened, a much more satisfactory job can be done if the deck lid is removed from the car and placed in a suitable holding device. A deck lid which has had the lower right-hand corner pushed in is shown correctly mounted in a holding unit in Fig. 62A. Inspection of the damage has shown that it will be possible to straighten the damage without cutting away a portion of the inner construction.

The first operation in straightening the damage can be done with an eighteen-inch rocker action spoon used in conjunction with a hydraulic jack. Fig. 62B shows the spoon in use. It is first necessary to insert the spoon through the small opening in the center of the deck lid, then position it so that it will push out as much damage at one time as possible. While pressure is maintained against the underside of the surface with the rocker action spoon, a spring hammering operation is done on the outer surface. This operation is shown in Fig. 63.

b. Hand Bumping. As soon as the surface is comparatively smooth (all sharp ridges have been removed), a bumping hammer and a deep-throated door spoon are employed (Figs. 64, 65). The great depth of the deep-throated door spoon (Fig. 65) allows you to reach to the very edge of the panel on most deck lids.

When the surface has been made as smooth as possible by bumping,

Fig. 63. Spring Hammering on Deck Lid

use a pick tool to raise the low spots. Fig. 66 shows a deep-throated pick tool being used on the deck lid to raise the low spots near the edge. Fig. 67 shows the same tool laid alongside the deck lid to enable you to see the reach which is possible with this tool.

Remove any low spots revealed by filing. A different type of pick tool, which has an offset to increase efficiency when working in close places, is shown in Fig. 68. This tool is shown inserted between the inner and outer construction ready for use in Fig. 69.

Fig. 64. Bumping Hammer and Deep Throated Spoon Being Used on Deck Lid

Fig. 65. Illustrating Depth of Deep Throated Spoon

(Courtesy H. K. Porter)

Fig. 66. Deep Throated Pick Tool in Use

Fig. 67. Illustrating Depth of Deep Throated Pick Tool

(Courtesy H. K. Porter)

Fig. 68. Deep Throated Pick with Offset Point

Fig. 69. Offset Pick Tool in Position, Ready for Use

(Courtesy H. K. Porter)

c. Metal Finishing. After all of the bumping operations are performed, any welding or shrinking necessary should be done before the finishing operations are started. When all the low spots are removed, the surface can be filed and sanded smooth. Fig. 70 shows a body file, which has been given a slight concave adjustment, being used on the deck lid. Care should be exercised not to remove too much metal. To make the surface ready for the painter, use a grinder with a No. 50 grit close-coat disk.

VII. DECK LID ALIGNMENT

Proper deck lid alignment should be maintained at all times. An improperly aligned deck lid will allow water and dust to enter the luggage compartment which may cause damage to anything which is being carried in it.

Whenever a deck lid is repaired or replaced because of damage, close attention should be given to its proper alignment. All surface damage must be corrected before you attempt to align the lid.

Several methods of aligning deck lids are commonly used depending on

Fig. 70. Body File Being Used on Deck Lid
(*Courtesy H. K. Porter*)

the type of equipment available and on the extent to which the lid is misaligned. How to check for deck lid misalignment, and how to achieve proper alignment when a condition of misalignment is evident is covered in the following paragraphs.

a. Proper Deck Lid Alignment. Proper deck lid alignment exists when the deck lid matches the contour of the body all around. Deck lid misalignment is easily checked in some cases by a visual inspection of the gap all around the deck lid between the deck lid and the body. However, it is often necessary to check more closely for deck lid alignment.

A simple but effective way to make this check is to chalk the edge of the body flange which contacts the deck lid weather strip. Be sure the chalk is rubbed on evenly all along the flange. Close the deck lid, then open it. The chalk will be transferred to the weather strip at each point where contact is made. If a chalk line is visible around the entire weather strip, the lid is sealing perfectly. Wherever the chalk line does not appear, the deck lid is not sealing properly, and realignment is necessary. If the trouble is in the contour, it will be necessary to perform a correction.

In some cases where the deck lid does not seal properly along the bottom edge, it may be possible to correct it by adjusting the latch or by making adjustment at the hinges. A typical adjustable hinge arrangement is shown in Fig. 71A. If, however, you make this adjustment and still do not get proper sealing or alignment, it may be necessary to bend or twist the deck lid.

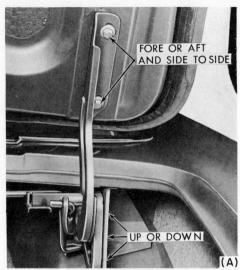

FORE OR AFT AND SIDE TO SIDE

UP OR DOWN

(A)

Fig. 71. (A) Deck Lid Hinge Adjustment; (B) Method of Twisting Deck Lid by Hand
(*Courtesy Ford Motor Company*)

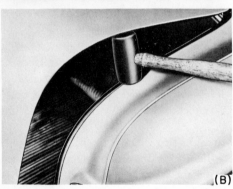

(B)

Bending or twisting operations can be done in some instances by hand with hand tools. They can be done in any instance with a door-bar unit or by the use of power tools. Some deck lids are more rigid than others due to the construction. In cases like these, it will be necessary to use a door-bar unit or power tools.

b. Twisting Deck Lid by Hand. Fig. 71B shows a method of providing a fulcrum point for raising one side of the lid, thereby forcing the other side down. No power tools are involved. In this case, the deck lid did not fit properly along the left side. A mallet was placed between the deck lid and the body as shown in Fig. 71B on the right-hand side. By closing the deck lid against the mallet, the side opposite the mallet (left side) was forced down. Never apply excessive pressure against the mallet. Check the alignment and sealing. If necessary, repeat the operation until the proper alignment is obtained.

c. **Use of Door-Bar Unit.** In another case involving misalignment in the same area, you may find it necessary to use a door-bar unit because the deck lid is more rigid. The same principles apply for using a door-bar unit on a deck lid as for using it on a regular door. A few experimental setups will give you an ample working knowledge.

d. **Matching Deck-Lid Contour with Body Contour.** Another situation you may encounter is that created when the deck lid does not fit the contour of the body. This condition may exist at several points around the deck lid, along the roof panel, along the extension panel, or along the lower back panel on either side of the deck lid. Sometimes it is not the fault of the deck lid. The panels adjacent to the deck lid may be misaligned.

If the deck lid does not follow the contour of the roof panel but works freely, the roof panel is out of alignment. Place a power jack between the floor pan and the underside of the roof panel just back of the drain gutter, as shown in Fig. 72.

Place the base of the jack against a 2 x 6 to distribute the strain on the floor pan over a larger area. Raise the roof panel until the proper contour is obtained. Do not apply excessive pressure against the roof panel with the first application. Check the fit along the roof panel. If necessary, repeat the operation until the proper contour is obtained.

Fig. 72. Hydraulic Jack in Place To Raise Roof Panel
(Courtesy Ford Motor Company)

If the misalignment is along the extension panel above or forward of the tail light openings, it can usually be corrected by the use of a rubber mallet only. First, determine the location of the misaligned section of the extension, then strike the top surface in the center of the misaligned area with the rubber mallet (Fig. 73). Be sure the blow is delivered close to the drain gutter with the flat surface of the mallet. It may be necessary to strike several blows to obtain alignment.

If the deck lid does not fit properly along the lower back panel, place a piece of paper between the deck lid and lower back panel. Close the deck lid, then pull the paper. If the deck lid is sealing properly, you will not be able to pull the paper out. You can make this same check at both ends and at the center of the deck lid next to the striker plate. If proper contact is not made at the striker plate, adjust the striker plate. If contact is made at both ends and not at the center after the striker plate has been adjusted, use two mallets, one at each corner, and ap-

ply pressure as shown in Fig. 74. You will encounter cases when you can hammer the lower back panel out toward the deck lid by striking the inside of the back panel with a mallet.

If the deck lid is tight at the center but no contact is obtained at either or both lower corners of the deck lid, one or two methods can be used to make the correction. The first is to hold the deck lid part way open, then to strike the corner of the lid that is not making contact with a rubber mallet. The

Fig. 73. Method of Aligning Center of Deck Lid Extension Panel
(*Courtesy Ford Motor Company*)

Fig. 74. Method of Aligning Center of Deck Lid with Lower Back Panel

Fig. 75. Fitting Deck Lid Lower Corner to Lower Back Panel

(*Courtesy Ford Motor Company*)

second is to place a mallet between the deck lid and the lower back panel at approximately the center of the panel. Apply pressure against the deck lid on the side that is not making contact as shown in Fig. 75. Repeat as many times as necessary to correct the damage.

TRADE COMPETENCY TESTS

The following questions, while they represent only a small portion of the material in this chapter, may be used to determine the percentage of the information retained.

1. Can doors, hoods, and deck lids become misaligned as a result of other than a collision? (p. 213)

2. What can be done to help prevent rusting at the bottom of door panels? (p. 214)

3. When is it necessary to remove the door lock during panel replacement? (p. 216)

4. When a door glass is left in the door during a panel replacement, what position should it be in? (p. 216)

5. When a door panel is replaced, is it always necessary to remove the interior trim from the door? (p. 216)

6. Why should the interior trim pad be removed before the belt moldings are removed? (p. 217)

7. When a door panel is to be replaced, is it practical to leave the door on the car? (p. 217)

8. What are the governing factors in establishing the type of joint to be used when a door panel is replaced? (p. 217)

9. What kind of joint is generally used when it falls under a molding or is otherwise concealed under a decorative strip? (p. 218)

10. When an entire panel is to be replaced, where is the old panel generally cut off? (p. 218)

11. Why are power saws or special cutters preferable to torch cutting when removing door panels? (p. 219)

12. How are the corners of a replacement panel prepared for flanging around the inner panel? (p. 229)

13. When scrub marks are found on a door sill or scuff plate, what kind of door misalignment is indicated? (p. 237)

14. What is the function of a door striker plate? A door dovetail? (p. 240)

15. What can be accomplished by a door dovetail adjustment? (p. 241)

16. What device is used with hinges to prevent the door from opening beyond the limit of the hinge travel? (p. 242)

17. In what ways can hinges generally be adjusted? (pp. 242, 243)

18. In either of what two ways are all contour alignment problems corrected? (pp. 245, 247)

19. What is the name of the equipment most commonly used for correcting door contour? (p. 245)

20. Why is it generally necessary to remove and hold a hood rigidly during a straightening process? (p. 253)

21. What adjustments are usually provided at the hinges of hoods? (p. 263)

22. When aligning a deck lid, is it possible to do any aligning operations with other than a door-bar unit? (p. 270)

23. Where is chalk applied in connection with checking decklid alignment? (p. 269)

24. What conditions may exist when the deck lid does not fit the contour of the body? (p. 271)

25. How is paper used to check the seal between the deck lid and the lower back panel? (p. 272)

26. Name three instances where a rubber mallet can be used to align the deck lid with body panel contours. (p. 272)

27. When is proper deck lid alignment said to exist? (p. 269)

FRAME STRAIGHTENING

As pointed out in Chapter 1 of this volume, the frame is the foundation of the automobile. The same holds true in unitized construction where the underbody takes the place of the frame. It is of the utmost importance, therefore, to first determine the extent of collision damage to the frame and then correct it. This chapter explains and illustrates how to determine and correct frame damage. We shall also see what the resulting damage to other units of the automobile can be when the frame is damaged.

Not only must the collision repairman be able to check a frame or underbody to determine what, if any, damage to it exists before attempting to repair it, but it is necessary also to determine if frame or underbody misalignment exists before you attempt to correct body alignment. The principles and the actual practice used in checking frame alignment are presented here in Section I.

The separate parts of an automobile or truck frame are usually riveted together. Unitized underbodies are almost exclusively welded. Rivets are used because of their great structural strength and their resistance to shearing. These properties exist only if the rivets are properly installed. Section II of this chapter explains rivets and their correct installation.

Some shops specialize in frame straightening only, and many small collision shops "farm out" their frame straightening jobs. These smaller shops, however, must be able to determine whether or not a frame is misaligned in order to know whether or not it must be sent to the frame shop.

Whether you will be working in a shop specializing in frame straightening and possessing large, expensive equipment or in a small shop with but little equipment, the principles involved in checking a damaged frame or an underbody are the same. These principles are discussed in sections III and IV.

Regardless of the equipment used, a bent frame member must be held at one or two points and the corrective force or pressure must be applied at another point. How this is done, along with illustrations showing typical setups, is described in Section V.

During the straightening processes, as a result of necessary heating or excessive "working," frame members often lose part of their original strength. It is entirely possible, too, that at some time you will encounter frames having inherent weaknesses. Some types of truck operation, moreover, result in unanticipated "shock" loads for which the manufacturer has not provided. In all of these cases, you will have to reinforce the frame. Section VI discusses the entire subject of frame reinforcements and shows you just how reinforcements are accomplished.

A misaligned or weakened frame may cause a number of other misalignments in a vehicle. For this reason, it is important that a frame be repaired immediately if it has been damaged or misaligned.

I. FRAME AND UNITIZED UNDERBODY MISALIGNMENT

(a) **Misalignment and Vehicle Control.** In addition to the structural significance of a weakened frame or underbody, the control of the vehicle can be affected. A car or truck with a damaged or weakened frame or underbody can be a menace on the highway, not only to the people who are riding in the vehicle, but also to people and property along the right of way. Frame or underbody misalignment or damage usually has an effect on the steering control. The steering mechanism is dependent on the frame for support. The suspension parts for both front and rear wheels are also attached directly to the frame. The proper control of the car depends on these units being correctly adjusted and in correct relationship, not only to each other, but to the center line of the vehicle as well. The adjustments in some cases are fine measurements which are immediately affected by any change in the shape or natural position of the frame or underbody.

You have undoubtedly seen examples of one type of misalignment in which a car seems to travel in a partially sidewise manner, commonly called "dog tracking." It is often necessary for the driver of such a vehicle to struggle constantly to maintain a straight course. The effort required to maintain a straight course with such a vehicle becomes greater as the speed of the vehicle is increased. Misalignment of frame or underbody also can cause tire wear, may affect the brakes, and, of course, is a factor in body alignment and can often account for binding of the controls.

(b) Misalignment and Vehicle Performance. Aside from the effect a damaged frame or underbody has on steering control and tire wear, it can also place undue stress on other mechanical parts of the vehicle. The alignment of the engine with the clutch and transmission may be affected. This could cause a manual transmission to jump out of gear, and might result in premature clutch failure. Any radical change in the angle of the transmission to the rear axle may cause excessive wear in the universal joints, noise in the rear axle, or axle failure. Moreover, whenever the frame or underbody has been damaged by a collision, there is a possibility of a partially ruptured hydraulic brake line which could ultimately lead to a complete brake failure. Electrical connections also may be broken or strained.

(c) Importance of Alignment. It is impossible to properly align any part of the body when the frame or underbody is out of alignment. If you attempt to align a door, deck lid, or hood before you correct the damage which has occurred, you will be unable to do a satisfactory job.

II. RIVETS AND RIVETING (RIGID FRAMES ONLY)

The various members of most automobile frames are riveted together. Since it is often necessary to remove a cross member to get at the transmission or clutch assembly for repairs, some center cross members may be fastened in place with bolts.

Always fasten a new frame member in place in the same way the original member was installed. If rivets were used, use rivets. If bolts were used, use bolts. However, if bolts were used and if the bolt holes have become enlarged from wear, redrill the holes so they are round, and install the next size larger bolt. This is generally necessary to prevent unwanted movement between the two members.

a. Equipment. Frame rivets can be satisfactorily installed with a ball-peen hammer and a backing-up tool. The surface of the backing-up tool that contacts the rivet can be flat. A better job, however, will result if the backing-up tool is provided with a depression which fits the rivet head.

The hammer should weigh at least 2 pounds and the backing-up tool at least 10 pounds. A 1½ to 2 in. diameter steel bar 20 in. long, with a rivet set in the end, will provide good backing for the operation.

Various air and electrically operated rivet guns are available. These, of course, require very little instruction since their use is obvious. There is danger in the use of these tools, however, that the head may be properly formed on each end without the hole being properly filled. When using these tools, make sure first of all that they have enough power to handle the rivet size being used. You should check, too, so as to determine if the rivets are hot enough so they can be expanded in the hole.

b. Riveting. In general, frame riveting is done with hot rivets only. Hot rivets are easier to form than cold rivets, and a much neater job can be done on forming the upset rivet head. The main reason for using hot rivets, however, is that when a rivet is installed in a hole that is not in complete alignment with the mating part, it may not fit the hole. A hot rivet will squash out and fill the entire hole so that a shearing action between the two parts is prevented.

If a rivet is installed so that looseness exists between the parts being riveted together, wear will develop. The slightest movement between the mated parts will set up a shearing action and the rivet will eventually be cut off or will break. Proper riveting, therefore, is most important.

(1) *PROCEDURE.* In all instances, the two frame members that are to be riveted together will have enough rivet holes so that two of them can be used to firmly bolt the two parts together. Use a long, tapered punch to pry the holes into alignment. Install the two bolts and tighten them securely.

Successful riveting requires fast work. Have everything you need right where you can put your hands on it. This will include the hammer, backing tool, tongs, and a punch.

The rivet must be white hot. Working fast:

(1) Grasp the rivet with the tongs right next to the rivet head and enter the rivet in the hole.

(2) Immediately hit the rivet head hard with the backing tool. This blow must be hard enough to assure that the flange of the rivet head will be tight against the frame member.

(3) With the backing tool held firmly against the rivet head, hit a

hard flat blow on the other end of the rivet. This is the blow which expands the rivet in the hole. Without this step well performed, any subsequent steps will fail to fill the hole. If you are too slow, the rivet will lose its heat and its ability to fill the hole. If the backing tool is not held firmly against the rivet head, the head will move away from the frame member, and it will be difficult to tighten the rivet. Work fast—hold the backing tool firmly against the head, and hit a hard flat blow with the hammer. The steps to this point are shown in Fig. 1.

(4) If a rivet head has not started to form as shown in the center illustration (Fig. 1), hit a second, harder blow.

(5) Use the ball end of the hammer and form a head on the rivet. The backing tool must be held firmly against the rivet throughout the entire operation.

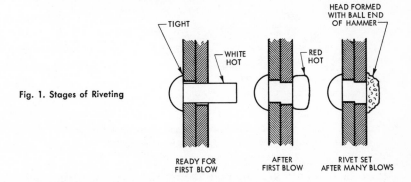

Fig. 1. Stages of Riveting

III. CHECKING FRAME ALIGNMENT

The principles of measurement presented in Chapter 1 of this volume apply to frames as well as to bodies. These principles remain the same regardless of the kind of equipment used. Less detailed instructions on how to put these principles to use are required, of course, if a complete frame checking and correcting machine, such as shown in Fig. 2, is used. If you understand the principles of frame alignment checking with an improvised setup, you will have no difficulty in applying what you have learned to one of these machines. Moreover, learning how to check frame alignment with a few basic tools which are generally available will give you a better appreciation of these machines, and will make you more self-reliant and better able to make quick preliminary checks of frames away from the shop, as may some-

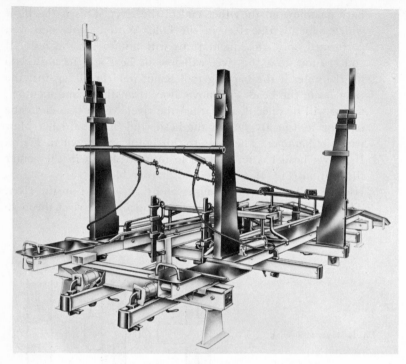

Fig. 2. Combination Body-Frame Correction Service
(*Courtesy Bear Manufacturing Company*)

times be necessary in estimating the repair costs. All frame checks not made on frame straightening machines should be made from a floor as level as possible.

The importance of frame alignment has been emphasized elsewhere throughout this entire volume. Assuming you have an appreciation of this importance, this section merely tells you how to check for misalignment. A frame may look like it is in alignment, but it may not be.

a. **Equipment.** Frame alignment can be checked with a steel tape, and a tram gauge which are generally available in even the smallest shops. The tram gauge used in body work (Fig. 3) is satisfactory. However, a larger gauge with a hinge in the center will be more versatile for frame work. The hinge in the center permits the tram gauge to be used like a pair of dividers. This permits you to check frame dimensions even though some intervening part makes it impossible to make

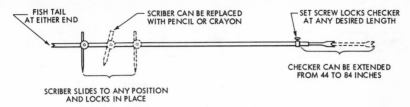

FISH TAIL
AT EITHER END

SCRIBER CAN BE REPLACED
WITH PENCIL OR CRAYON

SET SCREW LOCKS CHECKER
AT ANY DESIRED LENGTH

CHECKER CAN BE EXTENDED
FROM 44 TO 84 INCHES

SCRIBER SLIDES TO ANY POSITION
AND LOCKS IN PLACE

Fig. 3. Telescoping Tram Gauge
(*Courtesy H. K. Porter*)

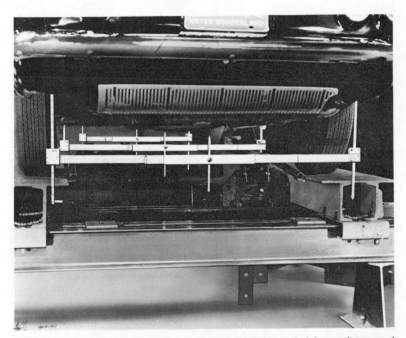

Fig. 4. When three self-centering gauges are used to check for vertical frame alignment, the frame is free from vertical misalignment only if all three gauges are in horizontal alignment.
(*Courtesy John Bean Corporation*)

a direct, point-to-point measurement with a tram gauge or a steel tape.

"Self-centering" gauges are also used to check frame alignment. The gauges are called "self-centering" because the pins in the center of the gauges always remain at the center of the gauges no matter how far the gauge is extended. Self-centering gauges are held in place by small pins which fit into the jig holes in the frame side rails (Fig. 4).

b. Center Section Alignment. In most cars, the center section of the frame is designed so that it will be level when the car is under the an-

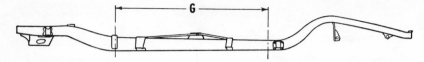

Fig. 5. "G" is the center section of the frame.

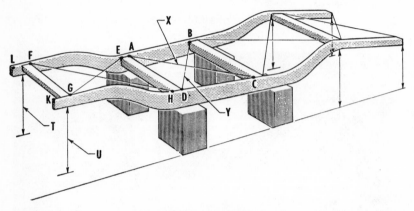

Fig. 6. Checking Frame Alignment

ticipated normal load. What is meant by frame center section is shown in Fig. 5. Area "G" is the center section.

(1) *LEVELING*. Place the four corners of the center section on horses of equal height so that they are the same distance from the floor. The frame must rest firmly on these horses. This will mean that instead of supporting the frame, the axles will be hanging from the frame. The springs should not be supporting any of the load. All these frame aligning operations should be done on a smooth, level floor. The floor is used as a reference point and is known as the "datum line" when measurements are taken. A frame setup on horses or blocks for an alignment check is shown in Fig. 6. It must be borne in mind, however, that most frame alignment checks are made with the frame in the vehicle.

(2) *MEASURING HEIGHT*. Make a visual check to see whether or not any of the corners do not touch the horses. If one corner doesn't touch the horse, either this corner is bent up or one of the other corners is bent down. Before any further checking is done, loosen all of the frame-to-body bolts. It is possible that some condition of misalignment in the body is holding the frame out of alignment.

If the corner is still up after the body bolts are loosened, continue with further checks of the center section, but keep this particular point of misalignment in mind.

(3) **X** *CHECKING.* When the four corners of the center section are established at the same height from the floor, all that remains is to **X** check the center section from one corner to the other, comparing the diagonals. These measurements are designated as *X* and *Y* in Fig. 5. If the diagonals are not the same, the frame is probably swayed at the center section or it has become diamond-shaped from a corner collision. Exaggerated forms of frame sway are shown in Figs. 14 and 16. An exaggerated diamond-shaped frame is shown in Fig. 23.

c. Front Section Alignment. After the alignment of the center section has been checked, the alignment of the front section can be checked. The front section of the frame is considered as all of the frame forward of the center section.

With the frame resting on the horses under the center section, make measurements *T* and *U* (Fig. 6). This will quickly establish whether any twist exists which has raised or lowered one corner. The front section is then **X** checked from *E* to *G* and *F* to *H* (Fig. 6). If these two measurements are not the same, the frame is either swayed, diamond-shaped, or buckled up or down. For example, if *EG* is longer than *FH*, the frame is swayed to the left. If *FH* is longer than *EG*, the frame is swayed to the right.

Further **X** measurements can be made out to the extreme ends of the frame *K* and *L* (Fig. 6). These measurements will establish whether or not the frame ends (or *horns,* as they are sometimes called) are out of alignment. The horns can be bent in or out or up or down. Height measurements from the tips of the horns to the floor will show which one is bent either up or down.

To isolate the exact point or area of misalignment, smaller areas of the front section can be **X** checked. Measurements also can be made at any point along the side of the frame to the floor. Always be sure to measure from like points at both sides of the frame. These measurements will be the same at each side of the frame except where the misalignment exists. If one side is higher from the floor than the other, the frame is either twisted or buckled upward at that point. If one side is lower than the other side, the frame is buckled downward at that point.

d. Rear Section Alignment. The rear section of the frame is considered as that portion of the frame from the center section to the rear.

The first measurements are height measurements from the two extreme rear corners to the floor. If one of these dimensions is more than

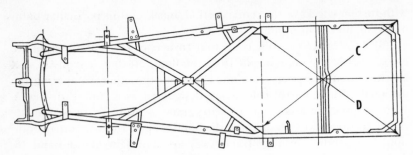

Fig. 7. Checking Frame Rear Section

the other, either one corner is up or the other is down or the frame rear section is twisted. Next, **X** check the rear section at C and D, Fig. 7. If C is more than D, the frame is swayed to the left. If D is more than C, the frame is swayed to the right. A diamond-shaped frame can also cause either of these measurements to be more than the other.

To locate the exact point or area where the misalignment exists, smaller areas of the rear section can be **X** checked. Always measure from like points at both sides of the frame. Measurements also can be made from any point along the frame to the floor. Measurements, when compared, should be the same. Any difference will indicate that the frame is either buckled or twisted in that area. How to correct both of these conditions is described in the following sections.

IV. CHECKING UNITIZED UNDERBODY ALIGNMENT

The same principles hold true for underbody misalignment and frame misalignment in a car that has regular rigid frame construction.

A regular frame machine with frame centering and leveling gauges is also equipped for handling unitized underbodies. A typical unitized underbody, with lineal dimensions and the master locating hole for checking alignment with a regular frame machine, is shown in Fig. 8. All frame dimensions are checked with reference to the master locating hole which is attached to a frame machine.

The body tram gauge (Fig. 9) is an accurate method of determining underbody alignment, but self-centering gauges are also widely used. On unitized bodies, self-centering gauges are mounted by means of **C** clamps, magnetic adapters, or special studs screwed into the bottom of the body.

Some typical alignment check and reference points are shown in

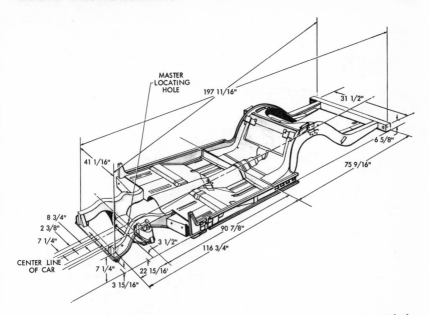

Fig. 8. A Typical Unitized Underbody With Lineal Dimensions and the Master Locating Hole for Checking Alignment With a Frame Machine.
(*Courtesy Lincoln-Mercury Division, Ford Motor Company*)

Fig. 9. X Checking a Vehicle and Frame with a Two-Point Tram Gauge
(*Courtesy John Bean Corporation*)

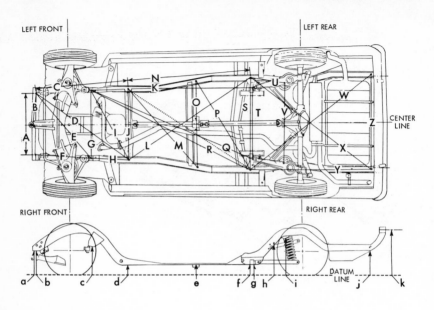

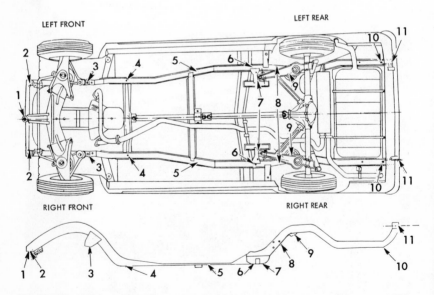

Fig. 10. This typical car frame shows vertical and horizontal dimensions and tram gauge reference points. The actual dimensions in inches can be found in Table I.

(Courtesy Buick Div.—General Motors Corporation)

TABLE I. DIMENSIONS AND
REFERENCE POINTS SHOWN IN FIGURE 10

HORIZONTAL:

Fig. Ref.	Dimension (Inches)	Ref. Point	Ref. to Point	
A	28–29/32	2	2	
B	14–15/32	1	2	(either side)
C	48	2	4	(same side)
D	56–5/8	2	4	(opp. side)
E	40–29/32	2	3	(opp. side)
F	27–23/32	2	3	(same side)
G	31–5/32	3	3	
H	20–9/32	3	4	(same side)
I	37–3/16	3	4	(opp. side)
J	31–5/32	4	4	
K	81–29/32	3	7	(same side)
L	69–1/2	4	6	(opp. side)
M	48–25/32	4	5	(opp. side)
N	59–7/8	4	6	(same side)
O	38–3/16	5	5	
P	46–11/16	5	6	(opp. side)
Q	87–23/32	3	7	(opp. side)
R	87–19/32	3	6	(opp. side)
S	40–1/8	6	6	
T	31–21/32	7	7	
U	17–23/32	6	9	(same side)
V	37–23/32	9	9	
W	69–23/32	6	10	(left side)
X	68–15/16	6	10	(right side)
Y	55–7/8	6	10	(same side)
Z	42	10	10	(same side)

VERTICAL

Fig. Ref.	Dimension (Inches)	Datum Line to Ref. Point
a	12–1/2	1
b	12–7/16	2
c	14–3/8	3
d	6–1/16	4
e	6–1/16	5
f	6	6
g	6–1/32	7
h	14–11/16	8
i	16–13/32	9
j	10	10
k	18–21/32	11

Fig. 10. All of the checks can be made with a tram gauge. Fig. 10 (top) shows letters which represent frame dimensions. Table I lists the same letters with the corresponding dimensions in inches. Fig. 10 (bottom) shows numbered tram gauge reference points. Table I lists the reference points and the distances between them.

V. STRAIGHTENING TYPICAL FRAME DAMAGE

Once you know where to hold and where to apply pressure, straightening of a frame is best accomplished on a frame straightener. Modern frame straighteners permit several setups to be made at one time. If you

Fig. 11. Wheel balancing as well as body and frame straightening may be done on this frame and body press

(Courtesy John Bean Corporation)

do not have access to a straightener, you can correct almost any damage by improvising setups.

Illustrations of typical damaged frames are shown in this section. Heavy black arrows show where corrective force is applied and heavy black blocks show where the frame is to be held. Light arrows indicate

Fig. 12. The hydraulic ram is one method of applying the push necessary to correct bodies and frames damaged by collision.

(Courtesy Ford Motor Company)

that the member should be pulled to simplify the correction. These illustrations also show where heat is to be applied.

A rack type frame and body press, which can be used for both frame straightening and underbody damage correction, is shown in Fig. 11. If a frame and body press is not available, portable hydraulic equipment as described in Chapter V may be used.

A "hydraulic ram" (Fig. 12) is a simple portable tool available for frame and underbody straightening. A hydraulic ram can often be applied directly against the damaged frame or underbody, thereby eliminating valuable time needed to set up more elaborate equipment. However, other equipment must be used if the hydraulic ram cannot be applied directly and at the correct angle to the damage.

The portable body and frame aligner shown in Fig. 13, uses the type of hydraulic ram shown in Fig. 12. With the hydraulic ram supplying mechanical power, the aligner is able to apply corrective force at any angle on all sections of the body or frame. However, the frame straightener and body press (Fig. 11) is a more complete tool than the portable body and frame aligner. Consequently, it often provides a faster repair because more than one hookup or correction can be made at the same time.

a. Use of Heat in Straightening. Frame side rails and cross members are usually formed from low-carbon steel. Strength is imparted to the frame members during the rolling and forming processes, but this surface hardness is, in a measure, sacrificed if heat is used during the frame straightening process. This loss of surface hardness, however, is the lesser of two evils. Any attempt to straighten a severely crimped or buckled frame cold may cause cracks in the bent part or ruptures in welds. Heat is also used in straightening underbody damage.

Because a frame is constructed from comparatively thick material, bending or otherwise distorting it work-hardens it in the area of the bend. Any further attempt to force it to another position may cause it to crack or break. For this reason, it is advisable to apply heat to the damaged portion of the frame, then to perform the straightening operations necessary while the frame is still red hot. Heat is applied with an oxyacetylene gas torch. If a sharp bend exists, heat should be used whether the frame is in the car or not. If the damage is such that the use of heat is called for at some point where it might damage the body, raise the body away from the work.

The heat should be applied directly on the damaged portion which you want to bend or reshape. The frame will bend in the heated area

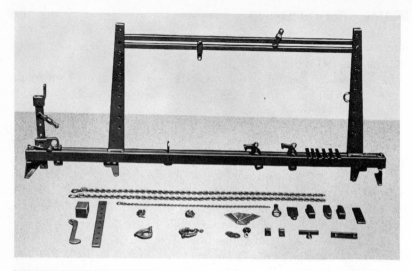

Fig. 13. TOP: A portable frame and body aligner is shown with its various clamps, chains, and pull plates in the foreground. When in use, a hydraulic ram is installed to apply force. BOTTOM: The portable aligner is straightening a unitized underbody. The underbody has no center cross member to exert force against. Therefore, clamps are installed on the "pinch" welds below the rocker panels. A length of tubing, along with the clamps and chains, serves as a temporary cross member against which corrective force is exerted.

(*Courtesy John Bean Corporation*)

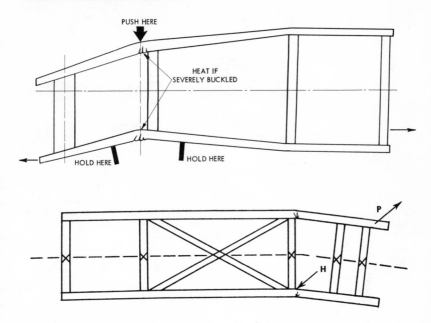

Fig. 14. Two Methods of Correcting Side Sway Damage From a Front End Collision
(*TOP: Courtesy Bear Manufacturing Company; BOTTOM: Courtesy John Bean Corporation*)

first. Unless the heat is applied properly, the corrective bend will not be made in the right place, and instead of having one bend to correct, you will have two.

If the frame is not deemed strong enough after the straightening is completed, it should be reinforced. (Frame reinforcing is discussed in Section VI of this chapter.)

(1) *APPLICATION OF HEAT*. Actually, only a very little heat is required to bring the color of the heated member to a dull red, at which time it is at the proper temperature to be worked.

Start to heat the buckled portion or damaged area well out near the edge. Fan the flame over the entire buckled area so that it is heated uniformly. Best results can be obtained by moving the flame in an ever decreasing circle until the area is entirely heated. Do not spot-heat any portion of the area. Spot-heating will be likely to damage the metal itself, and will undoubtedly make correction of the original damage more difficult. Heating well out toward the edge of a crimped or buckled area first, will remove the chill from the surrounding area. This prevents

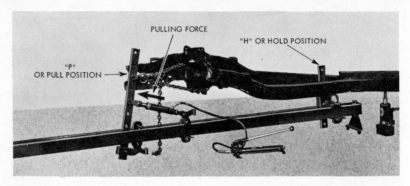

Fig. 15. The portable body and frame aligner is correcting an hour-glass type frame side rail for sway caused by a front end collision. A chain is wrapped around the rail at point "P" and a tool bar is placed against the tube at "H" position to provide a diagonal corrective force.
(*Courtesy John Bean Corporation*)

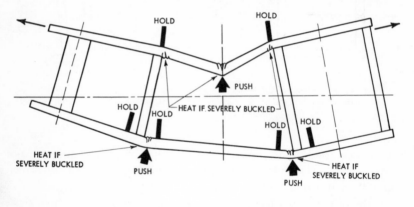

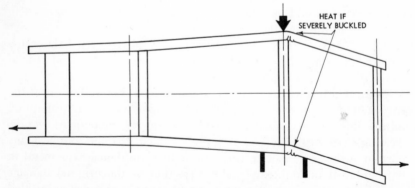

Fig. 16. TOP: Sway From Collision in Center; BOTTOM: Sway From Rear End Collision.
(*Courtesy John Bean Corporation*)

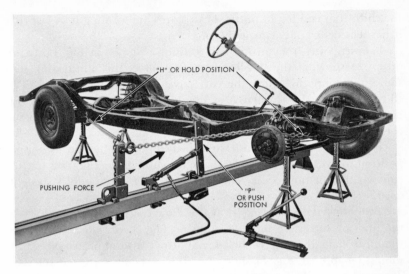

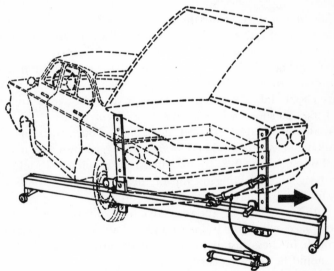

Fig. 17. TOP: The body and frame aligner in the process of correcting vehicle side sway. This method of alignment is often referred to as the "bow string" method. Push is applied against only one frame side rail and the vehicle body transmits the force of this push to the other rail. Therefore, the correcting force is applied to both rails through only one hookup. BOTTOM: The body and frame aligner correcting a unitized body for sway caused by a rear end collision. Notice that the diagonal push is exerted from inside the car, eliminating the need for outer sheet metal removal which would be necessary if the force were exerted from outside of the car.

(Courtesy John Bean Corporation)

the chill from rushing in on the heated area and cooling it so fast that it hardens before the damage is corrected.

b. Sway. Sway from a front end collision is shown in Fig. 14. In addition to showing the line of damaging force, this illustration also shows directions in which the corrective force can be applied. The illustration also shows where heat should be applied and two methods of correcting the frame. Fig. 15 shows a frame in the process of being corrected for front end sway.

It will be necessary to push the damaged portion beyond its normal position to overcome any spring back which might occur. You can decide whether or not to use reinforcements after the frame is straightened.

Two other types of frame sway are shown in Fig. 16. In both cases, the lines of corrective force are shown. The places where the frame should be held are clearly labeled, and arrows also indicate where heat should be applied. Fig. 17 shows two frames being corrected for sway damage.

c. Sag. Side rail sag is misalignment of the frame due to the bending downward of either or both side rails. Two different types of sag are shown in Figs. 18 and 19. In Fig. 18, the sag is caused by a front end collision. In Fig. 19, the sag is caused by a rear end collision. In both cases, the lines of corrective force and places where the frame should be held are clearly labeled. Places where heat should be used are also indicated. Fig. 20 shows a sagged frame being corrected.

d. Frame Mashed or Buckled. A mashed or buckled frame is more seriously damaged than either a swayed or sagged frame. A mashed or buckled frame results from an extremely severe impact. In addition to side rail sag and buckling on top of the side rail, the frame is bent down and buckled underneath the side rail.

In both Fig. 21 and 22, the corrective lines of force are shown along with the places where the frame should be held and where heat should be applied. In these instances, the damage nearest the middle of the frame should be corrected first.

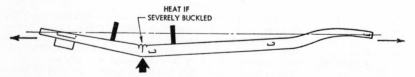

HEAT IF
SEVERELY BUCKLED

Fig. 18. Side Rail Sag from Front End Collision
(*Courtesy Bear Manufacturing Company*)

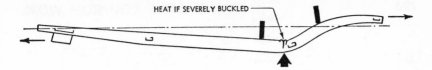

Fig. 19. Side Rail Sag from Rear End Collision
(*Courtesy Bear Manufacturing Company*)

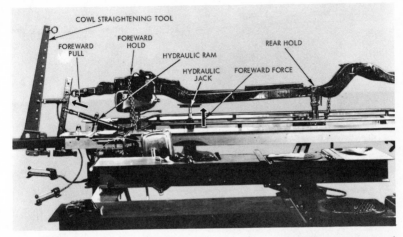

Fig. 20. The frame straightener and body press is correcting a sagged frame side rail. Note the various hookups for applying the correcting force plus the body upright tool for correcting damage in the cowl area of the body. Also note the position of the forward and rear holds.
(*Courtesy John Bean Corporation*)

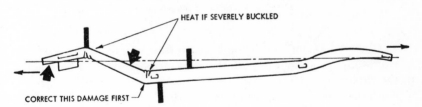

Fig. 21. Frame Mashed and Buckled from Front End Collision
(*Courtesy Bear Manufacturing Company*)

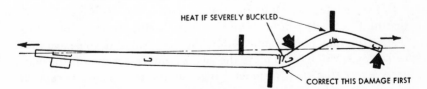

Fig. 22. Frame Mashed and Buckled from Rear End Collision
(*Courtesy Bear Manufacturing Company*)

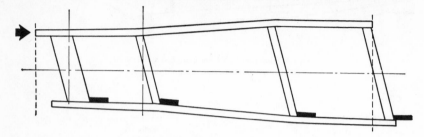

Fig. 23. Diamond Frame
(*Courtesy Bear Manufacturing Company*)

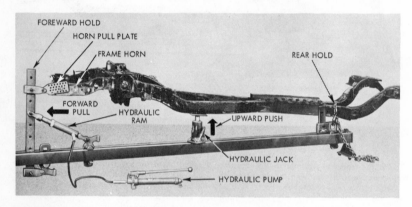

Fig. 24. The pull plate is bolted to the frame horn to help correct this hour-glass frame which has both sag and diamond damage
(*Courtesy John Bean Corporation*)

e. Diamond Frame. A diamond-shaped frame comes as the result of a lower impact, sufficient to push the cross members out of right angles to the side rails.

Such damage is shown in Fig. 23, and the way in which the damage should be corrected is indicated by arrows showing where corrective force should be applied and where the frame should be held. Fig. 24 shows a frame being corrected by a frame and body aligner.

f. Twisted Frame. Hold the frame down at the two points indicated in Fig. 25. If you have four separate jacks, pressure can be applied at the four points indicated at the same time. If you have only one jack, you will have to move the jack a number of times. If the damage is severe, the cross member flanges at the side members may be twisted. Apply heat at these points as the pressure is applied. Fig. 26 shows a twisted frame being corrected.

HIGH CORNER HIGH CORNER

LOW CORNER LOW CORNER

CORRECT ALL DAMAGE AT SAME TIME

Fig. 25. Twisted Frame
(Courtesy Bear Manufacturing Company)

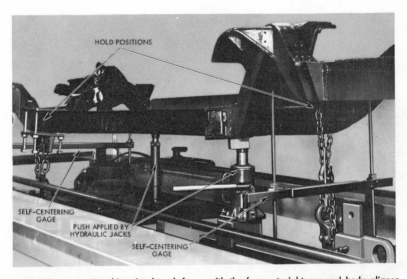

HOLD POSITIONS

SELF-CENTERING GAGE

PUSH APPLIED BY HYDRAULIC JACKS

SELF-CENTERING GAGE

Fig. 26. When correcting this twisted truck frame with the frame straightener and body aligner, chains are used to hold the carriage beams at the hold position while the hydraulic jacks apply a pushing force. The hydraulic jacks are used to lift the frame until all the self-centering gauges are in parallel alignment. Usually, the frame must be corrected past the misalignment, and in the opposite direction of the damage, in order to bring the frame to the correct position.
(Courtesy John Bean Corporation)

g. How to Hold. If you are working with a frame straightening machine such as shown in Fig. 26, the method of holding is obvious, since almost every possible requirement has been anticipated in the design. If you must improvise your setups, several things are possible.

(1) *EYEBOLTS IN THE FLOOR.* Some shops have been very successful in holding frames down by running a chain through the eye of an eyebolt and over the frame (Fig. 27). The eyebolt must be firmly anchored into the floor. Any number of eyebolts can be used.

An **I** beam, chains, and blocks can be used not only to hold the frame down, but can be used to hold the frame when straightening it

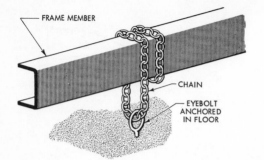

Fig. 27. Eyebolt and Chain Used
to Hold Down Frame

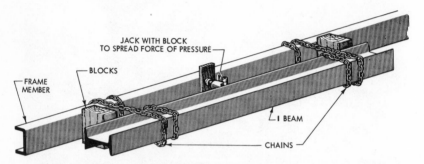

Fig. 28. Use of **I** Beam To Hold and To Provide a Base from which Pressure Is Applied
(Courtesy Bear Manufacturing Company)

in a horizontal plane as well. The **I** beam also provides a base for the jack or jacks with which the corrective force is applied. How this is accomplished is shown in Fig. 28.

h. How To Apply Pressure. The pressure required for straightening frames can be applied with the same hydraulic jacks used for correcting body damage. However, as a rule, larger heavier-duty jacks are used for straightening truck frames. Assistance to the jacks, of course, is afforded by the use of the heating torch.

Remember that all of these jacks are very powerful. Spread the force exerted by the jack by means of a suitable head on the jack or by means of a block (Fig. 28). This is particularly important when you are working on the comparatively light passenger car frames.

Some types of frame damage might permit pushing from one portion of the frame to another. In these cases, don't lose sight of the fact that the pressure is being delivered to both ends of the jack.

VI. REINFORCEMENT

Reinforcements are added to frames when there is doubt that the

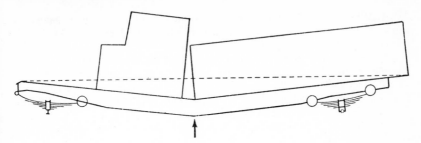

Fig. 29. Sagged Dump Truck Frame

frame will withstand the strains to which it will be subjected. A typical example of when a frame reinforcement is needed is when a dump truck frame has sagged and then been straightened. A sagged dump truck frame is illustrated in Fig. 29. Sometimes new trucks have their side members reinforced so that sag will not occur.

Most of the strain on a frame is vertical. For this reason, the reinforcement added would be positioned so that it will resist vertical stress. Reinforcements can be made from angle iron, flat plates, channels, or any type of section which will fit the contour of the frame in the area needing reinforcement. Reinforcements can be either welded or riveted into place, or they can be fastened by both welds and rivets.

In the example shown in Fig. 29, either a flat plate can be welded and riveted to each side member across the area needing reinforcement, or else a channel section which will fit inside the frame can be used. The type of reinforcement used depends on whether or not it can be installed without interfering with other members of the frame or working parts of the chassis.

Reinforcements can be made from any stock thickness which may seem desirable, depending on the use for which the vehicle is intended. The reinforcement should extend a considerable distance along the frame beyond the area being reinforced.

TRADE COMPETENCY TESTS

The following questions, while they represent only a small portion of the material in this chapter, may be used to determine the percentage of the information retained.

1. What is the most common method for fastening frame members together? (p. 277)

2. Can frame misalignment have a bearing on anything other than body alignment? (p. 276, 277)

3. What is meant by the term "dog tracking"? (p. 277)

4. When a new frame member is installed in place of a member which was bolted in place, how should the new member be fastened? (p. 277)

5. Why are hot rivets generally used for frame riveting? (p. 278)

6. What is the minimum equipment with which you can check frame alignment? (p. 280)

7. When checking the alignment of the center section of a frame, why is it a good idea to loosen the frame-to-body bolts if the frame does not rest squarely on the horses? (p. 282)

8. What do most passenger automobile frames have in common at the center section? (p. 281, 282)

9. What damage might occur if an attempt is made to straighten a severely bumped frame without the use of heat? (p. 289)

10. What color should a folded frame member be when it is at the proper temperature to be straightened? (p. 289)

11. In general, can the same hydraulic tools be used to apply pressure for frame straightening and for body straightening? (p. 298)

12. Reinforcements are usually positioned to resist stress in what direction? (p. 299)

13. How are frame reinforcements usually fastened in place? (p. 299)

14. Are frames sometimes reinforced before any actual damage has occurred? (p. 299)

CHAPTER 8

TYPICAL COLLISION JOBS

In the preceding chapters of this volume, most of the things involved in collision work have been presented. It is impossible, of course, to conceive, much less discuss, all of the possible kinds of damage that will be encountered. Nevertheless, every job you tackle will, in some respects, be like some other job, and some of the principles and techniques that have been presented will be used on every job. In a few cases in the preceding chapters, a typical damage and its correction were presented. In general, however, the purpose was to acquaint you with the separate techniques rather than to show you how to correct a particular damage.

This chapter, in a very real sense, can be called a summation of everything you have learned about collision work thus far. The explanations given will enable you to correctly apply the technical skills previously described to actual jobs. However, there is much more to collision work than the mere mastery of these skills. You must be able to apply these skills and the knowledge you have acquired both profitably and economically. The reasons why you should study any damage which you intend to correct before you start any of the corrective operations, and the kind of things you should look for and note, are re-emphasized in Section I. While a number of separate discussions of measuring have appeared in the preceding chapters, Section II gives you additional detailed information on how to make body measurements. Several sequences of damage correction are presented in Sections III through VI, so you can see the value of applying corrective measures in their proper sequence. Section VII explains how to evaluate the separate considerations involved in deciding whether a panel or part should be repaired or replaced. Section VIII gives the same type of treatment to the question of filling panels with solder or straightening them. The final section of this chapter brings together all of the technical information and its application you have learned from this volume and shows you how to apply it in estimating the cost for a repair.

All of the topics covered in this chapter have a definite bearing on reducing the cost of collision work while improving job quality.

I. STUDY THE DAMAGE

The ultimate success of any collision repair job depends on the accuracy of the analysis of what is damaged, and how the damage occurred. This principle is true whether you are working on a conventional body and frame or on a car of unit construction.

There is a definite five-step procedure to follow in correcting collision damage. This procedure is as follows:

1. Determine the exact extent of the damage.
2. Familiarize yourself with the construction of the vehicle on which you are working.
3. Decide upon a definite plan for correction, after careful study of the damage.
4. Perform the actual collision repair in progressive steps.
5. Check the work frequently until damage is corrected.

You cannot fix anything unless you know first, just what is wrong. Collision work must be approached on this same basis, but it goes a step further. Not only must you first determine what is wrong, but you must establish how it got that way. That is, you must learn what damage has occurred and the order in which it happened.

In collision work, the corrective forces must be applied in a manner directly opposite to and in the reverse order of the forces which caused the damage. When a damaged car or truck is brought to you for repair, determine all you can about the way in which the damage occurred. In addition to providing the order of procedure for correcting body and frame damage, your inquiries may reveal a number of things which will have a bearing on where you should look for hidden damage. The front and rear suspensions, the entire power train (transmission, drive shaft, rear axle, etc.), brakes, steering mechanism, the power plant (engine and related parts), and the electrical system all are subject to damage in a collision. By finding out wherever possible just how the damage occurred, you will know precisely where to look or check for parts needing repair or replacement. Always include a check of wheel alignment on every collision job of any consequence. Look for damage to the radiator, cracked cylinder block or transmission case, bent axle housings, broken engine supports, etc.

While the straightening of body panels and fenders represents the field in which the greatest volume of collision work is done, collision damage occurs on mechanical parts of the vehicle as well. The repair of mechanical parts is an important part of the repair of collision damage. When you are finished repairing a vehicle damaged in a collision or one that has turned over, it must run well, it must steer well, and the brakes and all of the electrical units must be in operating condition. Although the correction of mechanical difficulties caused by the collision involves other skills and techniques than are practiced by the collision expert, he cannot ignore them and must provide for their correction.

Make free use of your measuring facilities when you are studying the damage to a car. Sometimes a panel can be knocked out of line without actually distorting any visible part of it. When this occurs and you fail to make the necessary measurements, it is easy to miss the fact that it is not in its proper location. This will not be brought to light until you attempt to align it with the surrounding panels after they have been straightened. It is better to make too many measurements and find that most everything you have checked is in alignment than to make too few and find that nothing fits after you have straightened all of the bent parts or panels.

Where you cannot find out just what happened by asking someone, you will find, with a little practice and close attention to what you can see, that you can usually reconstruct the sequence in which the series of events occurred.

Consider a car which has rolled over. As the car moves along the highway, something occurs causing it to swerve into a deep ditch and turn over. First of all, the forward motion of the car would cause backward strain of the roof panel when it hit the ground. With the car turning over as well as traveling forward, hitting the ground will cause sideward strain as well. As the car rolls over onto its top, the impact causes downward strain of the whole top. When the car is righted, the top appears to be pushed back, to one side, and down.

Each of these damages occurred in the order just given. It is necessary to correct them in the reverse order of the way in which they occurred. Studying the damage permits you to reconstruct the sequence of events which caused the damage, thereby providing the proper order in which the damage should be corrected. Always correct first, the damage which occurred last.

II. MEASUREMENTS

The basic principles of measurements as used in collision work were presented in Chapter 1 of this volume. Further examples of measuring have been presented in most of the other chapters as well. The purpose of this section is not to repeat what has been covered before, but to emphasize some of the things already said and to provide some additional or more detailed instructions. The measurement of frames and unit construction underbodies was completely covered in Chapter 7. For this reason, this discussion will deal primarily with body measurements.

Body measurements are made in the same way in both unit construction cars and vehicles that have a conventional frame. Checking body measurements, of course, is done mostly by a system of diagonal comparisons commonly called **X** checking. The most widely used method of making these measurements is by use of a body alignment gauge, commonly called a body tram gauge (Chapter 7). Bodies are measured first to determine the location and extent of the damage before correction, and secondly, during the correction, to determine when alignment has been restored. In both cases, the system and principles of the measurements are the same.

In body measuring, the body is divided into sections. The area from the front door forward is the front section. The area from the front door to the rear door is the center section. The area from the rear door to the trunk compartment is the rear section. The trunk compartment is considered as a separate section.

Sometimes the damage is not confined to a single section. This makes it necessary to check from one section to another to find out just where the misalignment, if any, really lies. All of these measurements are explained in this section.

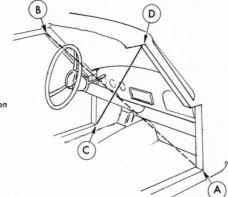

Fig. 1. Diagonals for Checking Front Section

a. Checking Individual Section. Fig. 1 shows how the diagonals are set up for checking the alignment of the front section. A convenient point, A, is located at or near the base of the right-front hinge pillar. The tram gauge is extended to reach from that point diagonally across to point B, located near the top of the left-front hinge pillar. The length of the gauge is locked at the length of the distance from A to B (Fig. 1).

It is absolutely essential that point C be in exactly the same relative position on the left side of the car body as point A on the right side. Likewise, points B and D must be in the same relative positions toward the top of the left- and right-front hinge pillars.

The tram gauge is then placed at point C and along the diagonal toward point D. If the length of the diagonal C to D exactly coincides with the length of the gauge, that is, if it is the same length as the diagonal A to B, then the front section is in alignment. However, if the tram gauge should not reach from point C to point D, as in Fig. 2, then it is obvious that the front section slants toward the right side. If, as in Fig. 3, the gauge projects from point C to beyond point D, then the front section slants to the left. Depending upon the extent of the damage, this procedure should be followed in **X** checking each section of the car body individually.

To assure accuracy in actual practice, points A, B, C, and D should be established before any **X** checking is done. Generally, points A and C can be most conveniently located at the corner formed by the juncture of the right- and left-front hinge pillars with the body sills. Here, the fishtail construction at the end of the gauge comes into

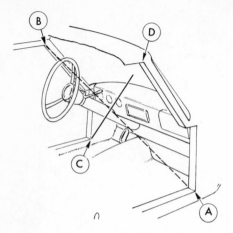

Fig. 2. Front Section Out of Alignment
Slanting to the Right

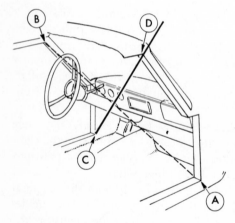

Fig. 3. Front Section Out of Alignment
Slanting to the Left

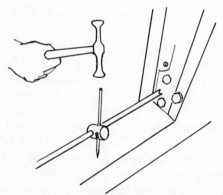

Fig. 4. Establishing Point on Sill

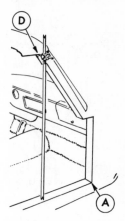

Fig. 5. Establishing Point on Pillar

practical use since it permits the gauge to be lodged against the corner.

The easiest and most accurate way to establish points B and D is to set and lock the scriber about 4 in. in from the end of the gauge. Place that end of the gauge against the front hinge pillar so that the scriber indicates a point on the body sill about 4 in. back of the pillar (Fig. 4). Use a light blow from a hammer to mark this point with the scriber. Repeat this procedure on the opposite body sill.

The next step is to extend the gauge straight up from the point you have just marked until the end of the gauge is about even with the top of the door opening and the scriber indicates a point on the front hinge pillar about 4 in. down from the opening. Lock the gauge in this position and mark the upper point with the scriber (Fig. 5). Follow this procedure on the opposite pillar, but do not change the length of the gauge. This will give you points B and D.

By similar procedure, you will be able accurately to establish other points within the car body which you will need for **X** checking the various sections. However, this **X** checking only determines alignment of the individual sections.

b. Checking Alignment of One Section with Another. In addition to checking the individual sections of the body, it must be determined whether or not all sections are in complete alignment with each other. That is, the front section must be in alignment with the center section, the center section must be in alignment with the rear section, and the rear section must be in alignment with the front section. Oc-

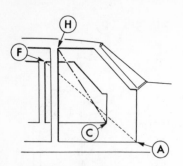

Fig. 6. Checking Alignment of Front
to Center Section

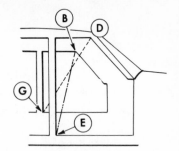

Fig. 7. Checking Alignment of
Center to Front Section

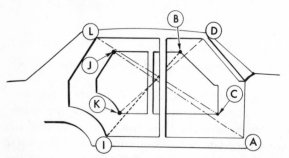

Fig. 8. Checking Align-
ment from Front to Rear
Section

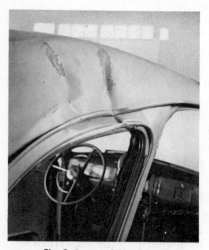

Fig. 9. Damaged Metal Top

Fig. 10. Pushing Out Upper Portion
of Lower Quarter Panel

(*Courtesy H. K. Porter*)

casionally, the trunk compartment must also be checked for alignment with the rear and center sections.

In checking the alignment of one section with another, the two sections are thought of as forming a cube or boxlike area. The diagonals are always run from one corner to the opposite corner so that they pass through the center of the cube or box. Just as in **X** checking individual sections, the opposite diagonals are compared with each other and must exactly coincide in length. Otherwise, the two sections are not in alignment. How to check the front with the center section for alignment is shown in Figs. 6 and 7.

In Fig. 6, the diagonal A to F is compared with its opposite diagonal, C to H. If the two diagonals coincide, that is, if A to F is the same distance as C to H, then the lower part of the front section is in alignment with the upper part of the center section.

In Fig. 7, the diagonal, B to E is compared with its opposite diagonal, D to G. If the two diagonals coincide, that is, if B to E is the same distance as D to G, then the upper part of the front section is in alignment with the lower portion of the center section. If, after all the diagonals of the boxlike area formed by the two sections are checked and found to be equal, the front and center sections are in alignment.

Fig. 8 shows the diagonal measurements used to check the alignment of the front section to the rear section.

First, points $A, B, D,$ and C and $I, J, K,$ and L are established. This, then, establishes the diagonals A to J, B to I, C to $L,$ and D to K. A comparison of diagonals B to I and D to K will determine whether the upper part of the front section is in alignment with the lower part of the rear section. A comparison of diagonals A to J and C to L will determine whether the upper part of the rear section is in alignment with the lower part of the front section. Any difference in the two sets of diagonals indicates misalignment. The length of the diagonals involved will indicate which way the body is slanting. You can then apply the corrective measures needed.

III. TOP

A damaged all-metal top is shown in Fig. 9. In this collision, the damage created backward strain on the lower portion of the lower crown section of the top. It caused a locking of the upper part of the quarter panel against the inner construction.

The first operation here is to push out the quarter panel upper portion. This is done with a power tool setup as shown in Fig. 10. A

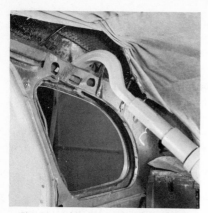

Fig. 11. Pushing Out Side of Metal Top

Fig. 12. Final Power Tool Operation in Pushing Out Side of Metal Top

(*Courtesy H. K. Porter*)

quarter panel molding spoon is used in conjunction with a remote-controlled jack.

You can see from the illustration that before any repair operations could be performed, it was necessary to remove the interior trim. Pushing the quarter panel inner construction back into place relieves the backward strain somewhat, and the next operation can be performed.

In Fig. 11, the side of the metal top is being pushed out by means of a top rail spoon which is being used with a remote-control jack. Pushing out the top in this manner relieves the downward strain, and the final straightening operations can be performed.

Another tool is shown in Fig. 12 in use for a further pushing operation on the top. This is a corner and header panel spoon,

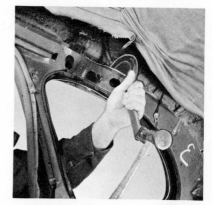

Fig. 13. Raising Low Spots with Hammer and Pick Tool

(*Courtesy H. K. Porter*)

and it, too, is used with a remote-control jack. This represents the final operation performed with power tools, and only the hand operations remain to finish the job.

The first hand operation is to raise all of the low spots. This is done

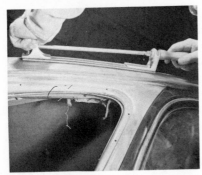

Fig. 14. Line Filing with Body File and Holder

Fig. 15. Completed Job Ready for the Refinishing Operation

(Courtesy H. K. Porter)

by using a pick tool of the proper shape for reaching this particular damage, and a metal bumping hammer (Fig. 13). A body file and holder, shown in use in Fig. 14, are used to reveal low spots by line filing. The final finished job, which has been properly ground with a disk grinder, is shown in Fig. 15 ready for the refinishing operation.

IV. FRONT QUARTER PANEL

In this next sequence of operations, you will be shown the method of straightening damage which has occurred in the left front quarter panel area. This is one of the most critical areas in the entire body. It is also one of the most difficult to straighten because of the complex construction.

Fig. 16. Badly Torn and Buckled Left Front Wheelhouse Inner Panel
(Courtesy Blackhawk Manufacturing Company)

Repair to this area can be made easier if you remember to study the damage carefully, then determine a way in which to proceed with the correction. Check your progress with tram gauges and alignment gauges while the corrections are being made.

Fig. 16 shows the left front wheelhouse inner panel assembly badly torn and buckled. The cowl was driven back on the left-hand side and the front frame member was badly kinked behind the rear engine mount. Note how the left front wheel has been driven back against the wheelhouse.

The first pull is made on the wheelhouse inner panel with a frame aligner (Fig. 17). A small jack is placed to exert an upward push against the sagged area while the frame aligner pulls the wheelhouse panel down and out. For heavy pulls, the pull plate may sometimes have to be welded to the frame member to avoid tearing the metal.

Next, the jack and frame aligner are placed to make a diagonal pull to swing the bottom of the wheelhouse inner panel into line (Fig. 18).

In Fig. 19, the top of the wheelhouse inner panel is being pulled out. Notice the effective method of anchoring the chain to the panel

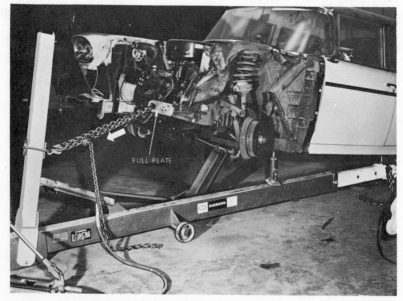

PULL PLATE

Fig. 17. Portable Frame Aligner and Jack in Place to Pull Wheelhouse Panel Down and Out
(*Courtesy Blackhawk Manufacturing Company*)

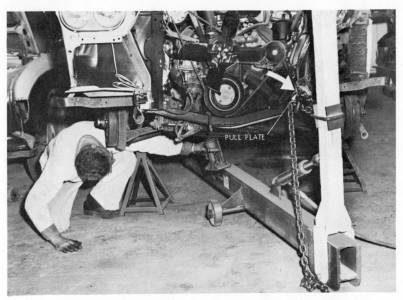

Fig. 18. Placing the Jack and Frame Aligner to Make a Diagonal Pull
(Courtesy Blackhawk Manufacturing Company)

Fig. 19. Pulling Out the Top of the Wheelhouse Inner Panel.
(Courtesy Blackhawk Manufacturing Company)

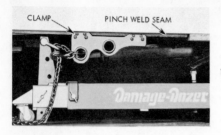

Fig. 20. An Underbody Clamp Fastened
to a "Pinch Weld" Seam
(*Courtesy Blackhawk Manufacturing Co.*)

by the use of a pry bar. With the setup shown, the pry bar presses against the reinforced panel section for a heavy pull.

An underbody clamp anchors the frame aligner to the car (Fig. 20). Because the car has a unitized body, the clamp must be fastened to the "pinch weld" seam beneath the rocker panel

In order to straighten the buckled bottom of the wheelhouse inner panel, a hydraulic ram (Fig. 21) exerts force while tension is applied with the frame aligner.

"Roughing out" means restoring panels to approximate shape and dimension even though they may later be replaced. If panels are not roughed out before any cutting is done, adjacent structures to which

Fig. 21. Using a Hydraulic Ram to Apply Additional Force Against the Frame Member
(*Courtesy Blackhawk Manufacturing Company*)

Fig. 22. The Wheelhouse Panel is Removed from the Car
(*Courtesy Blackhawk Manufacturing Company*)

the panels are welded may retain their damaged contours after cutting. If this occurs, the replacement panels will not fit and it is a losing battle trying to obtain a proper joint.

For instance, when a wheelhouse inner panel is badly buckled, the cowl is usually damaged. If the wheelhouse panel is cut loose from the cowl before a pull is exerted on it, the cowl will remain buckled and distorted. Then it will be extremely difficult to straighten the cowl area so that the replacement panel can be welded to it. Therefore, always work the damaged panels back to shape and dimension before attempting any cutting operations.

Up to this point in the repair, all of the work has been "roughing out." More than one pull has been made and the frame aligner and hydraulic jack have both been used to apply force.

Replacement of the damaged wheelhouse panel is considered more economical than repair, therefore the panel is removed (Fig. 22). Note the damaged areas of the cowl, and the buckling in the frame member just behind the engine mount.

After the wheelhouse panel is removed, the cowl is no longer reinforced and the remaining buckling can be straightened with the help

Fig. 23. A Hydraulic Ram Removing Buckles in the Cowl
(*Courtesy Blackhawk Manufacturing Company*)

of a hydraulic ram (Fig. 23). The repair is not attempted until after the reinforcing parts are removed. This reduces the strain on the sheet metal.

In order to swing the frame member back into its proper position,

Fig. 24. Using a Hydraulic Ram to Pull the Frame Member Back into Its Proper Position
(*Courtesy Blackhawk Manufacturing Company*)

Fig. 25. A Hydraulic Wedge Attachment Spreading the Top and Bottom Flanges of the Frame Member

(Courtesy Blackhawk Manufacturing Company)

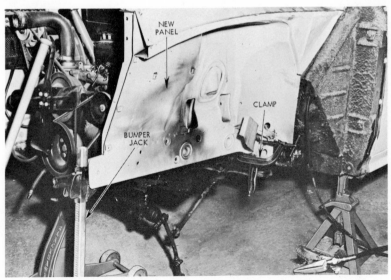

Fig. 26. The Replacement Wheelhouse Panel Fitted into Place

(Courtesy Blackhawk Manufacturing Company)

a hydraulic ram setup is used (Fig. 24). While the pull is maintained, the buckle in the frame member is pounded out.

Because the replacement wheelhouse panel nests inside an opening in the frame member, and because the opening collapsed during the collision, a hydraulic wedge attachment is used to spread the top and bottom flanges in the frame member (Fig. 25). Structural sections like the frame member must be restored to a near equivalent of original condition.

Next, the replacement panel is fitted in place and checked to see that all joining surfaces fit properly (Fig. 26). Careful measuring and proper pulling have made the replacement panel a close fit. This emphasizes the importance of checking with alignment gauges and tram gauges as the pulls are made.

A friction jack is used as shown in Fig. 27 to pull the new replacement panel back into place against the cowl. One hook is fastened to the panel, while a strap is used to fasten the other end of the jack to the cowl.

In Fig. 28, the new panel has been clamped in place and the hood has been installed to check for proper fit. Note the position of the

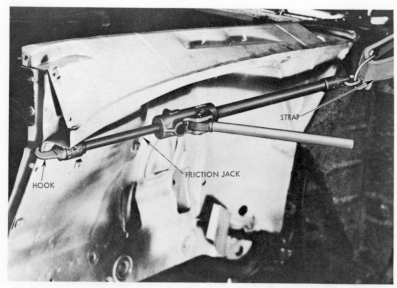

Fig. 27. Using a Friction Jack to Pull the Replacement Panel into Position Against the Cowl
(*Courtesy Blackhawk Manufacturing Company*)

Fig. 28. New Panel Clamped in Place with Hood Installed to Check for Proper Fit
(*Courtesy Blackhawk Manufacturing Company*)

Fig. 29. Gas Welding the New Panel to the Body
(*Courtesy Blackhawk Manufacturing Company*)

bumper jack and the friction jack. While the new panel is properly supported and clamped, it is gas welded to the body (Fig. 29).

Fig. 30 shows the new panel and hood installed. The next step involves installing and fitting the fender, suspension, radiator, etc.

In Fig. 31, the fender has been fitted and only the painting and mechanical work remain to be done. Fig. 32 shows the finished job after painting.

One factor that does not show in the preceding illustrations is the

Fig. 30. Installed Panel and Hood
(*Courtesy Blackhawk Manufacturing Company*)

Fig. 31. Car with Fender Fitted and Ready for Paint
(*Courtesy Blackhawk Manufacturing Company*)

Fig. 32. Completed Repair Job
(*Courtesy Blackhawk Manufacturing Company*)

Fig. 33. Car with Damaged Side
(*Courtesy Blackhawk Manufacturing Company*)

time spent in checking the damage and then deciding how to proceed. There is no substitute for planning the body repair job before doing the actual work.

V. SIDE REPAIR

Fig. 33 shows a car which has been hit in the left center pillar. The pillar is pushed in and the box sill in the area of the rocker panel is distorted.

First, the doors are removed so they can be straightened or replaced. Then the center pillar is pulled back to the proper position with a frame aligner. A timber is positioned as in Fig. 34 to prevent crushing the metal at the chain attachment point and to help remove bends in the pillar.

To anchor the frame aligner without injuring the body, a 4″x6″ timber is placed across the door opening on the opposite side of the

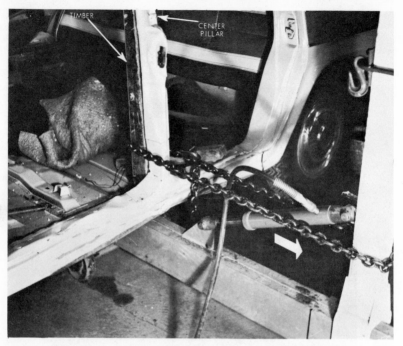

Fig. 34. Frame Aligner Pulling Against Timber to Straighten Pillar
(Courtesy Blackhawk Manufacturing Company)

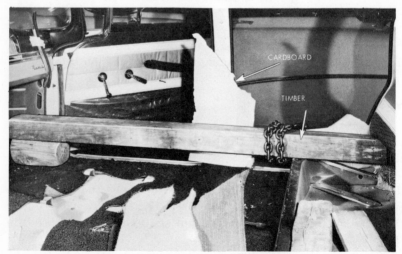

Fig. 35. Timber Being Used to Anchor Frame Aligner
(Courtesy Blackhawk Manufacturing Company)

car as shown in Fig. 35. Notice that the front trim is removed and a sheet of cardboard is used to protect the trim on the center pillar.

After the pillar is pulled out to its original position, the sill area is worked back into approximate shape by hammering as in Fig. 36. The hammering is done while pull is maintained by the frame aligner.

To pull out the sill area under the front and rear doors, openings are cut in the rocker panels so that a clamp can be attached (Fig. 37).

Fig. 36. Hammering Sill Area Back into Approximate Shape
(Courtesy Blackhawk Manufacturing Company)

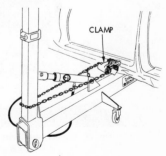

Fig. 37. Using Clamp to Pull Out Front Door Sill Area
(Courtesy Blackhawk Manufacturing Company)

Fig. 38. Straightening Distorted Inner Reinforcing Panels
(*Courtesy Blackhawk Manufacturing Company*)

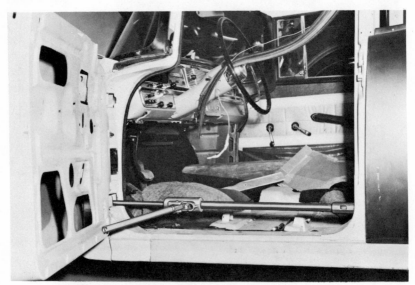

Fig. 39. Replacement Doors and Sill Panels in Place to Determine Door Fit
(*Courtesy Blackhawk Manufacturing Company*)

Fig. 40. Replacement Panels Welded in Place
(Courtesy Blackhawk Manufacturing Company)

Fig. 41. Car with Rear Collision Damage
(Courtesy Blackhawk Manufacturing Company)

The sill areas are then pulled out—first the front, and then the rear.

After the side is roughed out, the outer panels are cut off to gain access to the inner reinforcing panels which are distorted and require considerable straightening. The straightening is done with a hammer and a common pry bar (Fig. 38). The pry bar is used to reach behind the horizontal reinforcing panel. The "pinch weld" joining the sections at the bottom of the sill area is also straightened out by hammering after the reinforcing panel is straightened.

In the next step, the replacement doors and sill panels are set in place to determine door fit (Fig. 39). In order to obtain the proper door opening, a friction jack is used to hold the sill panels while they are spot welded in place.

Fig. 40 shows the replacement panels welded in place and the repairs substantially complete. The remainder of the repair will consist of hanging the doors, adding trim, and finishing.

VI. REAR END REPAIR

The car in Fig. 41 has been struck in the rear center. Both rear quarter panels are buckled out as shown, and the complete rear end has "dropped." The rear cross member is crushed and the rear glass is pulled out of place.

Fig. 42 shows the separation of the roof and quarter panels which is exactly the type of damage to be on the alert for. Sometimes, it may be difficult to detect, and a comparison must be made with another car of the same make and model.

The rear wheelhouse inner panel has buckled and the trunk floor pan has bulged up as shown in Fig. 43. This distortion occurred on both sides.

To correct the damage, a chain pull plate is attached from the body to a frame aligner (Fig. 44). The anchor post of the frame aligner is butted against the engine rear support member. A steel plate is used to spread the load on the engine rear support member to prevent dam-

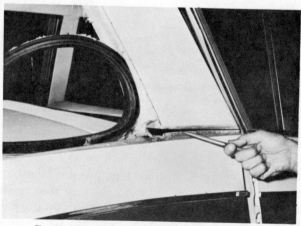

Fig. 42. Roof and Quarter Panel Separated by Collision
(*Courtesy Blackhawk Manufacturing Company*)

Fig. 43. Buckled Wheelhouse Inner Panel and Bulged Trunk Floor Pan
(Courtesy Blackhawk Manufacturing Company)

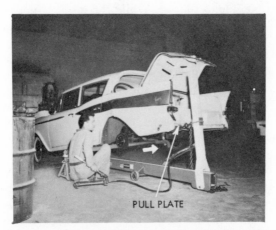

Fig. 44. Correcting Left-Side Rear End Damage with the Frame Aligner
(Courtesy Blackhawk Manufacturing Company)

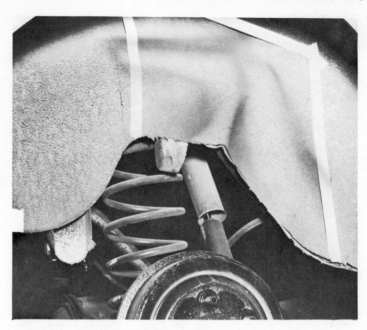

Fig. 45. Buckled Rear Wheelhouse Inner Panel
(Courtesy Blackhawk Manufacturing Company)

aging it. The car is then lowered onto stands, and an upward pull is made on the left side of the car. While the metal is under tension, a sledge is used to reduce the buckles in the trunk floor pan and the rear wheelhouse inner panel.

Fig. 45 shows the severe buckles in the frame member at the right rear wheelhouse inner panel. In order to straighten the dropped right rear end and remove the buckles, the frame aligner is set up as shown in Fig. 46. The rear cross member is then pulled out and, at this point, rough-out work is complete. The proper fit of doors, rear deck cover, and rear glass is checked and adjusted. The job is then ready for finishing.

Fig. 47 (top) shows the method used to hold down the area adjacent to the buckling by cutting holes through the wheelhouse panel. After the area is straightened, the holes are closed and brazed shut. When repairing unitized bodies, the collision man makes extensive use of underbody clamps for holding and pulling. In Fig. 47 (bottom) an eight-way clamp is shown. The holes in the clamp are positioned to

Fig. 46. Correcting Right-Side Rear End Damage with Frame Aligner
(Courtesy Blackhawk Manufacturing Company)

direct the chain pull toward the center of the clamp jaws to help prevent tearing the pinch weld.

In summing up this repair, notice that the job consisted not just of one operation, such as pulling, but a combination of pulling, hammering, and the use of hydraulic force. Also notice that some thought was given to "how to pull" and what steps were taken to assist the pull.

Always be sure to follow the following basic steps of collision damage repair:

1. Locate the damage.
2. Have a thorough knowledge of the body construction.
3. Plan the work.
4. Use the proper techniques.
5. Rough out the work.
6. Check the work.

VII. FENDER

A fender repair of an older car is discussed in the following para-

Fig. 47. TOP: Method of Holding Down Area Adjacent to Buckled Section; BOTTOM: An Eight-Way
Underbody Clamp for Holding or Pulling on Pinch Weld
(TOP: Courtesy Blackhawk Manufacturing Company; BOTTOM: Courtesy H. K. Porter)

graphs. Fig. 48 shows the fender as it looked after being damaged.
Fig. 49 shows the damaged fender after the running board has been
removed, leaving the fender ready for the corrective procedure.

The first operation in the straightening of this damaged fender is
performed with a fender beading tool and a roughing hammer (Fig.
50). In this operation, the fender beading tool is hooked over the
edge of the fender that is bent up and under. The roughing hammer is then used to strike a blow on the hammer pad on the beading

Fig. 48. Distorted Front Fender on Damaged
Car
(*Courtesy H. K. Porter*)

Fig. 49. Damaged Fender with Running Board
Removed
(*Courtesy H. K. Porter*)

Fig. 50. Hooking Down Edge of Fender with
Beading Tool and Hammer
(*Courtesy H. K. Porter*)

Fig. 51. Collision Tools Used for Correcting This
Damage
(*Courtesy H. K. Porter*)

tool. Hammering like this will bring the edge of the fender back down where it belongs. The roughing hammer is used for this operation because it is heavy enough to provide the impact necessary to reverse the kink in the fender at this point.

Fig. 51 shows all of the tools which will be used for the bumping operations necessary to straighten this fender. In this illustration, the toggle action spreader is shown inserted behind the fender skirt, ready for use.

The toggle action spreader is shown being used to push out the skirt area of the fender in Fig. 52. This portion of the fender is an unsupported area, and it was buckled in by the initial impact of the damaging force. For this pushing operation, the spreader is inserted between the fender skirt and the mudguard which is behind the fender skirt (Fig. 53). This mudguard is attached to the frame and to the bottom of the fender skirt at the bottom edge. This pushing operation will remove most of the damage from the skirt area. The balance of the operations required to completely remove the damage are performed with hand tools. It is necessary to have the skirt area of the fender restored to normal before the lower edge and fender bead can be restored. The finishing operation on the buckled skirt area is done with a surfacing spoon and a bumping hammer. This spring hammering will bring this surface back to its original contour (Fig. 54).

Notice in the illustration of spring hammering that the collision man is wearing gloves. When a bumping hammer is used directly against a spoon or dolly, a sting is sometimes imparted to the hands

Fig. 52. Pushing Out Fender Skirt with Toggle Action Spreader
(*Courtesy H. K. Porter*)

Fig. 53. Spreader Inserted Between Fender Skirt and Mud Guard
(*Courtesy H. K. Porter*)

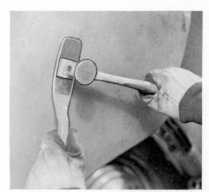

Fig. 54. Spring Hammering Fender Skirt
(*Courtesy H. K. Porter*)

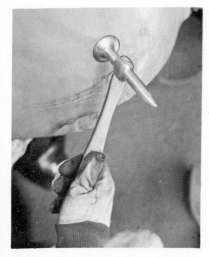

Fig. 55. Finish Hammering High-Crown Area
of Fender
(*Courtesy H. K. Porter*)

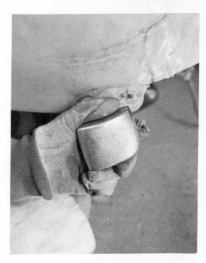

Fig. 56. High-Crown Dolly Used with Fender
Hammer
(*Courtesy H. K. Porter*)

upon the impact of the hammer with the dolly. Wearing gloves will prevent this from becoming annoying.

The final finish hammering is done with a fender hammer and a high-crown dolly (Fig. 55). The high-crown area above the front end of the running board is finished in this manner. Fig. 56 shows the high-crown dolly which is used with the fender hammer. This same hammer and dolly are used to reshape the flange on the fender to which the running board is bolted.

The low spots are brought up after the fender has been restored

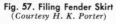

Fig. 57. Filing Fender Skirt
(*Courtesy H. K. Porter*)

Fig. 58. Repaired Fender with Tools Used
(*Courtesy H. K. Porter*)

to its normal contour. Any low spots which cannot be removed for one reason or another are then filled with solder. The solder is filed smooth with a body file (Fig. 57) at the same time the entire fender area is filed to prepare it for sanding.

The entire area is then sanded with a disk grinder and the job is ready for the paint shop. The finished job, with all of the collision and finishing tools used to effect it, is shown in Fig. 58.

VIII. REPLACEMENT VERSUS REPAIR

It is probably true that an ingenious collision man can repair anything that has been damaged in a collision. However, attempts to repair parts and panels that obviously should be replaced prove nothing except your poor judgment. As you gain experience in collision work, you will find that you are able at a glance to estimate the time required to do a particular job and can make your decision on the spot as to whether a particular part or panel will be replaced. You can do this, of course, only if you are familiar with, or have access to, the prices you will have to pay for the parts involved. Several independent companies have available complete body panel and parts lists, indexed with prices. Every progressive body shop should avail itself of this service.

On unit construction cars, replacement of panels is more common because the construction is of such a nature that damage is more localized. Shock is absorbed in the contacting panel.

The following parts and materials are almost always replaced rather than repaired. Bright metal parts, except in those instances where a compromise in quality is acceptable. Bright metal parts, due to their intricate design and to the nature of the material from which they are made, do not lend themselves to straightening or welding. Even in those cases where a satisfactory job of straightening is performed, the parts generally will have to be replated. The cost of replating often will be greater than the cost of a new part.

Interior trim panels generally can be cleaned and satisfactorily repaired to permit their re-use. Cardboard backing can be replaced, or in some instances, stiffened by gluing an additional cardboard reinforcement to them.

Body deadening material is replaced. Padding used for sound deadening usually tears apart as you attempt to remove it. An attempt to salvage this material generally is a waste of time, making it more costly than new material.

In collision work, you will have two extremes of quality that you will have to observe. Some variations in these extremes of quality also will be necessary. These two considerations depend upon whether you are working on used cars or on a vehicle where an insurance company will be paying for the damage on a client's car.

a. Used Cars. If you are working for a new or used car dealer, you will have the problem of restoring used cars to a salable condition. Some compromise in quality is necessary in these cases. Your goal is to determine quickly what you can do to restore the appearance of the vehicle to an acceptable standard with the amount of money the dealer is able to spend on the particular vehicle. In these cases, a good many compromises from the ideal are necessary. Particularly when working on older cars, the extra cost involved in striving for perfection is not justified since these costs will have to be added to the selling price of the vehicle, and will render that particular vehicle noncompetitive.

Privately owned automobiles which have become damaged and for which the owner must pay the repair charges, fall approximately in this same category. Here again, you must compare the benefits to be derived from perfection with what you can accomplish appearancewise with a minimum of time and material. You will often find that these owners welcome your suggestions for the more economical job and will become one of the best advertisers for your shop and practices.

Still another consideration arises in conjunction with jobs which are to be paid for by an insurance company and where the owner feels that he has every right to have his car restored to a like-new condition. On these jobs, you may encounter rusted-out fenders which do not lend themselves to repair. Here, you must keep in mind that it is the insurance company which is going to pay the bill. Where a minor damage to a fender tears it loose from the body due to the fact that the fender has rusted through, you may be required to improvise repairs which, while they may fall far short of restoring the vehicle to a like-new condition, will be satisfactory to both the owner and to the insurance company.

b. Where an Insurance Company Pays the Damage. Where an insurance company pays the damage or where an uninsured owner of a new car or nearly new car requires correction of collision damage, the quality of your work must be such that when you have finished, there is no indication of the damage having occurred. This does not necessarily mean that if the fender is damaged it must be replaced with a new one, though many owners will probably insist on this. As a matter of fact, you will find that if, in bidding for this work you consistently include the cost of replacement parts, the insurance company will send its business elsewhere. For this reason, you will have to be diplomatic with the owner of a shiny new car which has become damaged through no fault of his own and who insists on a new fender or a new door or whatever part happens to be damaged. If the kind of damage lends itself to repair, then you will have to repair it. If a more economical, yet equally satisfactory job can be done by repairing, don't argue with the owner. In the early stages of negotiations, submit your bid to the insurance company in a way that calls for repairing of the damage rather than replacement. Your attitude in this instance is not to pass the burden of responsibility on to the insurance company. Instead, you must protect them, since the company, rather than the owner of the vehicle, is your customer. In other words, minimize the damage to the owner. Indicate to him that the particular part is easily repaired and that replacement of the door or fender, or whatever the part happens to be, probably would not be as satisfactory as the mere pushing out and painting of the damaged part. In nearly all cases, you will find that you can appease the owner satisfactorily in this way without getting into trouble with the insurance company.

The uninsured new car owner is a little different. He is more apt to welcome your suggestion of repair rather than replacement, particularly when you can assure him that there will be no question of the quality. Sometimes you will find that the new or nearly new car owner will feel that the repaired part will not match the rest of the car. In these cases you can point out to him that a new fender or door will have to be refinished in your shop just as would any repaired part. After all, it is the paint that a person sees. Whether the part is replaced or repaired, the paint would be the same and would be applied by the same people. The desirability of a new part, therefore, becomes negligible.

Each of these cases may require a slightly different handling. For the most part, however, you will find that you can sell repair rather than replacement.

This discussion presumes, of course, that the repair can be performed more economically than the part involved can be replaced. The relationship of these two costs will vary among different shops. The car dealership doing collision work on the make of car it sells has a price advantage in obtaining new fenders, doors, panels, etc., that is not enjoyed by the independent collision shop. For this reason, the dealership can often replace a part more economically than it can repair it. The same damage in an independent shop might be repaired more economically than it could be replaced due to the shorter discount the independent shop might receive on the part involved.

In arriving at a conclusion as to whether a particular part should be replaced or repaired, don't lose sight of installation time. Installation time can be considerable as, in the case of a door, for example, for all of the door hardware, glass, and interior trim must be transferred from one door to the other. In the case of the front fender, you may have additional problems of grill and hood alignment when you have installed the part. All of these considerations must be a part of your evaluation as to whether or not you should repair or replace a part.

c. Cost. In most cases, the cost of the part as compared with the cost of the repair will be the determining factor as to which course you will follow. As mentioned in the discussion involving used cars, something less than perfection is generally acceptable in older automobiles. Often you will be working on fenders which have had innumerable previous repairs. When you start to work on them, you will find that they have been so filled with solder that you cannot make an economical repair. If the points favoring repair outweigh the points favoring replacement by only a small margin, it might be a good idea to determine whether or not the particular part has been filled with solder. If you find that it has been, recommend replacement rather than repair of that particular part.

When you are working on a car where the owner of the vehicle is personally paying the cost, it may be well to place yourself in his position. Again, if you are working on a used car, put yourself in the place of the person who would buy a car of that particular age group. A person who is driving an older car, or the person who buys a car of that type on the used car lot, probably does so for economic reasons. An extra thirty or forty dollars spent on the restoring of collision damage might amount to a hardship for this person. In most cases, a person in this group would rather have some slight imperfection in the car than to spend the extra money. On the other hand, the owner of a shiny new car generally has just paid, or contracted to pay, a substantial amount of money for the car, and he doesn't want to be reminded of the damage in any way by the appearance of the car after you have repaired it. In these cases, you will have to work for perfection.

Obviously, there are a number of intermediate steps between these extremes. It is important, therefore, that you recognize these differences in the problem, and match your recommendations to suit the vehicle wherever possible.

d. Quality. Throughout this volume, the instructions given have been toward achieving the skill and knowledge necessary to restore damaged parts to a like-new condition. This like-new condition refers not only to appearance, but to function as well. You, as a craftsman, will have pride in your workmanship, and even in those cases where sacrifice of quality is indicated as being acceptable, you will want to do just a little more than enough to make the job acceptable. This is good experience for you, and it is good practice because it keeps you in the quality habit.

e. Time. Time, of course, is always a factor in repairing collision jobs. However, after the first shock at seeing his automobile seriously damaged in a collision, the average vehicle owner becomes reconciled to the fact that he is going to be deprived of the use of his automobile for a few days. It is not unusual for the vehicle to set for a number of days before clearance is received from the insurance company to proceed with the work. When the OK to proceed is received, the owner is still quite anxious to get the car. If you let the situation get out of your control, he may demand some unreasonable delivery time. About the only satisfactory way you can meet this situation is to propose some alternate method of repair at either an increased cost or at some sacrifice of quality. Usually in an instance of this kind where, due to the owner's insistence that the car must be delivered more quickly, you point out to him that to do so would represent a sacrifice in quality or an increase in cost to him, the owner will change his mind and permit you to proceed as you originally planned.

In considering the question of repair versus replacement, don't be misled into believing that the replacement of a part always is more quickly effected than the repair of the part. This, in many cases, is not true. As previously mentioned throughout this volume, the replacement of a particular part often entails a considerable amount of work over and above the work that would be required to repair the part.

IX. FILLING VERSUS STRAIGHTENING

The question of whether to straighten out a sunken area or attempt to fill the depression with solder often arises. In general, there are not many times when it is more economical to use body solder to fill a depression than to straighten it.

If you lack equipment to get in behind inner construction satisfactorily, it may be necessary to fill with solder. Bring the surface up as far as you can by whatever means are available, even though you cannot bring it all the way up. This will reduce the amount of solder you will have to use. At any place where a low spot exists, you should consider filling the low spot with solder if the area is not extensive. This is particularly true if getting behind the damage involves a lot of work.

If there is a possibility that you can make a satisfactory repair of collision damage by straightening it without marring the paint, you can afford to remove a lot of parts for the cost of repainting. Soldering, of course, necessitates repainting the area involved.

Solder filling has an important part in collision work, and the advisability of filling with solder must be considered on jobs that lend themselves to this method. Since solder is expensive, you may find that the cost of the solder and the time to apply it is more than the cost of bumping out the damage.

In cases of minor damage to a door, either of the quarter panels, or to a rocker panel sill, it is sometimes more economical to fill the depressed area with solder. Repairing of damage in these areas usually involves the removal of interior trim and sometimes some of the exterior trim. The labor involved in removing and installing the trim so

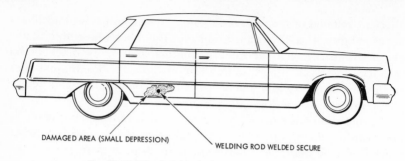

DAMAGED AREA (SMALL DEPRESSION)   WELDING ROD WELDED SECURE

Fig. 59. Welding Rod Attached to Pull Out Damaged Area
(Courtesy H. K. Porter)

that you could gain access to the damage from the inside, to push it out, sometimes is greater than the cost of filling with solder. This sometimes is particularly true if the panel is to be repainted anyway.

In damage of this type, it is sometimes possible to weld a piece of welding rod to the center of the lowest portion of the damage area. By pulling on the welding rod, you may be able to draw out the depressed portion of the panel (Fig. 59).

In some instances, you may have to drill a hole in the inner construction to gain access to the back of the damaged area. In other instances, you may have to drill a hole in the outer panel to work through. Of course, in this latter instance, you will have to fill the hole. If you are merely pulling the panel out so as to reduce the amount of solder required, filling the hole will be no problem, since a small hole is easily filled with solder as a part of the building up of the contour.

X. LOW COST, SHORT DURATION REPAIRS

Sometimes, it is desirable to make improvements in the appearance of a car, even though the resale value may be rather low. However, if the car is in good mechanical condition, it is probably a wise investment if the repairs can be made at a nominal cost.

a. Replacement Panels. Low cost, fiber glass panels are available for most cars. These fiber glass panels are for replacing rocker panels, splash shields, and lower back panels. These areas of a car body are the most susceptible to rust and damage from road debris which might damage the paint and result in a rusted-out condition. Replacement panels can be secured at local auto parts outlets or hot rod shops. Usually, they are provided with directions for installation.

The installation of the replacement panel is not difficult. It is necessary to remove the most rusted area of the old panel. Then fit the new panel in place and drill the required holes through the old and the new panel. Then secure the new panel to the old with sheet metal screws. The panel can then be sanded and finished to match the color of the car.

b. Body Filling. Another very acceptable and low cost method of repair is to use a plastic body filler. Plastic body filler usually comes in cans. It is mixed with a drying agent or thinner to give it the proper drying time for the desired job. Plastic body filler can be used to build up areas of a body that putties will not fill. Such areas include:

1. Sections of metal that cannot be worked.
2. Sections that cannot be restored to original contour.
3. Holes or tears in the edges of doors, fenders, or quarter panels.
4. Sections weakened by rust or rusted out altogether.
5. Welded sections where the weld cannot be filed smooth.

The drying time must permit time to fill the area and allow grinding and sanding time before the body filler sets hard, because then the body filler will flake off and drop down resulting in a minimum of dust in the air. If grinding and sanding are done after the filler has set hard, the dust is quite fine and will tend to float and contaminate the air.

When a hole or tear in the metal is mended, it should be backed up with a fiber glass screen or cloth. Thoroughly clean the back of the panel at least two inches around the hole to be mended. Saturate the screen or cloth with a plastic body filler and then place it over the hole from the back of the panel overlapping the metal in the cleaned area. After it has set, the hole can be filled a little higher than the panel to allow for sanding and finishing flush with the panel.

When a rusty area is reinforced, it should be done in the same way with the fabric extending at least two inches onto firm metal. If plastic filler is anchored on metal softened or weakened by rust, the metal is likely to pull out, taking the plastic with it.

If lead is selected as a body filler, the following steps should be followed:

1. Tin the areas to be leaded, using acid core, liquid, or paste solder.
2. When applying the lead, use a wide flame to melt the bar and concentrate the flame on the lead. If the flame is held on the metal, it may distort it.

3. A wooden paddle should be used to smooth out the lead. Beeswax or a similar lubricant should be used on the paddle to keep the lead from sticking to it.

4. Grind and sand smooth.

5. Neutralize the leaded area with a solution of equal parts of alcohol, ammonia and water. Then treat the entire area, including all bare metal, with rust inhibitor and metal conditioner.

XI. ESTIMATING

In collision work, estimating is the selling part of the operation. Most collision jobs are paid for by an insurance company. Insurance companies generally require at least two estimates, and with all other things being equal, the shop that submits the lowest estimate will get the work.

In collision work, all estimates are considered "firm." In other words, while a vehicle owner may not regard an estimate as a commitment to do the work involved for the amount of money shown, to the insurance company it is a firm pledge. If you "hedge" on your estimates, you will soon find that you will not secure future business from the insurance companies.

Actually, the estimate for repairing collision damage is a bid or proposal indicating the amount of money for which you will do the job. Your estimate should be detailed so that the insurance company can determine from the estimate just what it is you propose to do to the vehicle. The estimate must include the cost of the parts, labor, material, the shop overhead, and the shop profit. Parts and labor should be included at their list price. That is, the catalog price for the parts without discount and the selling rate or retail for labor in your shop should be quoted.

Most collision shops consider insurance companies as valuable customers to whom they are willing to give a discount on parts. The usual practice is to show the parts at full list price, but to include an additional entry, "discount on parts—20 per cent" (or whatever discount is being allowed). They then show the amount of the discount in dollars and deduct it from the total amount of the estimate. The difference is shown as net cost. The amount of discount you can allow on parts is controlled by the amount of discount which you receive in purchasing them. Don't give away all of your parts discount.

The cost of labor that you indicate on your estimate is based on the retail labor rate that has been established for your shop. A discussion of how a retail rate is established is presented in this section. This retail rate is multiplied by the number of hours and fractions thereof required to do the job. The number of hours required can be based on a flat rate schedule or based on the amount of time you estimate the jobs will take without regard to any published figures. These alternate methods are also discussed in this section.

a. The Retail Rate. The retail rate is the amount in dollars and cents that you charge to your customers for labor. This amount must include the actual cost of the labor; the cost of overhead, including such items as supervision, depreciation on equipment, supplies, etc.; and a profit for the shop.

The actual cost of the labor is the amount of money paid to the collision man. In the event some unskilled labor is used, this time should be charged for at the retail rate for the unskilled labor.

A highly skilled collision man should be worth between 40 and 60 per cent more than the prevailing rate for a first-class automobile repair mechanic in the same community. Of course, a lot of men are doing collision work who are not being paid this well. On the other hand, in many cases, these men may be semiskilled or amateurs who have acquired some but not all of the skills involved.

To command the top rate just indicated, the collision man must be able to do all of the things connected with collision work (exclusive of refinishing), and he must be able to do them fast. He must be able to size up a collision job quickly and to determine exactly how to go about correcting the damage with the minimum amount of labor and material.

The retail rate generally is established by multiplying the wages received by the collision man by two and one-half. This means that the collision man is receiving as compensation 40 per cent of the retail rate. This is a lower percentage than is paid in some parts of the country for automobile repair mechanics. However, the amount of supplies used in collision work makes it necessary that a larger amount be apportioned to overhead.

In some sections, where a working agreement between labor and management calls for the collision man receiving 50 per cent of the retail charge, the cost of supplies (solder, welding rod, gas, etc.) are listed separately on the estimate and are not considered as a part of the overhead.

From the foregoing, you can see that it is an easy matter to establish a retail labor rate for any community.

The cost of making estimates where you lose the job to some other shop, and the cost of supervision, rent, heat, light, electric power, welding gas, welding rod, solder, flux, and dozens of other items, make up the overhead of the shop. Overhead represents between 40 and 50 per cent of the retail rate. The remaining 10 to 20 per cent make up the shop profit, without which, of course, no business can long continue.

b. The Flat Rate. Most collision shops prepare their estimates from a flat rate time schedule as published by the automobile manufacturer or some flat rate service. In preparing these flat rates, the time allowance generally is quite liberal. The time shown is sufficient to permit the below-average collision man to do the job. The flat rate, however, generally does not take into account variations that exist in damage to a particular part. In using a flat rate manual to establish your estimate, there is a tendency for the estimate to be high unless you deliberately make allowances for those parts of the job that can be corrected simultaneously. Of course, this is not a serious factor as long as you are competing with other shops who also are using a flat rate basis for estimating.

c. Estimate Based on Time and Material. As you gain experience in collision work, you will be able to determine quickly just how you will go about correcting a particular collision job. A car that is pushed in for its entire length often can be pushed back in shape almost as a single operation by using a number of power jacks. If your competition is adhering to a flat rate price and if you are truly skilled and make an accurate estimate of the number of hours the job will take, you will find that in most cases your estimate will be the low one. This will be particularly true on the easy jobs. This means, of course, that you will be getting a large percentage of the easy, high-profit jobs. Your competitor, using a cut-and-dried flat rate for estimating, will be getting the tough, low-profit jobs that you lose.

Much has been written on collision work estimating. If there were but one or two things that you could learn, and from these become an infallible estimator of collision costs, these things would be listed at this point. However, this whole volume is filled with the things which are factors in estimating collision work. For example, the factor of quality, discussed in conjunction with used cars, is an important consideration for which the flat rate does not generally make allowances. How well you can evaluate the advisability of replacing a part as compared to repairing it as discussed elsewhere in this chapter is also an important consideration, as is the question of filling versus straightening. The amount of hardware and trim which you must remove are important considerations. In fact, every chapter of this volume contains information that is important in estimating the cost of a collision job.

Until such time as you have thoroughly mastered all the skills involved in collision work and have developed speed in practicing them, and until you are able to immediately envision the method or procedure by which you will repair the damage, it will be better for you to follow a flat rate rather than to use your own figures.

Regardless of whether you are figuring your estimates on a flat rate or on a time and material basis, the automobile body and frame must be considered by sections in order to locate and determine the extent of the damage.

TRADE COMPETENCY TESTS

The following questions, while they represent only a small portion of the material in this chapter, may be used to determine the percentage of the information retained.

1. Why should a study of collision damage be made before any attempt is made to straighten it? (p. 302)

2. In what direction must the corrective forces be applied in collision work? (p. 302)

3. How is it possible to determine sometimes just how a collision occurred without questioning someone as to the particulars? (p. 303)

4. When should the damage which occurred last be corrected? (p. 304)

5. What name is given to the system of diagonal comparison used for checking body alignment? (p. 304)

6. What piece of measuring equipment is most usually used for making body measurements? (p. 304)

7. Why is it necessary to make measurements at various stages in the correction of collision damage? (p. 304)

8. When a body is divided into sections for measurement, is the trunk compartment considered as part of the rear section? (p. 304)

9. Why is it sometimes necessary to check the alignment of one body section with another body section? (pp. 307, 309)

10. When the alignment of two sections is checked, what shape are the two sections considered as forming? (p. 309)

11. What are the principal considerations involved in determining whether to replace a part or repair it? (p. 335)

12. Is it usually best to repair or replace bright metal parts when they are damaged? (p. 335)

13. Is it usually possible to re-use interior trim panels after a collision repair? (p. 335)

14. When reconditioning used cars, is it always possible to do a high quality job? (p. 335)

CHAPTER **9**

REFINISHING

The straightening of damaged automobile bodies and their re-painting, two widely different crafts, are generally associated with each other. In smaller shops particularly, a single body shop man is often a combination collision man and painter. Even in shops where there is no overlapping between the body shop and the paint shop, each must be familiar with the techniques of the other.

Chapter 4 explains how the body shop prepares metal for the painter. Painters are sometimes required to repaint jobs on which a metal finisher has not worked, making it necessary for the painter to perform some metal finishing steps. A metal finisher who appreciates just how far the painter can go in filling up scratches is less liable to turn out work that cannot be properly refinished. Likewise, a painter who appreciates some of the problems confronting the metal finisher will not make unreasonable demands upon the body shop.

Painting is largely a matter of skill developed through practice, plus a thorough knowledge of painting materials. Skill can only be acquired through directed practice. This chapter will guide you in acquiring painting skill. The paint industry is constantly improving its products through continuing research, and, as a painter, you must keep your knowledge of materials up to date.

The difference between the paint job that sells for one price and one that costs four times as much is largely in the amount of care used, the attention to detail, and the compromises from perfection that are made. This chapter, plus some practice, should equip you to work on used car appearance reconditioning or price refinishing. The experience you need for the custom-shop quality jobs that sell for a higher price is acquired only through a lot of painting experience, with a constant striving for perfection on each job. This chapter presumes no previous knowledge of the subject; it is recommended that each section be studied, and that the exercises be performed in the order presented.

a. Materials. The major materials that you will be using fall into two broad groupings, i.e., lacquers and enamels. The basic difference between lacquers and enamels originally was that, after drying, the lacquer was essentially the same all the way through, whereas the enamel dried with a protective glaze on the surface. However, in recent years the same kinds of synthetic resins that caused the formation of the glaze on enamels have been added to lacquers. Now, modern lacquer automotive finishes also dry with a slight glaze on the surface.

One other basic difference, however, exists between lacquers and enamel. Lacquers, no matter how old the finish may be, are soluble (will dissolve or get soft) in lacquer thinners, whereas enamels, once properly dried, are not soluble in lacquer thinner or in enamel reducers.

b. Equipment. Some of the materials with which you will be working can be explosive under certain conditions, and almost all of them are inflammable. It is recommended, before you make your final deci-

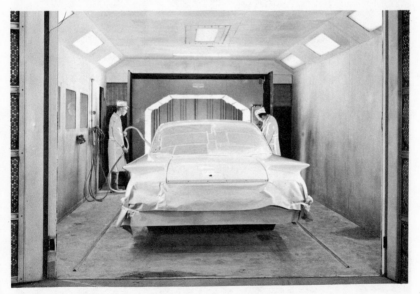

Fig. 1. Paint Spray Booth
(*Courtesy De Vilbiss Company*)

sions about the selection of paint shop equipment, that you obtain a copy of the National Fire Protection Association booklet, *Standards for Spray Finishing Using Flammable Materials.*

Where local ordinances permit it, and where no fire hazard exists, small spot repairs of lacquer can be accomplished without either a spray booth or drying oven.

On the other hand, if you plan a complete refinishing job with both lacquer and enamel, a paint spray booth which meets National Fire Protection Association standards and a drying oven are both desirable. Fig. 1 shows a modern paint spray booth. Notice that the painter holds the hose with his left hand so that it will not rub against or hit the newly applied paint. The booth doors are closed when paint is being applied. These doors are equipped with filters that remove dust particles from the air drawn into the booth. Fig. 2 shows an infrared type drying oven. The heat comes from special infrared lights which are usually equipped with gold-plated reflectors.

c. **Paint Identification Data.** As discussed under "a. **Materials,**" all cars are not covered with the same kind of paint. Some models are finished with enamel, while others are finished with lacquer. Later

Fig. 2. Removing Car From Infrared Drying Oven
(*Courtesy De Vilbiss Company*)

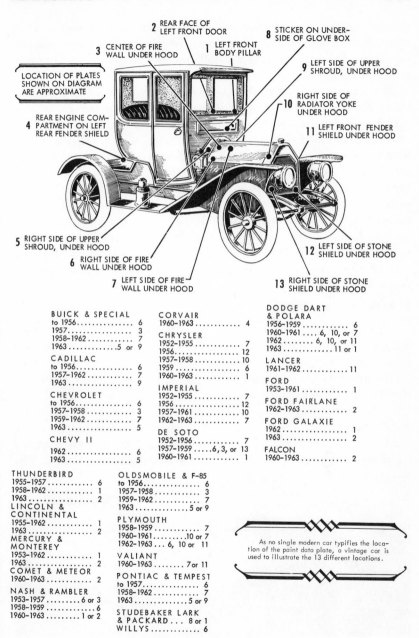

2   REAR FACE OF
LEFT FRONT DOOR

8   STICKER ON UNDER-
SIDE OF GLOVE BOX

3   CENTER OF FIRE
WALL UNDER HOOD

LEFT FRONT
BODY PILLAR

9   LEFT SIDE OF UPPER
SHROUD, UNDER HOOD

LOCATION OF PLATES
SHOWN ON DIAGRAM
ARE APPROXIMATE

10   RIGHT SIDE OF
RADIATOR YOKE
UNDER HOOD

4   REAR ENGINE COM-
PARTMENT ON LEFT
REAR FENDER SHIELD

11   LEFT FRONT FENDER
SHIELD UNDER HOOD

5   RIGHT SIDE OF UPPER
SHROUD, UNDER HOOD

6   RIGHT SIDE OF FIRE
WALL UNDER HOOD

12   LEFT SIDE OF STONE
SHIELD UNDER HOOD

7   LEFT SIDE OF FIRE
WALL UNDER HOOD

13   RIGHT SIDE OF STONE
SHIELD UNDER HOOD

BUICK & SPECIAL	**CORVAIR**	**DODGE DART & POLARA**
to 1956 6	1960–1963 4	1956–1959 6
1957 3	**CHRYSLER**	1960–1961 . . . . 6, 10, or 7
1958–1962 7	1952–1955 7	1962 . . . . . . 6, 10, or 11
1963 . . . . .5 or 9	1956 12	1963 . . . . .11 or 1
CADILLAC	1957–1958 10	**LANCER**
to 1956 6	1959 6	1961–1962 11
1957–1962 7	1960–1963 1	**FORD**
1963 9	**IMPERIAL**	1953–1961 1
CHEVROLET	1952–1955 7	**FORD FAIRLANE**
to 1956 6	1956 12	1962–1963 2
1957–1958 3	1957–1961 10	**FORD GALAXIE**
1959–1962 7	1962–1963 7	1962 1
1963 5	**DE SOTO**	1963 2
CHEVY II	1952–1956 7	**FALCON**
1962 6	1957–1959 . . . . .6, 3, or 13	1960–1963 2
1963 5	1960–1961 1	

THUNDERBIRD	**OLDSMOBILE & F–85**
1955–1957 6	to 1956 6
1958–1962 1	1957–1958 3
1963 2	1959–1962 7
LINCOLN & CONTINENTAL	1963 . . . . .5 or 9
1955–1962 1	**PLYMOUTH**
1963 2	1958–1959 7
MERCURY & MONTEREY	1960–1961 . . . . .10 or 7
1953–1962 1	1962–1963 . . . 6, 10 or 11
1963 2	**VALIANT**
COMET & METEOR	1960–1963 . . . . 7 or 11
1960–1963 2	**PONTIAC & TEMPEST**
NASH & RAMBLER	to 1957 6
1953–1957 . . . . .6 or 3	1958–1962 7
1958–1959 6	1963 . . . . .5 or 9
1960–1963 . . . . .1 or 2	**STUDEBAKER LARK & PACKARD** . . . 8 or 1
	WILLYS 6

As no single modern car typifies the location of the paint data plate, a vintage car is
used to illustrate the 13 different locations.

Fig. 3. Paint Data Location
(Courtesy Rinshed-Mason Company)

models may be finished with one of the newer, acrylic paints. Each manufacturer has his own trade name for the finish used on his particular product. However, it will fall into one of the three categories named above.

Naturally, then, the method of refinishing will depend on the material required. Therefore, identification of the type of paint used is of the utmost importance in obtaining a good paint job.

Each manufacturer provides a data number for each car. This number is sometimes stamped on a plate which is affixed to the body permanently or it may be stamped directly into a body panel such as the forward face of the cowl. Along with other identifying information, this number will contain a paint code which is in common use by all reputable manufacturers to identify color and material.

Fig. 3 shows the location of the paint identification plate on all model cars from 1956 through 1963. You should always check the plate very carefully to assure proper color matching when making spot or panel repairs.

I. PAINTING A FENDER OR PANEL

As a painter, you must inspect the metal finish first, making sure the metal finisher has prepared the fender for you. First, go over the entire repair with No. 120 grit metal cloth to remove any burrs raised by the grinder. Your fingers will feel any irregularities in the metal through the cloth as you work.

a. Featheredging. The second step is to *featheredge* the old paint. This is accomplished with No. 240-A grit waterproof paper on a rubber block, as shown in Fig. 4A. A wet sponge is held so that, with a slight pressure, water will run down over the surface being sanded. The

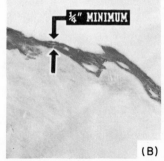

Fig. 4. (A) Featheredging Old Paint; (B) Taper Each Layer of Paint to at Least ¼ in. Wide
(*Courtesy Ford Motor Company*)

rubber block holds the sandpaper flat so that the high spots will be sanded down first. Work from at least 3 in. back from the bare metal. You are trying to sand the old paint so that the bare metal and the old paint form an uninterrupted, smooth surface. Properly feather-edged, each layer of the old finish will be no less than ¼ in. wide at its narrowest point. Fig. 4B shows a section of this fender properly featheredged. Keep the surface wet as you sand. This keeps the abrasives on the sandpaper from loading up with paint. Waterproof paper, kept wet during use, will last longer and cut faster.

b. Masking. Other parts of the car should be masked at this time so that paint will not get on them. Masking merely means the covering of surfaces with masking tape to protect them from unwanted paint.

Masking tape is waterproof paper gummed on one side. It comes in rolls of various widths from ¼ to 2 in. wide. In this case, the tail-light was completely covered with masking tape. Care must be used not to have the tape cover anything that you want painted. When you are going to be sanding near chrome parts, it is a good practice to mask the chrome so as not to scratch it during the sanding.

This fender was *spot repaired*. However, as a beginner, you should learn by painting an entire fender or panel rather than attempt the

more difficult spot repair at this time. In painting the entire fender on this particular car, you might remove the bumper bar rather than mask it. On later model cars this involves too much work, so you should mask the bumper. The rest of the car would also be masked with masking tape and paper. Fig. 5 shows an *apron taper* that will apply about half of the width of the masking

Fig. 5. Applying Masking Tape with Apron Taper
(*Courtesy Minnesota Mining and Manufacturing Company*)

tape to paper. Such a device saves considerable time. An equally satisfactory job, however, can be done by putting masking tape on the edge of wrapping paper or newspaper. Lay the paper on a clean, flat surface and apply the masking tape so that half of its width is on the paper.

The taped edge of the paper is then placed on the car to protect

Fig. 6. Using Paper to Mask Rear Body Panel
(Courtesy De Vilbiss Company)

the surface which is not to be painted (Fig. 6). If you are painting a fender or body panel, all other parts of the car within a foot of where you will be applying paint should be masked. As a beginner, it may be wise to mask everything within 18 in. of where the new paint will be applied.

c. Sanding. To repaint all of this fender, all of the old paint should be wet-sanded with No. 320 grit waterproof paper, either on a rubber block such as used for featheredging, or with a felt pad. Use a wet sponge to keep the surface wet during the sanding. While sanding, always keep your strokes going in the same direction. The strokes may vary from 6 to 12 in. in length. Use a stroke length that seems to come natural to you.

The purpose of this sanding is to obtain a smooth surface that will provide *tooth* for the new paint. Stop sanding when the surface is smooth. Check your progress frequently by pulling the edge of a *squeegee* over the wet surface. The squeegee will remove the water from the smooth surface; any pits or depressions in the paint will remain wet, and thus will become apparent. The squeegee used by a sander works like the squeegees used for cleaning windows. It wipes the water off of the surface. This squeegee, however, is merely a rubber block about ¼ in. thick, 1½ in. wide, and 2½ in. long.

d. Putty Glazing. If you encounter deep pits that do not go down to bare metal, it is not necessary to sand them out. These pits can be filled with *glazing putty,* which is packaged in both cans and tubes. Glazing putty packaged in tubes is better for use in small shops because it will keep longer.

Only a small amount of putty is pressed into the pit with a putty knife. The surplus is then scraped off, but *do not scrape off too much.* Leave enough so that there will be something to sand after it has dried.

e. Cleaning. When all of the surface to be repainted, including any putty-glazed spots, has been sanded, the entire surface must be cleaned. Wet sanding leaves a mud-like accumulation on the surface. This mud and all traces of water must be removed. Wipe the surface clean and, with a *duster gun,* use compressed air to blow out any water or mud that may have lodged in crevices or behind decorative trim.

Small areas or particles of wax, or other protective coatings that were on the surface, are apt to remain even after sanding; all traces of

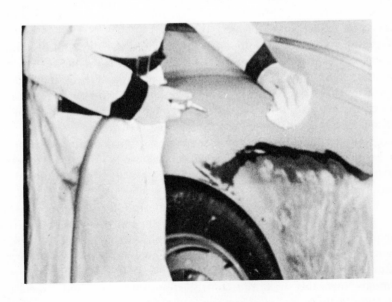

Fig. 7. Surface Must Be Chemically Clean
(Courtesy Ford Motor Company)

these materials must be removed. Removal of these particles is accomplished by wiping the surface with a clean cloth dipped in a special solvent designed for this purpose. All major automotive paint companies sell solvents, under various trade names, for dissolving these protective agents. These materials will make the surface *chemically clean,* a prime requisite of a good paint job.

CAUTION: *Avoid touching the surfaces with your hands from this point on. The small amount of natural oils in the skin can affect the final paint job.*

In spot repairs, *dewax* at least 12 in. beyond the spot to be repaired (Fig. 7).

f. Foundation Coats. Two different foundation coats are used under the final color or finish coat. The first coat material is called the *primer.* It functions as an adherent to bare metal. The second foundation coat material is called the *surfacer.* Several coats of surfacer are used to build up the surface. This is necessary to provide enough thickness to permit sanding without cutting through the primer to bare metal.

In most retail paint shops a combination *primer-surfacer* is in general use. This material provides a good starting place for learning to use a spray gun. First, however, you must understand the equipment with which you will work.

g. Spray Gun. Most automotive paint shops use the kind of spray gun shown in Fig. 8. This gun has a cup that holds the paint. A trigger on the gun allows compressed air to blow through the gun and out of the nozzle. Paint is drawn up into the center of this air stream and out of the nozzle. To flatten this paint-and-air stream, two additional streams of air are directed at its sides through two *horn holes.*

Some guns are provided with several additional air jets that help to break up the more viscous (sticky) materials such as synthetic enamels (Fig. 9A). The nozzle shown in Fig. 9B is primarily intended for lacquers.

The paint spray gun shown in Fig. 8 is a siphon type gun in which the air velocity through the gun creates a suction or siphon effect on the paint in the cup. The paint is drawn out of the cup and into the air stream. The siphon type of gun is the most commonly used in spray paint shops because it is the least expensive. It does not, however compare favorably with the controlled-pressure spray guns used in car manufacturers' paint operations.

One gun which does compare favorably to production plant spray

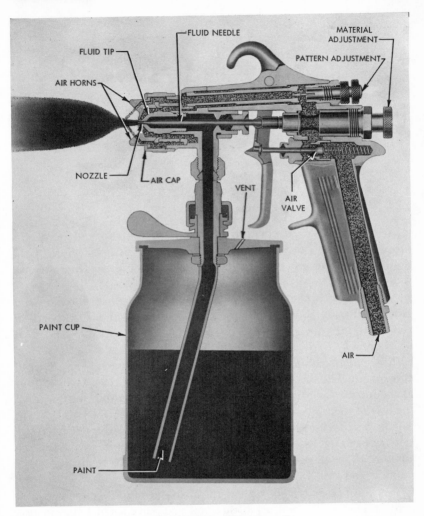

Fig. 8. Sectional View of Paint Spray Gun
(Courtesy De Vilbiss Company)

guns is the "remote-cup gun" (Fig. 10). With this gun, the paint is delivered from a remote cup, under pressure, to the spray gun itself. An air supply, fed to the gun, controls the spray pattern only and is not required to siphon paint from the paint cup; therefore, less actual air pressure is required. The arrangement provides more even pressures than with the siphon type of gun. The remote-cup gun is easier

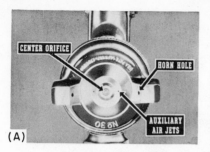

Fig. 9. (A) Spray Gun for Synthetic Enamel; (B) Spray Gun for Lacquer
(*Courtesy Ford Motor Company*)

to handle because the operator does not lift the cup and the paint supply. The gun can be used in a horizontal or an upside-down position, Fig. 10 (bottom), with no danger of dripping paint from the cup vent.

In any shop which does a large amount of paint work, remote-cup gun installation should be considered because of the advantages of controlled-pressure spraying.

(1) *MATERIAL ADJUSTMENT.* Paint spray guns are provided with a *material adjustment* and a *pattern adjustment.* The material adjustment, Fig. 11, controls the amount of paint that will flow out of the nozzle. In learning to use a spray gun, turn this adjustment all the way to the right (clockwise) to completely shut off the paint. Then, as you start to use the gun, turn the adjustment to the left (counterclockwise) to increase the amount of paint until you have it set to the amount of paint you can handle. You will be able to handle more paint as you gain experience.

At the beginning, if you cut the material adjustment down, you will be less apt to spoil a job that you may have spent hours in preparing for paint. With experience, you will be able to handle the gun with the material adjustment all the way open for some materials.

(2) *PATTERN ADJUSTMENT.* The pattern adjustment controls the air to the horn holes. Fig. 12 shows that the shape of the stream of paint and air from the gun can be adjusted. Except when making small spot repairs or painting narrow surfaces, the pattern is usually set wide open.

h. Selecting the Material for the Foundation Coats. All bare metal must be covered with either a coat of primer and several coats of sur-

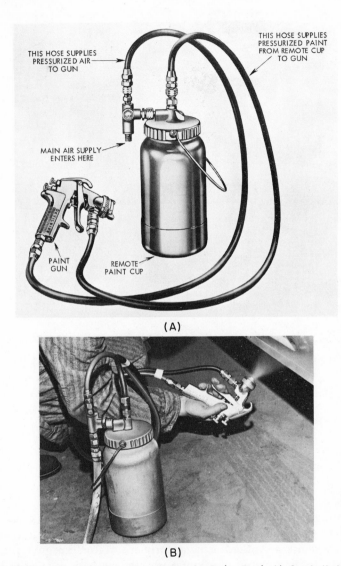

THIS HOSE SUPPLIES
PRESSURIZED PAINT
FROM REMOTE CUP
TO GUN

THIS HOSE SUPPLIES
PRESSURIZED AIR
TO GUN

MAIN AIR SUPPLY
ENTERS HERE

PAINT
GUN

REMOTE
PAINT CUP

(A)

(B)

Fig. 10. (A) Remote-Cup Paint Spray Gun; (B) Spraying Rocker Panel with Gun in Upside-Down
Position
(*Courtesy De Vilbiss Company*)

facer or with several coats of primer-surfacer. At first, it is better to start with a primer-surfacer rather than to use the two different materials.

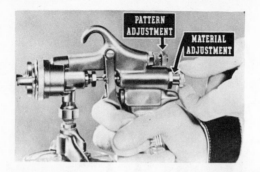

Fig. 11. Spray Gun Adjustments
(*Courtesy Ford Motor Company*)

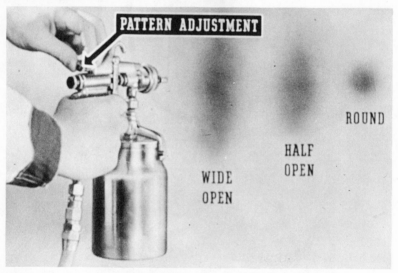

Fig. 12. Setting the Pattern Adjustment
(*Courtesy Ford Motor Company*)

Ordinarily, if the final or color coat is to be lacquer, you would use a lacquer primer-surfacer. If the color coat is to be synthetic enamel, you should use a synthetic enamel primer-surfacer. Lacquer primer-surfacers dry in a matter of minutes whereas synthetic enamel primer-surfacers must generally be left to dry over night so that they are dry enough to sand.

For the first attempt at painting a single panel or fender, it may be advisable to use a synthetic enamel primer-surfacer. While the synthetic enamel primer-surfacer requires overnight drying, it has the advantage of not being soluble in lacquer thinner. Later, when you apply the lacquer color coat, the new color coat can be washed off with thinner without damaging the primer-surfacer coat should you make a mistake or have an accident.

i. Reduce and Strain Primer-Surfacer. If the color coat is to be put on the same day, use lacquer primer-surfacer. Stir the material you use in the can until it is thoroughly mixed. Use a metal stirrer with square corners that will reach and stir up the material in the corners at the bottom of the can.

Using a clean can for mixing, follow the manufacturer's directions and reduce the material to the specified consistency. When using lacquer primer-surfacer, pour the specified amount of lacquer thinner into the mixing can. If you are using synthetic enamel primer-surfacer, add the specified amount of synthetic *enamel reducer*. Wipe the stirrer clean, and thoroughly mix the primer-surfacer with the thinner or reducer. Strain the reduced and thoroughly mixed primer-surfacer directly into the spray gun cup.

j. The Air Pressure System. A spray gun uses approximately nine cubic feet of air per minute. Air compressor capacity usually averages about four cubic feet of air per minute for each one horsepower of the compressor motor. Thus, two spray guns in simultaneous use require a five horsepower (20 cubic feet per minute) air compressor.

If the compressor lacks the capacity to keep the required quantity of compressed air flowing to the spray gun, the additional air needed must come from the reserve tank. As you use more air than the compressor is supplying, the pressure in the tank and the pressure at the gun are gradually reduced. *A change of pressure while you are applying paint can cause considerable trouble.* This will be particularly true later, as you spray color containing metal particles. Metallic paints are very popular but difficult to apply uniformly unless the air pressure to the spray gun remains constant.

Another cause of pressure loss is air-line resistance. Both the air lines and the air hose running to the spray gun must be of adequate size; otherwise, the pressure at the gun will drop as soon as you start to paint. This will result in more paint coming out of the nozzle during the first instant you pull the trigger than during the rest of the stroke. Any variation in pressure will cause trouble with almost any kind of paint, and will make a good job with metallic paints almost impossible.

Some shops make the mistake of using hose designed for use with grease guns instead of air hose designed for use with paint spray guns. To avoid excessive line loss, the hose carrying air to your spray gun should have a $\frac{5}{16}$ in. diameter passage to handle the volume of air required by the spray gun without excessive line loss.

The entire air system must be installed so as to be self draining. The moisture in the air condenses when the air is released from under

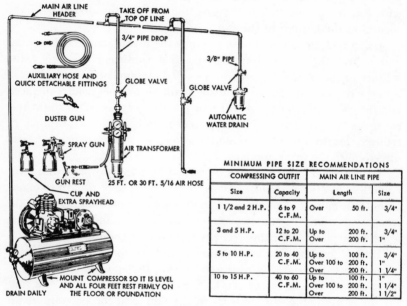

MINIMUM PIPE SIZE RECOMMENDATIONS			
COMPRESSING OUTFIT		MAIN AIR LINE PIPE	
Size	Capacity	Length	Size
1 1/2 and 2 H.P.	6 to 9 C.F.M.	Over 50 ft.	3/4"
3 and 5 H.P.	12 to 20 C.F.M.	Up to 200 ft. Over 200 ft.	3/4" 1"
5 to 10 H.P.	20 to 40 C.F.M.	Up to 100 ft. Over 100 to 200 ft. Over 200 ft.	3/4" 1" 1 1/4"
10 to 15 H.P.	40 to 60 C.F.M.	Up to 100 ft. Over 100 to 200 ft. Over 200 ft.	1" 1 1/4" 1 1/2"

Fig. 13. Typical Compressor, Air Transformer, and Spray Gun Installation
(Courtesy De Vilbiss Company)

pressure or is cooled. If this water gets into your paint, or on the surface you are painting, it will spoil the job.

Fig. 13 illustrates a typical satisfactory installation. *The water that condenses in the reserve tank should be drained out every day.* The main air line or header is sloped to allow any water that condenses there to drain away from the compressor; a means of draining the line or an automatic water drain is provided at the other end. Both of the take-off lines are installed so that the line goes up from the header and then down, which prevents water in the main line from running down to the transformer.

Even with these precautions, some water can condense in the line running down from the main air line or header. An air transformer must be used to insure a flow of clean, dry air at the correct pressures. A typical air transformer is illustrated in Fig. 14. *It is extremely important to use exactly the pressure specified by the paint manufacturer.* In general, a pressure of 50 psi at the transformer is required for lacquer material and 60 psi at the transformer for synthetic enamels.

To use the spray gun, connect the air hose and spray gun to the transformer. Shut off the material adjustment on the spray gun. Hold

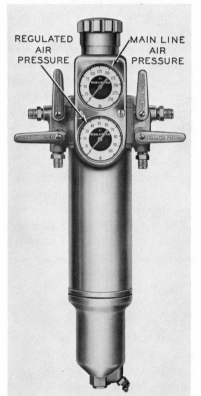

REGULATED AIR PRESSURE

MAIN LINE AIR PRESSURE

Fig. 14. (*Left*) Air Transformer with Automatic Drain
(*Courtesy De Vilbiss Company*)

Fig. 15. (*Below*) "T" and Gauge to Check Pressure at the Gun
(*Courtesy De Vilbiss Company*)

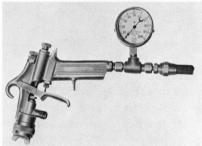

the spray gun trigger all the way back (wide open) and adjust the air transformer to the desired pressure.

Excessive air pressure wastes thinners when spraying lacquer. Insufficient air pressure will not supply enough volume or velocity of air to properly atomize the more viscous synthetic enamels.

k. Checking Line Drop. To determine the drop in air pressure between transformer and the spray gun, it is necessary to install a **T**

and a pressure gauge between the air hose and the spray gun (Fig. 15). Hold the gun wide open again and compare the pressure reading at the gun to the regulated pressure reading at the transformer. The difference in these two readings is the pressure loss in the hose running from the transformer to the spray gun. You will find that it is impossible to do good paint work if you have excessive pressure drop at the gun. However, if some compromise in quality is acceptable, or if you possess enough skill to overcome this handicap, you may wish to readjust the pressure at the regulator to raise the pressure at the gun to the recommended reading.

l. **Adjust the Spray Gun.** With the air pressure adjusted, the material adjustment shut off, and the gun cup filled with properly strained and reduced primer-surfacer, you are ready to adjust the spray gun. First, you must establish the correct spray pattern and the correct material adjustment. To accomplish this, you hang a piece of paper on the wall with masking tape. This paper is used to test your adjustments. It can also be used for practicing with the spray gun until you get the feel of the gun and acquire enough skill to start working on an automobile. Secondly, position yourself in front of this paper so that your feet are 15 to 20 in. apart, and you can hold the spray gun comfortably with the head directly in front of you and about 8 in. away from the paper. Now, hold the spray gun trigger open and turn the material adjustment out, i.e., counterclockwise, until paint starts to appear on the paper. Fig. 12 shows a range of patterns that are possible.

As a beginner, you will probably find it better to start with the pattern adjustment half open. If the pattern coming from the gun is horizontal rather than vertical, loosen the air cap collar on the spray gun head (Fig. 8) and turn the horns so that they are horizontal instead of vertical. This will turn the spray pattern 90°.

If the paint pattern looks like those illustrated in Fig. 16, your spray gun is dirty. Thoroughly clean the gun head and nozzle. Don't attempt to paint with an imperfect pattern. If the paint pattern is heavy in the center as shown in Fig. 17, either the material in the gun needs further reduction (add more thinner or reducer), or higher air pressure is required.

If the spray pattern looks like the one illustrated in Fig. 18, the air pressure is too high for the consistency of the material in the gun; reduce the air pressure. When correct gun adjustments, proper air pressures, clean gun, properly mixed paint, and the correct distance between the gun and the surface are employed, a perfect pattern such as shown in Fig. 19 can be obtained.

m. Spraying Exercise. You are now ready to use the spray gun. Without pulling the trigger, practice moving the gun across the paper,

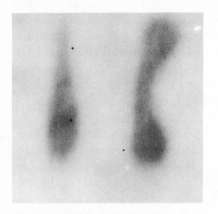

Fig. 16. Spray Pattern of Dirty Spray Gun
(*Courtesy Ford Motor Company*)

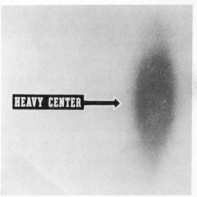

Fig. 17. Pattern with Paint Too Thick or Pressure Too Low
(*Courtesy Ford Motor Company*)

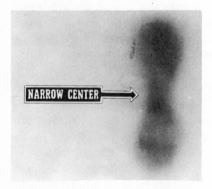

Fig. 18. Spray Pattern with Pressure Too High
(*Courtesy Ford Motor Company*)

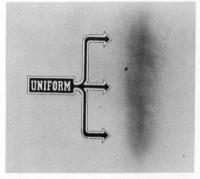

Fig. 19. Correctly Adjusted Spray Pattern
(*Courtesy Ford Motor Company*)

holding or maintaining the distance between the gun head and the paper. You will find that this is easier to do if your head, shoulders, arm, and the spray gun all move together. Confine the movement to your waist, hips, and legs.

Once you have developed the ability to make a stroke about 16 or

18 in. long, while maintaining the correct distance between the gun and tne paper, close the material adjustment. Then, pulling and releasing the trigger each stroke, again practice the stroke.

CAUTION: *Remember that the trigger must never be opened when the gun is not in motion.* This means that the trigger is not pulled until the gun is already in motion at the beginning of each stroke. Likewise, the trigger is released just before the end of each stroke. Keeping this in mind, open the material adjustment slightly and start to spray. You will find that the half open spray pattern previously set will be the easiest for you to handle at first. Keep increasing the material adjustment until the paint on the surface of the paper appears wet.

If your strokes slow down, too much paint will pile in one place and the paint will sag. The paint will also sag if the spray gun gets too close to the surface you are painting. If you get the gun too far away from the surface you are painting at any part of the stroke, the material may go on dry.

You will probably want to change your practice paper several times before you actually start working on the car. Once you have mastered the technique of the correct stroke and proper timing in triggering the gun, start to cover the surface of the paper with overlapping strokes, attempting to apply a uniform thickness of paint. You may have to make a number of trials before you get the kind of surface you want, and several different patterns and material adjustments may be necessary as well.

If the paint appears like that shown in Fig. 20 (orange peel), the cause is usually one or a combination of the following things: improper air pressures, paint not thoroughly mixed, or the incorrect distance between the surface and the spray gun. Regardless of the cause, the trouble must be corrected before you start working on the car.

Once you feel that you have mastered the handling of the spray gun and its adjustments, you should be ready to apply primer-surfacer to a car fender or body panel.

n. Applying Primer-Surfacer. During your practice exercises, you were applying paint to a flat piece of paper and the strokes made were straight. However, since practically no surface on an automotive vehicle is flat, to maintain the proper distance between the spray gun and a curved surface, it is necessary that the spray gun strokes conform to the contour of the surface you are painting.

Fig. 21 shows a student getting ready to paint the same fender discussed earlier in this chapter. You will note that he is establishing the distance between the spray gun and the surface to be painted with his left hand. With the little finger and thumb extended, the hand is used as a gauge to establish that distance.

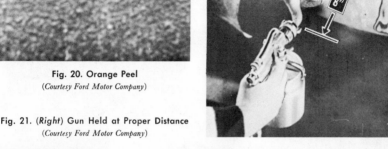

Fig. 20. Orange Peel
(*Courtesy Ford Motor Company*)

Fig. 21. (*Right*) Gun Held at Proper Distance
(*Courtesy Ford Motor Company*)

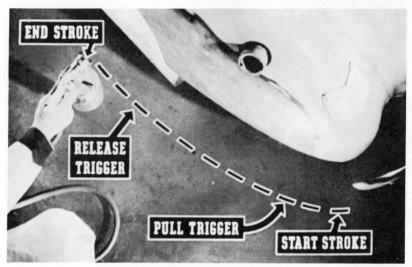

Fig. 22. Stroke Curved to Match Contour
(*Courtesy Ford Motor Company*)

Fig. 22 shows what the correct stroke should be for the fender previously discussed. Practice making such a stroke without pulling the trigger. It may be helpful if you can have someone looking down from above to tell you how well you are following the contour of the surface and if you are maintaining the proper distance between the spray gun and the surface.

Now wipe the surface clean and again practice the stroke illustrated in Fig. 23. When you feel you have mastered it, start pulling the spray gun trigger after the stroke is under way and releasing the trigger before stopping the movement of the gun, as in Fig. 22. After the first stroke, raise the gun slightly and put on a second, overlapping stroke; continue until you have covered the entire surface to be

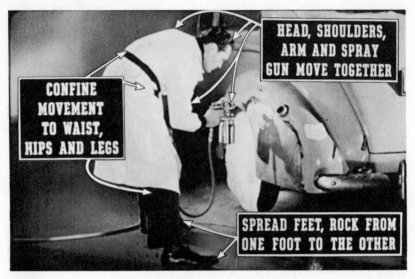

Fig. 23. Correct Stance for Spray Gun Stroke
(Courtesy Ford Motor Company)

painted. Remember, strokes should be made with the whole body; space the feet wide apart and shift your weight from one foot to the other as you make each stroke. Confine your movement to your waist, hips, and legs. This will permit your head, shoulders, arm, and spray gun to move together as a unit. *Avoid using your wrist.* Use of your wrist during the stroke will turn the spray gun away from right angles to the surface, and excessive spray dust will be blown on areas that you do not want to paint.

If you make a mistake or if the paint sags or runs, it can be removed with lacquer thinner, and you can start over. Small imperfections are not serious; however, all of the bare metal must be covered. Several coats are required to provide enough thickness to permit sanding later. It may be advisable to spray a small amount of primer-surfacer over any portions of the fender that may have been putty glazed.

o. Preparing for Color Coat. If you are using synthetic enamel primer-surfacer, allow it to dry overnight; if you are using a lacquer primer-surfacer, allow it to dry from 30 to 60 minutes. In either case, when the primer-surfacer is thoroughly dry, wet-sand it with No. 360-A grit waterproof paper, using a pad and water to level off and remove all orange peel from the surface.

If you are working on a spot repair, during the sanding (Fig. 24), sand beyond the resurfaced area at least 6 in. Slightly scuffing or roughening the old finish provides adhesion or tooth where the color coat is to be tapered off.

After sanding, the surface again must be cleaned. All traces of sanding mud and water must be removed. Wipe clean and blow off the surface. Then, just before you are ready to spray on the color coat, wipe the entire area to be sprayed with a *tack rag* to remove all dust and lint.

TACK RAG: *A tack rag is a rag treated with a varnish containing excessive oils that resist drying. Such a treated rag will pick up dust and lint from the surface. Tack rags can be purchased from all automotive paint supply houses, or you can, in an emergency, make one yourself by spraying a piece of muslin with synthetic enamel.*

p. Applying Lacquer Color Coat. Thoroughly clean your spray gun and gun cup. Pour a clean can about one-quarter full of lacquer color that has been thoroughly stirred. Add the specified amount of lacquer thinner. Making sure your stirrer is clean, thoroughly mix the thinner and lacquer. Strain the reduced and mixed material into the gun cup and install it on the gun. You are now ready to apply color to the fender. For your first experience in applying color, confine yourself to lacquer rather than synthetic enamel.

You will find that lacquer is easier to apply and, therefore, a better instructive medium for you at this time. Using the same techniques that were discussed for the application of primer-surfacer to the fender, spray the entire fender or body panel with horizontal strokes of the spray gun. As soon as you have covered the surface with the strokes in one direction, go over it again with strokes in the opposite direction. That is, if, for first time over, you used horizontal strokes, with a vertical pattern, the next time over, turn the air horns on the spray head so as to provide a horizontal pattern and then go over the surface again with overlapping vertical strokes. Be sure, during both of these coats, that you maintain the distance between the spray gun nozzle and the surface being painted, and that your gun at all times is at right angles to the surface. Make sure that the speed of each stroke is uniform throughout the stroke.

If you used a synthetic enamel primer-surfacer for the foundation coats, and if you have an accident or make a mistake in applying the lacquer color, wash the color coat off with a lacquer thinner and, after it's dry, make another attempt. As shown in Fig. 25, the paint you

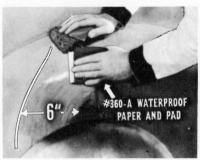

Fig. 24. Sand Beyond Surfaced Area
(*Courtesy Ford Motor Company*)

Fig. 25. Removing Lacquer Just Applied
(*Courtesy Ford Motor Company*)

have just put on is entirely soluble in lacquer thinner while the synthetic enamel undercoat is not; so, the new paint can be washed right off without damaging the undercoat. In this illustration the paint has sagged approximately half way down below the gasoline tank filler. Whenever this occurs, it is better to wash off the paint and start over. This is not accomplished as easily if you used a lacquer primer-surfacer. In this case, the thinner used to remove the color coat also will remove the primer-surfacer and you will find yourself wiping the surface back to bare metal. If this should happen, you must reapply and sand the primer-surfacer coat.

q. Finishing the Job. When the lacquer color coat is thoroughly dry, all traces of orange peel or any slight imperfections can be removed with No. 600 grit wet or dry sandpaper and water.

Again clean and dry the surface and apply a mist coat of clear lacquer thinner. Clean all traces of color from the spray gun cup and head and put a small amount of thinner in the cup. To apply a mist coat, hold the gun nozzle about 12 in. away from the surface. As soon as the paint appears wet, stop the mist coat. Too much thinner will soften the color coat and may cause it to run.

The purpose of the mist coat is to remove the minute scratches caused by the sanding. Lacquer is soluble in thinner; so, if you hold the gun too close, the thinner will go on wet, and its velocity will be great enough to damage the new paint.

After the job is thoroughly dry again, carefully remove the masking tape and paper and go over the new surface with a liquid polish. If the new paint on the fender or panel makes the rest of the car look dull, recommend that the balance of the car be compounded and polished, or that wax or one of the other protective materials be applied to the entire car.

II. SPOT REPAIRS

Weathering tends to lighten colors and reduce gloss. Extreme weathering imparts a chalklike appearance to the finish. For these reasons, it is usually advisable to repaint an entire fender or body panel rather than to make a spot repair.

Spot repairs, however, can be made on either a lacquer or synthetic enamel finish. Such spot repairs are made with lacquer, regardless of the original finish.

First, the oxidized paint must be removed from the entire fender or panel. This is best accomplished with rubbing compound. Rubbing compound is an abrasive that is applied to a rag or a polishing wheel for the purpose of grinding or rubbing off this unwanted material. Rubbing compounds come in fine and coarse grits. Until you have gained experience in the use of rubbing compound, it is best to confine yourself to fine compounds. Similar materials are used in preparing cars for wax or other surface protection.

You will occasionally see cars on which the finish has compounded through the color so that the undercoating or foundation coats are visible. Such exposed surfacer can be recovered with a color coat by means of a spot repair. Whether the original finish was lacquer or synthetic enamel, the spot repair is always made with lacquer.

The entire fender or panel involved is first compounded to restore the original color.

It is impractical to try to tint or blend colors so that they match the aged paint on the balance of the fender or panel. Rather, the spot repair is made with the original color blended into the old finish by the technique explained in this section.

Place a color chip of what you believe to be the original color on the fender or panel, and wet both surfaces (Fig. 26). The water on the old paint will give it gloss so that it will have approximately the same luster as the color chip. While wet, it is easy to determine whether or not the color chip is the same color as the original finish.

In making spot repairs, always use the original color. In case the original color was synthetic enamel, use the same color in lacquer.

The old surface must be prepared for the color coat in the manner explained in the preceding section. If the paint has worn through to bare metal, primer-surfacer must be applied and sanded smooth. In addition to sanding the actual spot to be repaired, sand or scuff the

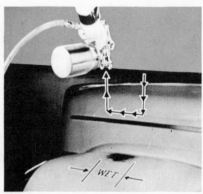

Fig. 26. Wetting Old Surface for Comparison with Color Chip
(*Courtesy Ford Motor Company*)

Fig. 27. Movement of Spray Gun to Blend In a Spot
(*Courtesy Ford Motor Company*)

old paint from 6 to 10 in. in all directions from the spot. This scuffed or roughened area beyond the surfacer is used to taper the paint, so that there will be no definite point at which the new color coat ends. This is accomplished as illustrated in Fig. 27. Hold the gun far enough away from the job so that the material momentarily goes on dry. Immediately move the gun directly toward the job to normal spraying distance and make a stroke across the surfaced area, pulling the gun away from the job at the end of a stroke.

The marked-off areas in Fig. 28 show just how the color coat goes on. In the area where primer-surfacer was exposed, the paint must go on wet. Immediately adjacent to this wet area the lacquer goes on dry; beyond this, less dust and beyond that, nothing. This tapers off the amount of color so that if a difference in color exists between the old and new paint, it will not be marked by a distinct line between the two colors.

After the lacquer color coat has been applied, clean the spray gun, and put lacquer thinner in the cup. The lacquer thinner will be applied to the surface in the form of a mist with insufficient velocity to displace any of the previously applied paint. This mist of lacquer thinner (without any color) will dissolve whatever color went on in the previous operation in the form of dust. The wet lacquer dust will level out and fill the small scratches in the scuffed area, forming a good bond.

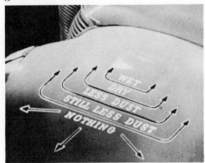 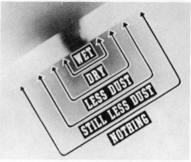

Fig. 28. Stages in Spot Repair
(*Courtesy Ford Motor Company*)

Fig. 29. Application of Paint in Blending
(*Courtesy Ford Motor Company*)

Since the dust was tapered off to nothing (Fig. 28), a blend of the old color without a joint of any kind will result. To illustrate this method of color blending, Fig. 29 shows the blending of two different colors. A piece of masking tape was placed over a portion of the surface to be spot repaired. After blending in the manner outlined in the preceding instructions, the masking tape was removed. Notice that there is no line of demarcation between the two colors except where the tape was removed. This is a severe example in which an almost black gray was blended onto a white surface. You will never be required to blend such extreme differences in color.

After the spot repair has dried, compound the entire fender, or panel, *including the new paint*. Go over the entire surface with a liquid polish or apply a paint protecting material if it is desired.

III. COMPLETE PAINT JOB

After you have acquired enough experience with refinishing single fenders or panels, and have learned how to handle the gun on spot repairs, you can start working on complete paint jobs. In painting a complete car, you do the same things you have previously learned, only on a larger scale.

On the first few complete paint jobs that you do, it may be advisable to remove the hood and hang it so that you will be painting a vertical rather than a horizontal surface. If the hood is removed, it is painted first.

a. Masking. Fig. 30 shows how a door, an instrument panel, and headlining of a car could be masked to keep paint off of them when

Fig. 30. Masked Door Edge and Hinge Pillar
(*Courtesy Ford Motor Company*)

the edges of the door and the hinge pillar are painted. Fig. 31 shows one method of masking windows. In this case, a piece of paper is placed over the top of each window, and the window is then raised to hold the paper at the top. If possible, some of the paper is pushed down inside the body at the bottom, and the edges are secured to the glass with masking tape as illustrated.

The wider the masking tape, the harder it is to apply on a curve. You can usually save considerable time by masking around curves with ¼ in. tape first (Fig. 32). More tape is used this way, but tape is inexpensive and considerable time is thus saved in applying the masking paper.

As illustrated in Fig. 33, decorative chrome strips, hub caps, wheel rings, headlights, windshield wipers, etc., are masked with either masking tape alone or a combination of masking tape and paper. Fig. 33 shows the completed masking of the windshield. Note that the grille, headlights, and chrome strips have all been masked. Likewise, the hub caps have been removed. Fig. 34 shows the door handle and lock

Fig. 31. Masking of Windows
(Courtesy Ford Motor Company)

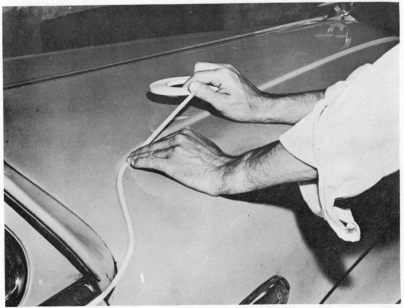

Fig. 32. Use of ¼ in. Tape To Separate Two-Tone Paint Job
(Courtesy Minnesota Mining and Manufacturing Company)

cylinder completely covered with masking tape. On this old car, the running board had to be masked.

Fig. 33. Masking of Glass, Trim, Lights, etc.
(Courtesy Ford Motor Company)

Fig. 34. Putty Glazing Surface Pits
(Courtesy Ford Motor Company)

Fig. 33 shows a wheel masked while the fender is painted. Masking rings are available to mask the tires when the wheels are painted. These rings consist of 2-in.-wide strips of thin sheet metal. These strips are wrapped around the outside of the wheel rims and the ends. are held together with small C clamps. This shields the tires from paint when the wheels are painted.

b. Water Sand. Water sand the entire car until smooth, using No. 320 grit waterproof paper on a rubber block (Fig. 35). Check your

Fig. 35. Water Sanding
(Courtesy Ford Motor Company)

Fig. 36. Checking Progress with a Squeegee
(Courtesy Ford Motor Company)

progress with a squeegee (Fig. 36). If you encounter scratches, pits, or bare metal, you will have to putty glaze, featheredge, and/or resurface them.

c. Putty Glaze. Unless putty glaze is completely dry all the way through, it will sink after the sanding. This will result in a slight depression on the finished surface. It is a good plan to do whatever putty glazing has to be done as soon as practical. Stone marks and any small pits in the paint should be filled with glazing putty when the pit does not go all the way down to the bare metal (Fig. 34).

Fig. 37. Machine Featheredging
(*Courtesy Minnesota Mining and Manufacturing Company*)

d. Featheredge. Featheredge the paint in any areas where the bare metal is exposed, using No. 240 grit waterproof paper and water. Featheredge scratches or pits that go down to the metal. Fig. 37 shows a special head for a portable grinder that reduces the labor of featheredging.

e. Resurface Bare Metal. Apply two coats of primer-surfacer to all bare metal, and cover all spots that have been featheredged or putty glazed. When the surfacer is completely dry (one hour for lacquer; overnight for synthetic enamel primer-surfacer), water sand it with No. 320 grit waterproof paper on a rubber block (Figs. 35, 36).

f. Clean and Dewax. Remove all moisture and dust, being especially particular at crevices, corners, and seams. Render the entire surface chemically clean with solvent to remove wax or other protective material.

g. Reduce, Stir, and Strain Paint. Pour the paint into a clean can and reduce as specified in manufacturer's directions. Before reducing the paint, be sure that it is well mixed by stirring vigorously and thoroughly with a square stirrer, as recommended previously. Use lacquer thinner for lacquer color coat. Use synthetic enamel reducer for synthetic enamel. Reducers and thinners are rated as slow, medium, and fast, to permit matching the material to the spraying temperature. Use a slower thinner than normal for your first complete paint jobs. Be sure your gun is clean, and strain the material directly into the gun cup.

h. Apply Color. Go completely over the car with a tack rag. Keep the tack rag handy so you can again tack the surface of each area just before applying the paint.

(1) *ROOF.* Provide yourself with a bench about 30 in. high to stand on as you paint the car roof. The bench must be long enough so that you can walk the full length of the roof.

When you paint an entire car, you always end up at the point where you started. Half way up on the windshield pillar is the best

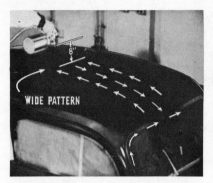

Fig. 38. Start Halfway Up the Hinge Pillar
(*Courtesy Ford Motor Company*)

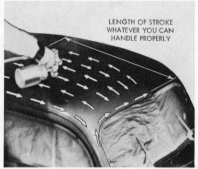

Fig. 39. Direction of First Coat Overlapping Strokes
(*Courtesy Ford Motor Company*)

place to start. With the air pressure properly set, the paint mixed, reduced, and strained, and a bench to stand on, go over the side of the roof you are going to paint first with a tack rag. Tack as much of the roof as you can reach. Starting halfway up the windshield pillar, apply a wet coat of paint, with a wide pattern, in a continuous stroke to the center of the top of the windshield. Make a second stroke back to your starting point. The spray gun for at least one of these strokes should be pointed slightly up. Start spraying one side of the top. Start the first stroke at the center of the top and windshield, moving toward the back window. The return stroke is closer to the side of the car, and must overlap the first (Figs. 38 and 39). The stroke length should be whatever you can conveniently handle. Most people can cover half of the distance from the windshield to the back window without much trouble.

Begin the movement of the gun, and then pull the trigger. Release the trigger before completing the stroke. This action *feathers* the material and reduces the amount of *overspray*. Cover the area as quickly as possible. Turn your wrist so that the spray pattern is lengthwise with the car and cross-spray a second coat (Fig. 40), feathering the paint out at the center.

As soon as the double coat of color is applied, move back and, following the same technique, apply a double coat to the back half of that side of the roof. Move your bench to the other side of the car and immediately paint that side of the roof. Again start at front of the roof. Cut the pattern to half width when overlapping the paint you put on from the other side of the car. This will reduce the amount of overspray from both coats.

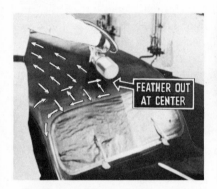

Fig. 40. Cross Spraying the Second Coat
(*Courtesy Ford Motor Company*)

Fig. 41. Use of Cardboard as a Shield
(*Courtesy Ford Motor Company*)

(2) *BODY.* When the roof has been completely covered with a double coat, remove the bench, starting with the front door on the side where the last half of the roof was painted. Open the door and paint the door edges, lock pillar, header, and hinge pillar. As shown in Fig. 41, a cardboard in your other hand will reduce the amount of overspray that goes inside the car.

Close the door to the first latch only. Spray around the windshield and then paint the cowl. Do not paint the hood or front fender at this time. Rather, paint the door next. Use a double coat on all surfaces. You may want to set the spray pattern at half width for vertical panels. Paint the next door or panel to the rear, and so on until you have worked around the back of the car to the point where you started to paint the roof. Don't forget to open each door and the deck lid and paint their edges, lock pillars, etc. With synthetic enamels, it is important to get back to your starting point as soon as possible. About

20 minutes probably will elapse. If you take longer than this, the surface will have started to dry on the first enamel applied, and the overspray from the last paint you apply will not readily fuse with the first paint, and the joint will appear dull.

(3) *HOOD AND FRONT FENDERS.* Paint to the middle of the hood and the fender on that side. Start at the back of the fender and work toward the front. Paint the front of the fenders, hood, and grille. Next, paint the other half of the hood and the other fender.

(4) *MIST-SPRAY START AND STOP JOINT.* As soon as you have completely covered the car, empty the paint from the gun cup and fill it with lacquer thinner. Hold the spray gun near a piece of paper and squeeze the trigger until the thinner comes out of the gun clean. Immediately apply a mist coat of lacquer thinner to the overspray at the start and stop joint (Fig. 42).

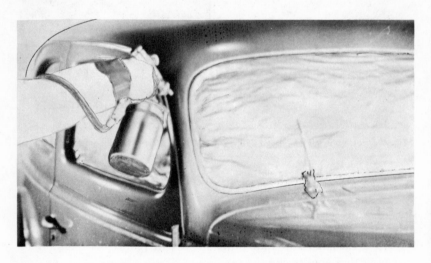

Fig. 42. Spraying Lacquer Thinner on Overspray at the Joint
(Courtesy Ford Motor Company)

(5) *SPECIAL INSTRUCTIONS FOR SYNTHETIC ENAMEL.* When working with synthetic enamel, it is important, once you start, to continue until the job is finished. Before you start, make sure that you have paint, reducer, strainer, stirrer, and tack rag handy. You can't afford to lose time looking for things. If the enamel sets, you will probably have to compound the overspray. Lacquer thinner will dissolve the overspray and fuse it with the first paint you applied, only if you

put the lacquer thinner mist coat on within 20 minutes of the time the job is started. Use lacquer thinner because synthetic enamel reducer will not dissolve the overspray.

(6) *REMOVE MASKS AND TOUCH UP PAINT.* While synthetic enamel dries dust free in as little as 30 minutes, it remains soft for sometime, so the masks must not be removed until the enamel is hard. If the paint is air dried, it should set overnight to harden. If the paint is oven dried, allow the car to set at least an hour after it has cooled down to room temperature before removing the masking.

If the car was painted with lacquer, the masks can be removed in one hour after painting is completed.

Once you have removed the masks, inspect the entire car for areas where small particles of paint may have been pulled off by the masking tape. Touch up these spots, as well as any others that you may find, with a stripping brush. Carefully check all door and deck lid edges.

i. Synthetic Enamel. Clean up and polish the entire car, using a liquid polish. For a more expensive job, the finish may be compounded to reduce orange peel and remove the shine. *This should not be done, however, before the new paint has aged at least two weeks.*

j. Lacquer. While the material for painting a car in lacquer will usually cost more than synthetic enamel, lacquer has the advantage of producing a perfectly smooth finish with some additional work. This accounts for the use of lacquer for work on the highest priced cars. This smooth finish is accomplished by sanding the new paint with No. 600 grit paper to remove all orange peel. A mist coat of lacquer thinner is then sprayed over the completed job, dissolving the scratches and producing a smooth finish. An even smoother finish is accomplished by compounding after the mist coat has thoroughly dried.

TRADE COMPETENCY TESTS

The following questions will help you to determine how well you have retained the information presented in this chapter. If you don't know the answer to any one or several of these questions, reread the page indicated.

1. Why should an automotive painter have some knowledge of metal finishing? (p. 346)

2. What are two basic differences in lacquers and synthetic enamels? (p. 347)

3. How do you keep the spray-gun hose from rubbing on the new paint? (p. 348)

4. What is the purpose of featheredging? What kind of paper is used? What grit number? (p. 350)

5. How does the water help you when sanding old paint? (p. 351)

6. What grit paper is used for sanding the old paint? (p. 352)

7. What does the squeegee show you? (p. 352)

8. What is putty glazing? (p. 353)

9. How is the surface to be painted rendered chemically clean? (p. 354)

10. What is the function of the primer-surfacer? (p. 354)

11. How is the paint-and-air stream from a spray gun flattened? (p. 354)

12. What two adjustments are provided on a spray gun? (p. 356)

13. Ordinarily, what kind of primer-surfacer would be used as a foundation for a lacquer finish coat? (p. 358)

14. Why should a stirrer have square corners? (p. 359)

15. How much air does a paint spray gun use? (p. 359)

16. What is the purpose of the air transformer? (pp. 360, 361)

17. Which requires the greater air pressure, synthetic enamel or lacquer? (p. 361)

18. How is pressure line drop checked? (pp. 361, 362)

19. What things are required for a perfect paint pattern? (p. 362)

20. What must be happening when you pull the spray gun trigger? (p. 364)

21. The spray gun trigger is released before what? (p. 364)

22. Why must you avoid using your wrist at either end of the paint stroke? (p. 366)

23. How long should lacquer primer-surfacer dry before you attempt to sand it? (p. 367)

24. What grit paper can be used to remove orange peel from lacquer finish coats? (p. 367)

25. What is a mist coat? (p. 368)

26. What is ¼ in. wide masking tape used for? (p. 372)

27. Why must putty glaze be completely dry before sanding? (p. 375)

28. How long should you wait before removing the masks from a car that has just had the paint baked on? (p. 379)

INDEX